List of Tables

OPTICAL RECORDING
A Technical Overview

Alan B. Marchant
Verbatim Corporation

Addison-Wesley Publishing Company
Reading, Massachusetts • Menlo Park, California • New York
Don Mills, Ontario • Wokingham, England • Amsterdam
Bonn • Sydney • Singapore • Tokyo • Madrid • San Juan

This book is in the Addison-Wesley Series in New Horizons in Technology

Many of the designations used by manufacturers and sellers to distinguish their products are claimed as trademarks. Where those designations appear in this book, and Addison-Wesley was aware of a trademark claim, the designations have been printed in initial caps or all caps.

Library of Congress Cataloging-in-Publication Data
Marchant, Alan B.
     Optical recording : a technical overview / Alan B.
       Marchant.
       p.   cm.
     Bibliography: p.
     Includes index.
     ISBN 0–201–76247–1
     1. Optical storage devices.   I. Title.
TA1635.M37   1990
621.38—dc19   89–176
                                               CIP

To my teachers—Don Groom, Stuart Shapiro, and Dennis Howe—
and to many friends at TMO for motivation and experience.

Preface

This book is intended as a technical description of optical recording, with emphasis on the development of optical disk systems for digital data storage. The general emphasis is on recording systems—the combinations of media, hardware, applications, etc., which provide functionality to the user. Much of the technical discussion is presented in the form of system design trade-offs. A number of important design alternatives are described and compared in the context of practical design scenarios. These design choices also illuminate the underlying science and technology.

Part I (Chapters 1–4) begins with a brief historical review of the ideas and inventions that created the technology of optical recording, a mention of some attempts to draw products from the technology, and a brief discussion of the basic pros and cons of optical recording compared with competing technologies. Further chapters add a motivational foundation by describing the three classes of optical recording systems and the applications to which they are best suited. Some current optical disk products are described in these chapters. The discussions include the functional requirements that the (many and diverse) products are intended to satisfy.

The technical core of this book is contained in Parts II–IV (Chapters 5–14), which describe the basic principles and practice of optical head design, focus and tracking servos, signal processing, error correction, and media design. These chapters review all the major concepts and challenges that are unique to optical recording. Topics such as mechanical design, electronic design, and computer interface issues are quite thoroughly neglected here; these issues are dealt with adequately elsewhere—for example, in the many reviews of magnetic recording systems.

No attempt has been made to consolidate the technical discussions of any class of optical recording systems. For instance, various aspects of magneto-optic recording are described in each part of the book. There is sufficient unity between the different types of optical recording so that each can be better understood by comparison with the others.

The book ends with a glossary of terms from the developing jargon of optical recording. The reader should refer to this section for possible help whenever the discussion seems confusing. Some of the terms in the glossary have yet to be officially defined; it is hoped that the definitions here will serve to clarify this situation rather than cause further confusion.

The level and content of this book are intended for professionals in the storage technology industry who have not had a thorough introduction to optical recording technology. The presentation and derivations are not particularly complex, so even nontechnical readers should find most of the material understandable. On the other hand, the author's past contributions to the field of optical recording have been mainly theoretical, and a theoretic treatment is used in this book to clarify some technical problems and design trade-offs. The limited mathematics employed should not be daunting to any reader with a modest technical background.

I would like to thank Chi H. Chung of Laserdrive Ltd. and James J. Burke of the Optical Data Storage Center at the University of Arizona for reviewing the manuscript.

Alan B. Marchant
Sunnyvale, California

Contents

List of Figures

PART I

NEW APPLICATIONS

Optical recording is not a very new idea; serious design proposals and even product-development projects date back nearly to the invention of the laser. Chapter 1 gives a brief overview of the history of optical recording, summarizing the apparent advantages that motivated its development and the early commercial applications that made it a practical technology.

Optical recording products are grouped into three categories according to their degree of functionality: read-only systems, which reproduce only prerecorded information; write-once systems, in which file updates are accomplished by recording new versions without erasure; and erasable systems, which can erase and rewrite data files with the same flexibility as traditional magnetic storage systems. This three-way categorization is most applicable to the various types of optical recording media. Drives present a more complicated picture because in the future multifunctional drives might appear, which will use different types of media for different applications. Chapters 2, 3, and 4 qualitatively describe the three types of systems using existing products as examples. The descriptions include summaries of typical performance characteristics and the most popular or promising applications.

CHAPTER 1

Optical Recording: The Bright Idea

1.1 A Brief History

Most of us are intimately familiar with light as a source of information. Our brains emphasize vision more than any other sense, and visual display has always been a major mode of communication. Pictograms and the various forms of prehistoric art demonstrated that images could convey experience and knowledge through time to future generations. But the most significant development in optical storage occurred 5000 years ago, when the Egyptians invented alphabetic and hieroglyphic writing. True writing systems, as opposed to drawings or pictograms, are essentially methods for the digital transmission of language information. A written description can convey a very precise understanding of an idea. Barring misspellings, the message can be copied many times without any loss of meaning— witness the remarkable preservation of ancient records through generations of handwritten manuscripts.

Figure 1.1 illustrates some of the dramatic developments in information storage that were motivated by the need for more convenient access and more efficient storage. This technological evolution has been both a consequence and a cause of the rapidly increasing production of information. As the information age intensified its search for new storage techniques, many of the resulting inventions reemphasized the importance of light and optics for information storage and communication.

In current usage, *optical data storage* refers to systems that use light to record as well as to recover information. Photography was the earliest example of optical recording. Silver-halide photography, developed over the last 200 years, has demonstrated remarkable

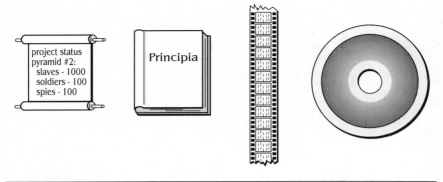

Figure 1.1 *Here we see the evolution of digital optical data storage.*

achievements in (analog) image recording. Consider, for instance, the recording rate on 35-mm color film. In 1 ms, an amateur photographer can record an image with an effective information content of 10 Mbits (an effective recording rate of 10 Gbit/s!). Recent developments in electrophotography and holography have further extended our ability to record analog images and text rapidly, cheaply, and compactly. However, the utility of analog images for information storage is limited. Digital computers, the centerpiece of the information age, require inputs that are electronic, digital, and (essentially) serial. A considerable amount of processing is required to convert any analog signal into a machine-readable form. It is advantageous to convert information into a digital data stream at the earliest possibility, but then the corresponding storage system must be suited to recording and storing arbitrary digital information.

Photography can be adapted for digital data recording and storage. A number of high-speed, film-based data recorders have been built, for instance, the RCA system described by Pierson (1979). In these systems a laser beam is modulated by the data signal as it scans rapidly and repetitively across a reel of film. Data rates of 20 Mbit/s and storage densities of 10^4 bit/mm^2 have been demonstrated. However, these photographic film systems are limited to specialty applications (e.g., streaming data recorders) because the "tape" format inhibits rapid data access and because post-processing, either chemical or thermal, is necessary.

The modern concept of optical recording, in which a light beam is used as a multi-purpose tool for both marking and reading information, developed as an application for lasers. An unmodulated laser beam was used to write thermally on thin metal films as early as 1966. The concept of pulsing the beam to create discrete, micron-sized marks followed shortly. In fact, the first such proposal (Chen, Ready, and Bernal, 1968) was for recording in thin films of MnBi; this prescription for magneto-optical recording corresponds quite closely with current practice. In a seminal paper, Maydan (1971) demonstrated "micromachining" of small holes in metal films and described the basic optical and thermal characteristics of the optical stylus. This work was the foundation for modern write-once optical recording.

Throughout this book, we will use the term *optical stylus* to refer to a tightly focused spot of light that is used to write and read marks on the surface of an optical recording medium. Figure 1.2 illustrates how light is focused by an objective lens to form the optical stylus. Diffraction effects related to the wavelike nature of light limit the minimum size of the focused spot. The tightest possible focus is achieved using a coherent light source such as a laser. (*Coherence* means that the light at any two points has a constant phase relation-

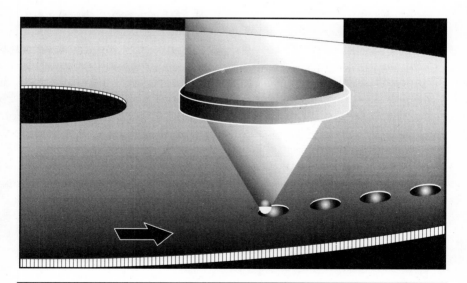

Figure 1.2 *A tightly focused spot of light, the optical stylus, is used to write and read.*

ship.) The smallest possible spot diameter (full width at half maximum intensity) is approximately

$$FWHM \cong 0.6\lambda/NA \qquad (1.1)$$

where λ is the wavelength and NA is the numerical aperture of the focusing lens (the sine of the incidence angle of a marginal focused ray). In practical systems, the wavelength is typically $\lambda \cong 800$ nm and the numerical aperture is approximately 0.5 (limited by laser and lens technologies). The size of the optical stylus can therefore be less than 1 μm.

The obvious possibility of data densities on the order of 10^6 bit/mm^2 led to a flurry of research into optical data recording and the development of many materials for real-time optical recording. However, the first class of product to use a laser for recording (or rather, mastering) and playback was the read-only videodisc. The videodisc was developed as a means for mass replication and distribution of video programs, something like an LP for television.

Video programs are carried on analog, not digital, channels. The voltage level of the video signal is interpreted as the screen brightness (or luminance level). In the NTSC format, the video image is repeated or updated 30 times per second (25 times in the European PAL format). Each scan consists of 550 horizontal lines across the screen. These are displayed as two half-frames (lines 1, 3, 5, . . . , and then lines 2, 4, 6, . . .) so that the image is apparently refreshed 60 (or 50) times each second. The scan time per horizontal line is about 1 s/30/550 = 60 μs. Since the horizontal scan lines are independent, they create a vertical resolution of nearly 275 cycles. The horizontal resolution should be comparable to the vertical resolution. To support a horizontal resolution of 200 cycles, the total luminance bandwidth would have to be greater than 200/60 μs = 3.3 MHz. The actual bandwidth for NTSC video is 4.2 MHz.

In principle, the need for ideal color fidelity triples the video bandwidth requirement. However, the information about hue and saturation is contained in two chroma channels that are encoded as the phase and amplitude of a high-frequency carrier and mixed with the luminance channel. This technique results in relatively poor independent resolution for the red, green, and blue parts of the image, but the overall video image is esthetically pleasing.

Bandwidth-efficient analog video signals cannot be recorded directly on a videodisc. The original videodisc master is made by laser recording in a thin layer of photoresist (see Chapter 12, Section 4). After development, the recorded marks take the form of pits whose lengths and positions are determined by the laser pulses, but all the pits have essentially the same width and depth. Readout of such a pattern is not suitable for reproducing continuous signal levels because the readout signal switches between just two possible values— a low value where a pit is present, and a high value where the surface is unmarked. On the other hand, because the lengths and positions of the pits can be varied in a continuous fashion, frequency-modulated (FM) analog signals can be easily reproduced on a videodisc. Figure 1.3 illustrates how the composite video signal is frequency-

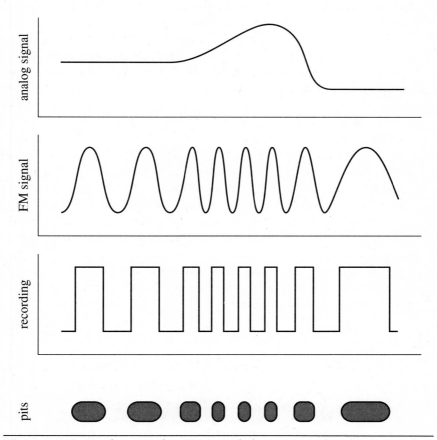

Figure 1.3 *An analog signal is FM encoded as pits on a videodisc in this manner.*

modulated and recorded onto a videodisc master as a track of variable-length pits. The process is reversed to reproduce an analog video signal at readout. This technique of FM encoding is similar to the method used to record on video tape.

In some videodisc formats (i.e., Philips' LaserVision), the composite video is FM encoded and recorded without further modification. In the LaserVision format, the entire range of luminance voltages, from the "blacker than black" synch signals to full white, is transformed to the frequency band 7.6 to 9.3 MHz. The image information expands the actual signal bandwidth considerably, but it leaves a lot of unused bandwidth at the lower frequencies (below 4 MHz). Two analog audio channels are usually added in this frequency range, and enough unused bandwidth may remain for the addition of a complete digital audio channel (see Chapter 2, Section 3).

A standard videodisc has a diameter of 300 mm (just like an LP). It is composed of two PMMA substrates, mastered and injection molded using the processes described in Chapter 12, Section 4. The formatted, information-bearing sides of the plastic disks are coated with aluminum and then laminated together face to face, protecting the coatings. The tracks extend from an inner radius of 55 mm to an outer radius of 145 mm. At a track pitch of 1.67 μm, each side of the disk can hold up to 54,000 tracks. If a single video frame is recorded on each track, each side of the videodisc contains up to 30 minutes of programming. Under these conditions, the pit lengths and spacings are much smaller on the inner tracks than on the outer tracks. If a freeze-frame video display is not a requirement, the amount of programming can be nearly doubled using the CLV mode (see Chapter 10, Section 1).

Still-framing is possible only when the rotation rate is 1800 rpm (1500 rpm for PAL). For full-bandwidth video, the corresponding pit lengths may be as short as

$$L_{min} = 2 \cdot \pi \cdot r \cdot 30 \text{ s}^{-1} / (2 \cdot f_{max}) = 1.05 \cdot 10^{-5} \cdot r \qquad (1.2)$$

for a maximum FM frequency of $f_{max} = 9.3$ MHz. On the innermost track at a radius $r = 55$ mm, the minimum pit length is about 0.6 μm and the minimum pit spacing is about 1.2 μm. Given the basic restrictions on the size of the optical stylus, these are about the smallest readable features. Full-bandwidth video can be stored on a small disc, but the inner radius must not be smaller than 55 mm. For smaller videodisc formats (i.e., a 200 mm disk) the bandwidth is usually reduced in order to make shorter tracks possible and to increase the number of frames per disk. The video bandwidth can be reduced by separating out the chroma signal and then filtering out the high-frequency part of the luminance. This kind of compression causes a loss of fine resolution in the image.

Thomson CSF and Kodak have both developed concepts for very low-cost videodisc systems. Thomson invented a player that could handle a flexible, transparent disk. The disk pattern was replicated by step-and-repeat embossing on a relatively thin plastic web (plastic sheet material in roll form) from which videodiscs were punched. (Embossing is much faster and cheaper than injection molding; it is the process used to make LPs.) The player included a nonplanar reference surface that aerodynamically stabilized the disk using airflow driven by the disk rotation. This type of stabilization is now applied in the Bernouli Box magnetic disk drives from I-Omega.

Eastman Kodak Company developed another cost-effective means of replicating flexible videodiscs (Howe, Thomas, and Wrobel, 1979). Their system used a transmissive master that was essentially a write-once optical disk. The video information on this master was contact-printed onto a plastic web coated with diazo. Contact printing is a very rapid process, well suited to efficient manufacturing. Diazo is a photographic material that is developed by ammonia gas without any wet chemistry, an intrinsically clean process. A major technical achievement in the development of this process was a technique for causing intimate contact between the web and the master while avoiding severe wear on the master. Air bubbles or tent-poles of any size interfere with contact printing of submicron features.

A relatively low-cost videodisc system was commercialized by RCA. Their nonoptical system used a relatively simple stylus that tracked in a groove in contact with the disc surface. It picked up capacitance variations associated with submicron features in the groove. Masters for the capacitive system were cut mechanically into metal blanks (soft copper) and the single-piece videodiscs were embossed on both sides.

Unfortunately, no low-cost videodisc systems ever gained wide market acceptance. A complete explanation of this failure would take us far afield of our technical discussion, but the basic reason can be summarized in one acronym—VCR. Erasability (full-function recording by the user) and a long, uninterrupted playing time made video tape more desirable than the videodisc, even though the signal quality from a videodisc is superior.

Since this book is about optical recording for digital data storage, a more complete discussion of the videodisc would be out of place. However, optical videodisc system designs formed the foundation for many aspects of modern optical recording technology, such as the design and manufacture of read-only media, servo and head designs, and mastering techniques. The pioneering videodisc project at Philips led to the first publicized demonstration of write-once optical recording in 1972. That same project also spun off the very successful CD program (see Chapter 2, Section 1). See Isailovic (1985), the *Philips Technical Review* (vol. 40, 1982), and the *RCA Review* (vol. 39, 1978) for detailed descriptions of videodisc systems.

Although the videodisc market is not growing rapidly, major applications have developed in the area of training. There are clear signs that optical videodisc technology is ascendant there (over capacitive systems). Several companies with established VHD product lines (using the capacitive technology) have now begun to offer laser-based systems and new videodisc players that incorporate the latest electronic and optical technology. Chapter 2, Section 3 describes multifunctional players that combine videodisc capabilities with the digital read-only functionality.

1.2 Basic Advantages

Optical recording is usually considered as a potential replacement for magnetic recording. This is understandable, since magnetic tape and disk products completely dominate all digital data storage applications. (Computer cards and punched tape linger only as unpleasant memories.) Table 1.1 is a qualitative comparison of the performance potential of optical disk systems versus that of magnetic disks and magnetic tape. See Section 1.4 for detailed definitions of some of these figures of merit. The reader should recognize that a fair comparison of future potential is fraught with difficulty, particularly because only a few types of optical recording systems have yet been fully developed, while magnetic systems possess the design maturity that comes after many generations of product design. The performance figures in Table 1.1 do not describe any particular products; rather, they reflect state-of-the-art performance from high-end products and practical R&D demonstrations.

TABLE 1.1 Optical vs. Magnetic Performance Expectations

	OPTICAL DISK	MAGNETIC DISK	TAPE
Data density (bits/mm²)	10^6	$2 \cdot 10^5$	10^4
Data capacity (bits/media unit)	$5 \cdot 10^{10}$	10^{10}	10^{10}
Access time (ms)	10^2	20	10^4
Data rate (Mbit/s)	10^2	10^2	10^2
Removability applications	Yes	Lower performance	Yes
Reliability problems	Unproven	Head crashes	Print-through; binder failure; wear

The principal motivation behind the development of optical re-cording was the excitement over its high areal data density—the amount of information that can be stored per unit area on the media surface. The data density is much higher than in magnetic systems because the tracks are spaced so closely together. High-end magnetic and optical storage systems can both achieve in-track data densities much higher than 10,000 bits/cm. However, the track pitch in magnetic systems is limited by mechanical constraints for tape (usually > 100 μm) and by track runout and signal-to-noise ratio (SNR) considerations for high-end disk drives (>15 μm). (Using rotary-head techniques developed for the VCR, future tape systems might have densities comparable to those of high-performance disks.) By contrast, the track width and pitch for optical recording must be comparable to the size of the optical stylus, ~ 1 μm. This fully accounts for the data density and capacity advantages of optical recording in Table 1.1.

Early estimates of optical disk pricing were colored by optimism and by hype surrounding the introduction of the videodisc. Projections in the popular press in 1979 predicted media prices as low as 1 ¢/Mbyte. At the present time (1988), these hopes have not yet been realized. Typical write-once disk prices are about $100 each, retail, or >10¢/Mbyte. $5\frac{1}{4}''$ erasable magneto-optic disks with a ca-

pacity of about 250 Mbyte cost more than $200; they are not likely
to be much cheaper than $100 in the near future (40¢/Mbyte).
Nevertheless, optical disks are already competitive with conventional
magnetic media on a per-Mbyte basis, and much lower prices are
expected when production passes from the pilot phase into volume
manufacturing.

Optical recording systems have a potential for much greater reliability than magnetic systems. The optical stylus provides a large
working distance between any part of the head and the rotating disk.
So head crashes, which are a serious risk in magnetic disk drives,
should never occur. And unlike magnetic tape systems, no wear is
associated with repeated use. Dust that accumulates on the head and
on the exposed surface of the disk should cause no catastrophic problem because it is out of focus with respect to the imaging system.
However, because long-term experience with the technology is rather
scant, questions about the overall reliability of optical systems per-
sist. Will the diode lasers have a long enough lifetime? Can the precise optical alignment tolerances be maintained? Is the media sufficiently resistant to corrosion?

Closely related to the issue of reliability is that of removability.
Many types of magnetic recording systems with removable media
exist. There are even removable Winchester systems. However, long-
term reliability has been a continuing problem with such systems.
The optical disk, with its built-in dust protection and noncontact
operation, is perfectly suited to removable applications. In the long
run, optical recording might come to dominate just those applications where removability is desirable. These include low-end needs
currently filled by floppy disks and high-end peripherals like mass-
storage "juke boxes."

Most optical recording systems operate at low data rates: < 1
Mbyte/s. Contemporary Winchester disk drives operate several
times faster. As discussed in Section 1.4, the data rate is often of
secondary interest compared to the access time. But in applications
that handle very large blocks of data (e.g., for image storage or back-
up) the data rate is of primary importance. The data rate in an optical system is usually limited by the laser power and disk rotation rate
(both of which are likely to increase in the near future). Another
technique that can greatly increase the data rate is unique to optical
recording: multichannel operation with a single head. Multiple, in-

dependent laser beams can be focused through one objective lens, to create a recording system with a very high data rate. Recording rates exceeding 10 Mbyte/s were demonstrated in an early RCA system (see Chapter 8, Section 5), but at present, multichannel optical recording remains in the realm of R&D demonstrations and specialty products.

Mass data replication (through substrate molding) is a special advantage of the optical disk that has motivated the creation of read-only applications. In the case of the videodisc, the advantage of replicability did not outweigh the importance of recordability. But in the professional markets of data publishing, the reverse is likely to be true.

1.3   Disadvantages

Optical disk systems are often described as having extremely high error rates as compared to magnetic systems. This perception results from a misinterpretation of the error-rate specifications of magnetic systems and very vocal public discussions of the raw error rates from optical disks. As discussed in the following section, the usual systems specifications refer to the *net* error rate, after defective media are rejected, questionable areas are fenced off, and an error-correction technique is applied. The *raw* error rate of an optical disk might be slightly higher than that of a high-density magnetic disk, but any difference can be explained by the higher density of information. (Smaller defects can cause errors.) And the more powerful error-correction codes developed for optical disk systems more than compensate for a slightly increased raw error rate. In fact, the error-correction strategies developed for optical recording are being adapted for new generations of magnetic recording systems.

The greatest real drawback to optical disk systems, vis-a-vis magnetic systems, is slow access. This problem is partly due to the large head mass; moving a head mass of 100 g across the disk in 20 ms can be a challenge. Tracking difficulties also increase the access time. Because the track pitch on an optical disk is so small, the servo must be extremely precise; the necessary servo accuracy is more easily achieved with slower disk rotation and lower actuator velocity. The laser power constraints that limit the data rate also limit the rotation rate of the disk, adding to the access time through increased latency. Note that all of the causes of slow access are related to the immaturity of optical recording systems. Lighter heads, improved actuators, and more powerful lasers will facilitate much faster optical disk systems.

Another disadvantage of optical disk systems is a relatively high drive cost. Magnetic disc drives are much cheaper. The optical drives can be justified only for applications that exploit the removability feature. However, this disadvantage, too, is a matter of immature technology. Optical and magnetic disk drives have basically the same components: load mechanism, spindle, drive electronics, and controller. The only major difference is that an optical head is more complex than a magnetic head. As designs and manufacturing techniques mature, optical disk drives should not cost much more than magnetic disk drives; perhaps they will be significantly less expensive on a basis of price per Mbyte.

Most optical recording systems are not erasable. As long as this is true, they will not be able to compete against magnetic recording systems except in strictly archival applications. As a consequence, erasability has always been a major topic of research in optical recording. Early work on M-O concepts resulted in a flurry of patents and research, including some very advanced ideas. Unfortunately, the first material of choice, MnBi, was too noisy to support very-high-density data storage. When this was realized, most M-O development programs in the United States were scaled back. The erasable optical disk was reinvigorated by the invention at IBM of an amorphous, low-noise magneto-optic material. See Chapter 4 for the updated status of erasable optical recording.

As we concentrate on optical recording technology, we should remember that magnetic recording "presents a moving target." In recent years, new ideas such as vertical recording, thin-film heads and media, and rotary heads have resulted in impressive demonstrations of technology. However, in terms of achievable data density, magnetic recording research may be entering a phase of diminishing returns. There is increasing evidence that magnetic recording technology has "ripened" and will not yield dramatic improvements in the future. Most previous increases in magnetic storage density have come about by simultaneously decreasing the gap length, head/media spacing, and recording-layer thickness. But present Winchester drives operate near the practical limit for flying height, and there is good evidence for an effective head/media spacing even when the head is pressed into contact (as in tape systems). In addition, any future generations of magnetic drives must include tracking servos and sophisticated error correction to solve problems inherent in any high-density media. These are problems that optical recording systems have already addressed head-on.

Archival, write-once optical recording is particularly suited to document and image storage applications. Here, optical recording is competing against a storage technology with an even longer history and an equally devoted technical cadre: photography. But the relatively slow pace of innovation in photography is a signal that fundamental and practical limits exist in any technology. As the optical disk becomes more familiar, it will be recognized as the natural successor to microfilm and microfiche.

1.4 Performance Parameters

For comparison and general discussion, the performance of a recording system is usually described by just a few figures of merit: access time, data rate, capacity, and error rate. The size of the drive is usually identified by its form-factor. Since all of these numbers are subject to misinterpretation and (sometimes) misuse, we need to define them carefully. The definitions below are specifically directed at optical disk systems, but they can be applied generally to any other recording format.

Access Time: The average time required to move from one data location to another (chosen at random) and begin reading or writing data is the access time. The access time is a combination of various drive motions and delays, as illustrated in Figure 1.4.

$$t_{access} = t_{seek} + t_{settling} + t_{latency} + \cdots \qquad (1.3)$$

Seek is the motion required to reach a new track. *Settling* is a delay period while transient tracking errors die down. *Latency* is a delay unique to disk systems. It is the time taken to rotate the correct sector into place after finding the correct track. The cautious reader should be aware that the term "access time" is sometimes used as if it were

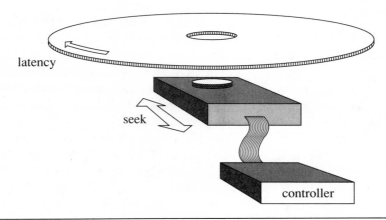

Figure 1.4 *Various delays contribute to the total access time.*

synonymous with seek time. In product specifications, this usage has the "advantage" of understating the access time. For subsequent discussions we define *access time* as the total of all delays as in Eq. (1.3). The combined total is much more relevant to comparisons of system performance than any single contributor.

Suppose data files are scattered randomly on an optical disk with a uniform distribution, independent of radius (this would be the case if the disk has the same capacity on each track and is nearly full). If r_{min} and r_{max} are the radial limits of the recording zone, the average radial distance between two files is

$$<\Delta r> = \int_{r_{min}}^{r_{max}} dr \cdot \int dr' \cdot |r\text{-}r'| / (r_{max} - r_{min})^2 = \tfrac{1}{3} \cdot (r_{max} - r_{min}). \qquad (1.4)$$

In words, the average seek distance is one third the width of the recording zone. This is why the seek speed of a drive is usually quoted as the time to travel one-third full stroke. In optical disk systems, the data are not always organized with the same number of sectors on each track (see Chapter 9, Section 1). The average seek distance then involves a more intricate integral than Eq. (1.4), but the final result is not much different.

The average seek time (distinct from Δr) is not a simple function of the average seek distance. Especially with high-performance actuators, the seek time is not proportional to distance because the head is being accelerated (and then decelerated) during most of a seek operation. In addition, the seek procedure might be more complicated than a simple jump from one radius to another. If many tracks must be crossed rapidly, the tracking subsystem may fail to keep a precise count as tracks are crossed. After the actuator stops, the actual track address is read, then one or more fine seeks may be required to reach the precise destination. The delay for these fine seeks (more than 1 ms each) must be included in the net seek time.

As the seek time is shortened, settling becomes a more significant component of the access time. When the bandwidths of the focus and tracking servos are much greater than 1 kHz, the system should settle within 1 ms after the coarse tracking actuator stops. However, if the head motion is very rapid, residual vibration, over-travel, etc., could degrade the servo accuracy for a while.

Of all the contributors to access time, latency is the easiest to compute. At the moment when the correct track has been accessed and the servos have settled, the optical stylus could be located anywhere on the track. On average, half a rotation period, $T/2$, will pass before the desired sector comes around. Therefore, latency depends only on the disk rotation rate: 33 ms at 900 rpm, 17 ms at 1800 rpm, 12.5 ms at 2400 rpm, etc. Usually the latency is kept comparable to, but smaller than, the seek time; for example, a high-performance magnetic disk drive with a seek time of 20 ms would probably be designed with a rotation rate of 3600 rpm. By contrast, the seek times of many optical disk drives exceed 100 ms, so latency does not contribute much to the access time, whatever the rotation rate.

In magneto-optic recording, the latency may have an additional component. Before recording data in a sector, the drive must first erase all existing data; a full disk rotation must be dedicated to the erasure step. In effect, the latency during one combined erase/write operation is $3T/2$, though the latency for readout operations is still $T/2$. Therefore, the rotation rate has a much higher priority in the design of this type of magneto-optic system. See Chapter 4, Section 4 for overwriting techniques that could eliminate this extra latency.

Other factors sometimes increase the access time. For instance, if the rotation rate is radially dependent, the motor must change speed during an access operation. Depending on the disk mass and motor torque, this change in spin speed could take longer than all other motions combined.

Data Rate: In some cases, it is necessary to discuss the instantaneous data rate, the rate at which bits of information are recorded onto or read from the disk. But as a description of system performance, the data rate should refer to the average speed at which user data are written or read. The user data rate may be considerably smaller than the instantaneous, raw data rate, because much of the channel may be taken up by overhead information and digital delays.

An example in Chapter 3, Section 2 demonstrates that the data rate may be a function of the file size. Several types of delays occur only once per readout event. They reduce the channel efficiency most when very small files of data are handled. Their fractional contribution is small when a very long, continuous file is written or read. One obvious delay is the time to read the header before each sector. Headers interrupt the flow of user data at regular intervals. The error detection and correction system (Chapter 11, Sections 2 and 3) adds both regular and irregular delays. During readout of an error-free file (and during any recording event) the user data must be manipulated to create the correct check bits or parity overhead. To do these calculations, the data pass through an electronic pipeline, creating a one-time delay in addition to the continuous channel overhead for the parity information. On those occasions when data are read and found to have a correctable error, the error correction system may impose unpredictable delays to find and correct the errors. The operating system can impose additional data-rate penalties, for instance if a sector interleaving strategy spreads out a single file onto a few sectors on each of several tracks.

In some product literature, the term *data rate* is used to describe the rate at which the drive controller can communicate with the host computer. But the bus rate is simply a characteristic of the controller electronics; it yields no comparative information about drives. Occasionally, a data rate for "channel bits" (Chapter 9, Section 1) is cited. These are artificial time intervals that do not relate to actual information.

Capacity: The data capacity is mutually determined by the drive and media. It is the amount of user data immediately accessible to the drive from one media unit. The capacity is usually specified in units of kbytes, Mbytes, or Gbytes. If the drive has a head on only one side of the disk, then any information stored on the opposite side of a two-sided disk is inaccessible (without first ejecting the disk). In the future, double-headed optical disk drives may be developed; the corresponding capacity would then include both sides of the disk, just as with double-sided floppy disk drives.

The capacity of a media unit is the product of its recording area, areal data density, and overall efficiency. The areal data density is given by the in-track data density divided by the track pitch. Since the track pitch is approximately the same for all optical disks, different data densities primarily reflect differences in the in-track density (code efficiency, data rate, overhead, etc.). The overall efficiency depends on the layout of sectors on the disk; see the discussion of CAV vs. CLV in Chapter 10, Section 1.

Unless otherwise noted, we will use the word *capacity* to refer to the net user capacity, which should not be confused with the raw capacity. The difference, which is called overhead, is used up in several ways. The area associated with headers (or the equivalent amount of data at the in-track data density) is one major source of overhead. Another is the parity information added for error detection and correction. Other peculiarities of the sector format can add significant overhead (see Chapter 10, Section 2). And part of each track can be wasted if each track must hold an integral number of sectors. Sources of overhead are measured as fractional additions to the user data. Hence an overhead greater than 100% is possible; the total overhead for CDROM is almost exactly 100%.

Data capacity, data rate, and access time are closely linked. An increased spin speed may be desired to reduce the access time (i.e., latency). The data rate must be increased proportionately in order to preserve the data capacity. Likewise, the data capacity may be increased by increasing the in-track density. Then the data rate must also be increased in order to keep the access time (latency) constant.

Error Rate: The BER, or raw bit error rate, is measured as the fraction of bits in error using some digital channel. For a meaningful system evaluation, the drive's recording and readout channel should be used. In these tests, it is best to use pseudo-random data, not some fixed pattern of repeating bits, because the worst-case pattern is not always obvious. The BER should be understood as underestimating the number of potentially error-causing defects. Such a defect might be missed if the error is "soft" (marginal amplitude) or if it looks like a mark that is supposed to be present anyway. On the other hand, large defects might cause synchronization failures, exaggerating the lengths of long error bursts and overestimating the error rate.

The BER is essentially a global property of the media; it usually refers to an average over an entire disk or at least a statistically significant fraction of it. However, the distribution of media defects on a recording surface is seldom uniform. A few small regions with high defect densities can be the dominant causes of system failure, even if they do not add much to the average BER. It would be desirable to define an additional statistic to describe local variations in the BER.

The BER is not really a performance figure of merit; it is mainly useful for system design and diagnosis. The user should be most concerned about the errors that slip through the error detection and correction (EDAC) system. The *net error rate* depends on the BER, the type of error correction code, and the uniformity of the error distribution. The net error rate is defined as the reciprocal of the average number of bits recovered between decoder failures. Failures include both uncorrectable error patterns (which the ECC can detect but not fix) and undetectable errors (which mimic valid patterns or elicit false corrections from the ECC). Systems are designed to achieve a very low net error rate (usually $<10^{-13}$ is required), given some nominal media error rate. The true test of the system is whether it can avoid errors when the channel performance is somewhat degraded or when the media defect distribution is realistically irregular. See Chapter 11, Section 1 for a more detailed discussion of error rates.

Form Factor: Optical disk systems have been designed in all the sizes popularized by magnetic disk drives—$14''$, $8''$, $5\frac{1}{4}''$, and $3\frac{1}{2}''$—as well as the important $12''$ size peculiar to optical recording. For purposes of standardization, the size of a system is described in terms of the slot into which the drive should fit. Strictly speaking, the form factor is only a drive limitation, though the original system design must determine the allowable disk or cartridge size consistent with the drive envelope.

The names of various form factors ($5\frac{1}{4}''$ full-height, $3\frac{1}{2}''$ half-height, etc.) are only indirectly indicative of the actual dimensional restrictions; they have largely historical significance. Consider for instance the $3\frac{1}{2}''$ half-height form factor. The term $3\frac{1}{2}''$ refers to the approximate disk size; the precise disc diameter may be 86 mm, 89 mm, or even greater than 90 mm (for magnetic Winchester systems).

The corresponding slot width into which the drive must fit is 101.6 mm. The slot height is 41.5 mm, which was chosen so that two half-height drives can be stacked into an 83 mm full-height slot. The slot length has not been clearly standardized; actual drives ranges from 146 to 155 mm in length.

Form factors provide useful guidance for drive designers, but unfortunately, the list of preferred sizes is always in a state of flux. Recently, third-height and even smaller floppy and Winchester drives have emerged. As smaller drives are developed, system integrators can readily adopt them into existing systems as well as new products, where they change design expectations and create pressure for new form-factor standards.

MAJOR CONCEPTS

- Optical recording and readout are accomplished using an optical stylus with a diffraction-limited diameter of $0.6 \cdot \lambda / NA$ (Eq. 1.1).

- Optical recording signals have a binary character. Analog optical disks, such as videodiscs, are FM encoded (Figure 1.3).

- The principle advantages of optical disks over magnetic disks are higher data density (narrower tracks), media ruggedness, and removability (Table 1.1).

- System performance is parameterized by access time, data rate, data capacity, data integrity (error rate), and size (form factor).

REFERENCES

Carlson, C., E. Stone, H. Bernstein, W. Tomita, and W. Myers, "HeNe laser: Thermal high-resolution recording," *Science,* **154,** 1550 (1966). Probably the first demonstration of immediate marking with a laser beam.

Chen, D., J. Ready, and E. Bernal, "MnBi thin films: Physical properties and memory applications," *Journal of Applied Physics,* **39,** 3916 (1968). The first description of true optical recording, and the basis for magneto-optic recording technology.

Howe, D., H. Thomas, and J. Wrobel, "Replication of very high density videodisc master recording via contact printing," *Photographic Science and Engineering,* **23,** 370 (1979). A description of videodiscs manufactured by contact exposure in diazo.

Isailovic, J., *Videodisc and Optical Memory Systems,* Prentice-Hall, Englewood Cliffs, N.J. (1985). A detailed review of videodisc technology, both optical and capacitive.

Itao, K., and S. Hara, "High-performance optical disk storage system," *International Symposium on Optical Memory 1987, Technical Digest,* 133 (1987). A discussion of the causes of the performance limitations of optical disk drives, with speculations on future improvements.

Maydan, D., "Micromachining and image recording on thin films by laser beam," *The Bell System Technical Journal,* **50,** 1761 (1971). This paper laid the technical foundation for write-once optical recording.

Philips Technical Review, **40** (1982). A review of technology for the Laser-Vision videodisc and the Compact Disc.

Pierson, P., "Design considerations for a flexible high-resolution film recording system," *SPIE Proceedings,* **200,** 100 (1979). A description of a 20-Mbit/s digital image recorder using laser exposure of photographic film.

RCA Review, **39** (1978). An issue devoted to videodisc technology, specifically RCA's capacitive system.

CHAPTER 2

Read-Only Systems

R ead-only disks, including the CD audio disk and CDROM, are technological successors to the videodisc. Digital information is replicated into these disks and cannot be altered during operation (except by way of damage). Strictly speaking, read-only products do not qualify as recording systems, but they are important to our discussion because they are forging the optical disk marketplace and because they provided the technical base for more advanced optical recording devices. Substrate manufacturing methods for read-only disks are used to make substrates for write-once and erasable disks. And the design concepts, components, and manufacturing techniques developed for read-only heads have strongly influenced the more advanced head designs discussed in Chapter 8.

2.1 The Compact Disc

The audio Compact Disc (or CD) system is the prototypical read-only optical disk product. Working from their base in videodisc technology, Philips engineers conceived of a read-only optical disk for digitized audio programs. In a joint development program, Philips combined their experience in optical heads and media with SONY's expertise in digital electronics and manufacturing. They jointly introduced the CD product in 1983, and it immediately became the de facto quality standard for audio reproduction. The introduction of the CD was the culmination of nearly a decade of careful systems engineering. The substrate replication and drive technology of the optical videodisc were combined with state-of-the-art digital signal processing technology to create a product that advanced the state of the audio art in every important respect—fidelity, convenience, and ruggedness.

A CD is a plastic (polycarbonate) disk with an outer diameter of 120 mm, an inner diameter of 15 mm, and a thickness of 1.2 mm, as illustrated in Figure 2.1. In operation, the optical stylus is tightly focused through the transparent substrate with $NA \sim 0.45$, substantially reducing the visibility of any dust or scratches on the uncoated disk surface. The substrate is manufactured by injection molding, using high precision molding techniques and equipment developed specifically for optical disks. Special requirements for the molding process include: precise thickness control across the disk and from shot to shot; elimination of stress, to maintain flatness and minimize birefringence; cleanliness at the disk surfaces and inside the molded part; center-hole profile, roundness, and concentricity with the CD format; and reliable replication of the microscopic format pattern.

A flexible nickel stamper is mounted against one side of the mold cavity. Its surface is finely patterned according to the CD format with a tightly wound spiral track of micron-sized features which represent the digitally encoded music. Each feature is replicated as a pit in the molded substrate. Methods for mastering, stamper-making, and injection-molding are described in greater detail in Chapter 12, Section 4.

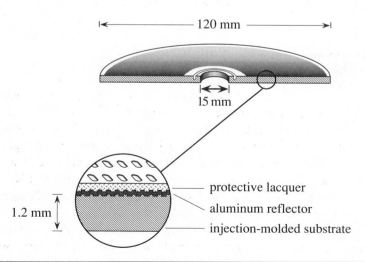

Figure 2.1 *The design and dimensions of the CD are shown here.*

After molding, the patterned side of the CD substrate is sputtered with a thin coating of aluminum, ~ 100 nm thick. The purpose of the Al coating is to make the formatted surface reflective. The pits are visible in reflection through the substrate as small, dark marks. Aluminum is thermally conductive and resistant to heat, so the disk is very resistant to thermal damage from moderate laser exposures during readout.

A protective plastic film, 10–20 μm thick, is applied over the aluminum to protect it from scratching and other handling damage. Without lacquer coating, any handling would scratch the thin Al layer and create large error bursts. This lacquer layer is usually a UV-cured acrylate, applied by spin-coating. Title information is printed on the CD over the lacquer layer, usually using UV-cured inks.

The CD disk looks superficially like a 45-rpm record with an undersized center-hole, but one immediately notices much more colorful diffraction patterns on the CD; the diffraction is more obvious because the CD is more reflective and its track spacing is much smaller than in a vinyl phonograph record. The CD also looks similar to many write-once and erasable optical disks, especially in its format appearance. But most writable optical disks are much darker (low reflection is a prerequisite for recording sensitivity) and double-sided (two CD-like substrates bonded face-to-face).

The basic performance characteristics of the CD system are summarized in Table 2.1. The single replicated surface holds 700 Mbytes of music information, plus an additional 300 Mbytes to cover the

TABLE 2.1 Performance of a CD System

Disk diameter	120 mm, single-sided
Data capacity	700 Mbytes of music (about 1 hour) plus 40% overhead
Access time	600 ms, average
Data rate	2 Mbit/s, directly from the disk
Drive size	Drives range from full-size stereo components, to car stereos, to hand-held portables
EDAC strategy	CIRC error-correction code plus concealment techniques to hide net errors

overhead requirements for a reliable digital channel. The raw data rate from the disk is 2 Mbit/s, or 1.4 Mbit/s for the digitized audio information. The spiral track makes as many as 20,000 revolutions from a radius of 25 mm out to 58 mm. At a scanning velocity of 1.2 m/s, this permits an uninterrupted playing time greater than 1 hour. The access time of a CD drive is relatively long compared to that of magnetic disk drives; it is even slow compared to inexpensive floppy disk drives. However, the CD drive is still much faster than any tape drive or audio turntable. Because of the extremely high data density, the signal from most CDs has a relatively high error rate; so several special techniques are used to minimize the effects of errors. This was the first consumer application of a high-performance error-correction code, or ECC.

Much of the CD's product appeal arises not from specific performance specifications, but rather from its digital (i.e., essentially perfect) fidelity as contrasted to conventional records and tapes, which rely on analog reproduction. Analog audio reproduction is degraded by noise from the media, transducers, and preamplifiers. Transport mechanisms introduce speed fluctuations, or wow and flutter. At high levels, there is usually a significant amount of signal nonlinearity, or distortion. But digital reproduction, as long as the data are reliable, eliminates all this noise and distortion; only slight digitizing errors and amplifier noise remain. Standard analog discs and tapes suffer from noticeable signal degradation after a few playings, but the Compact Disc can be played an unlimited number of times without any reduction in quality.

According to the CD standard, the audio signal is digitized at a rate of 44,000 samples per second per channel, a rate that accommodates an analog bandwidth from 20 Hz to 20 kHz. Actually the digital channel reproduces audio frequencies down to 0 Hz (DC); the 20 Hz cutoff is due to other electronic constraints. Each sample consists of an instantaneous 16–bit digitization of the analog waveform. For a signal of maximum amplitude, the voltage errors due to digitization are about one part in 2^{16}. Therefore, the ratio of signal power to noise power, or SNR, available from a CD system is about

$$\text{SNR} \approx (2^{16})^2 \cong 10^9 = 90 \text{ dB.} \qquad (2.1)$$

Some CD units contain features that further improve on the standard CD signal quality. For example, digital over-sampling is a technique in which intermediate signal levels are calculated by interpolation between the recorded signal samples. In some systems, additional (insignificant) bits are calculated by a smoothing algorithm and appended to each sample. These types of digital enhancement do not make the reproduction more accurate, but they do make the sound more pleasing by smoothing out the spectral response and masking digitization noise when the signal level is low.

The magnificent SNR, which is due entirely to the 16-bit signal digitization, is responsible for the perceived quality of CD audio reproductions. But digitization is not free; it greatly increases the required bandwidth, disk capacity, and channel complexity. The information rate for two-channel CD stereo is $2 \cdot 16 \cdot 44,000 = 1.4$ Mbit/s. In the CD format, an ECC redundancy of 33% is added to detect and eliminate errors. An additional 7% overhead for synchronization and 4% for display and control raise the total required data rate to 2 Mbit/s. The modulation code (the channel waveform that carries digital information to and from the disk) has a maximum frequency of 1.4 MHz. Therefore the quality of digital audio reproduction is purchased at the cost of a 35× increase in bandwidth compared to the analog audio signal (1.4 MHz vs. 2×20 kHz).

The raw CD digital channel is organized into blocks of 33 bytes: 24 bytes of music (6 stereo samples), 1 display and control byte, and 8 parity bytes for the ECC. The display and control (D&C) bytes provide the user with miscellaneous information, such as the song title or selection number, which can be displayed while the program is playing. See Bouwhuis, Braat, Huijser, Pasman, van Rosmalen, and Immink, (1985) for details of data encoding in the CD system. The ECC employed here is called CIRC, or cross-interleaved Reed-Solomon code. See Chapter 11, Section 3 for a functional description of the CIRC code and other powerful error-correction techniques. CIRC was optimized to simplify decoding in the presence of multiple errors and to accommodate very large error bursts. Because of the large overhead, it is not the optimal ECC for most other optical disk systems. Large error rates are frequently seen on CDs because of the manufacturing strategy (no certification) and the disk handling method (loading by hand from an open box). CIRC is very effective in detecting these errors. But when the defect rate is very large, some error patterns may not be correctable. The complete EDAC strategy includes additional tactics for handling uncorrectable errors. An isolated uncorrectable error is patched up by interpolation between adjacent readings. Only six audio samples (0.14 ms) are involved in an isolated, uncorrectable sequence. Interpolation over this interval is usually a good approximation that reduces the high-frequency response of the system only momentarily. Several consecutive errors call a blanking circuit into play, so the listener would hear only a brief silence (no hiss, pop, or click). An instantaneous cutoff can produce harsh overtones, so better-quality CD systems include a digital fader, which rolls off the output amplitude whenever blanking is required. At a relatively high BER of 10^{-3} this type of signal failure should (theoretically) occur only about once in a month of random disk play. In a common demonstration of ruggedness, many millimeter-sized holes are drilled through a CD but the disk still plays without any obvious disturbance.

The physical layout of data on the CD was designed to maximize its storage capacity. The data are arranged in a spiral track of pits, with a pitch of 1.6 μm starting at the inner diameter. The minimum pit length is 0.9 μm. Data are encoded with a run-length-limited (RLL) modulation code called EFM at an in-track density of 1.6 bits per μm. Chapter 9, Section 2 describes EFM and other useful RLL modulation codes in some detail. In order to maximize data capacity and keep the readout signal as steady as possible, the pit lengths and data density are held constant over the entire data band. The raw data capacity of one single-sided disk is just the area of the data band times the in-track data density divided by the track pitch. For a data band running from 25-mm to 58-mm radius, this amounts to

$$C = \pi(58^2 - 25^2)\text{mm}^2(1.6 \text{ bit}/\mu\text{m})/1.6 \ \mu\text{m} = 8.6 \cdot 10^9 \text{ bits}. \quad (2.2)$$

Thus, one CD could support a 2-Mbit/s data channel for 4300 seconds, more than 1 hour. Despite the inefficiencies of digitization, the overhead associated with error correction, and its small size, a single-sided CD can hold more audio programming than a two-sided LP.

Audio information must be recovered at a very constant rate, because the ear is very sensitive to slight frequency fluctuations. In a CD system the scanning velocity is continuously adjusted (by changing the speed of the spindle motor) to maintain a constant rate. This procedure is called constant linear velocity, or CLV, operation. After readout, the data pass through a small FIFO data buffer. The data are clocked out to the A-D converters at a crystal-controlled rate, ensuring that slight variations in motor-speed result in no wow or flutter. A major drawback to CLV operation is that any change of radius to access a new program requires additional time for the motor speed change. The overall access time in CD systems is about 1 second, including radial movement, rpm changes, and latency. This would be poor performance for a computer peripheral, but it is very attractive in comparison to phonograph turntables and tape players.

From the viewpoint of the recording industry, the read-only character of the CD is attractive because it discourages both piracy and home copying. Analog copies of CDs and even digital recordings off the air cannot approach the quality of a digitally mastered CD. Bootleg copying may eventually be possible with low-cost digital drives and recording media, but the legitimate read-only manufacturing techniques will still be much cheaper. Effective piracy would require access to full-scale, high-tech manufacturing facilities. Of course consumers may view this argument differently. They would probably prefer erasable optical disk systems. However, erasable CD disks and drives are not likely to be cost-competitive in the foreseeable future.

Viewed strictly as a means of distribution for digital information, the CD is very cost-effective. Each disk replicates up to 700 Mbytes of user information for a manufacturing cost estimated at less than $1. With a molding-cycle time of about 10 seconds, the effective rate of replication is over 500 Mbit/s. And because CD disks are compact, lightweight, and rugged, they permit very low-cost distribution.

The characteristics of low-cost manufacturing, ease of distribution, and intrinsic copy protection that make CD media technology attractive in the audio market make it useful for other applications as well. The next sections describe how the CD is being modified for use in data distribution, training, software distribution, and a host of new applications.

Typical CD drives are also cost-effective, compact, and rugged. They are less expensive than good audio turntables; they can be made virtually pocket-sized; and because recording is not required, their optical and mechanical specifications are less stringent than for other types of optical disk drives. Figure 2.2 is a photograph of a miniature CD drive, model D-10 from SONY. This unit measures 127 mm × 133 mm × 19 mm and weighs only 420 g. The system is rugged enough for operation inside an automobile and efficient enough to be battery powered.

Recently, a magnetic tape system that may compete with the CD has been proposed. The R-DAT, or Rotary-Head Digital Audio Tape system can record data at a linear density of 2.5 bit/μm and a track pitch of 12 μm for a raw data density of 0.2 bit/μm^2. Although this

Figure 2.2 *An ultra-compact CD player, model D–10 from SONY, weighs only 420 g. Photo courtesy of SONY Corporation.*

is only 20% of the data density on a CD, R-DAT capitalizes on the tape format to pack a digitally encoded album in a package that is even more compact than the CD. This particular technological competition is unusual because CDs are already established worldwide, while their magnetic counterpart, R-DAT, has not yet reached the U.S. market. A comparison of the two systems is a good illustration of the basic functional differences between optical and magnetic recording. Higher in-track data density can be achieved by magnetic recording, but optical recording enjoys the advantage in cross-track density. Mature methods are available for compact packaging of magnetic drives and media. On the other hand, R-DAT systems cannot be as reliable as CD systems, in part because of the head–tape interface. (The head rubs against the tape at 3 m/s.) The winning technology for digital audio may eventually be decided by the relative importance of convenient access (CD) versus recordability (R-DAT).

2.2 CDROM

The primary disadvantage of read-only optical storage is that it is new and obviously different. The basic markets for information storage have developed around the specific characteristics of conventional recording products such as magnetic tape, floppy disks, etc.

In order for a new technology to succeed, it must find appropriate niches or develop new markets. The CD, for example, has been very successful in developing a new market for digital audio. It is now in the process of diversifying into other major niches in the form of the Compact Disc Read-Only Memory, or CDROM (Lambert and Ropiequet, 1986).

CDROM can be defined as a direct extension of the CD system for general distribution of digital information. The disks are intended to store software, catalogs, abstracts, reference works, documentation, etc. Among many reference materials available on CDROM are *Books in Print* and *Grolier's Encyclopedia*. Read-only optical disks are an inexpensive means of data replication and a convenient medium for data distribution. In addition to high capacity, a CD-like system provides fast access in comparison with all the previous alternative distribution technologies (books, microforms, floppy disks, and modem-connected, on-line data bases). Table 2.2 compares the data capacity of these systems in terms of ASCII-encoded pages of text (40 lines × 80 characters, or 3 kbytes per page; see the discussion in Chapter 3, Section 2). One CDROM disk could replace 40 microfilm cartridges or 500 cards of fiche, and the disk is so much more convenient. In this information age, data bases of all kinds have increased rapidly in number and size. As the data bases grow larger and as their frequency of update increases, the costs of reproduction and distribution eventually dominate. CDROM is perceived as an answer to this problem of data-base replication and distribution. For instance, distributed CDROM systems could replace many on-line data bases, at great savings in telephone bills and increased convenience to the user. Experience has shown that the convenience (i.e., access speed) of optical-disk systems dramatically increases the

TABLE 2.2 Capacity of Media Used for Data Distribution

MEDIA TYPE	DATA PER UNIT	PAGE EQUIVALENTS
Book	1000 pages	1000
Microfilm	4000 pages	4000
Microfiche	300 pages	300
$3\frac{1}{2}''$ microdisk	800 kbytes	300
CDROM	500 Mbytes	170,000

use of the converted data base, substantiating earlier predictions of a library revolution based on CDROM (see Irving, 1986).

The CD system is appropriate for general data storage in the sense that its channel is truly digital; the disk-duplication process demonstrates the fact that digital data can be replicated an unlimited number of times without *any* degradation. However, the general usefulness of the CD system is limited for several reasons:

- The major disadvantage compared to standard magnetic media is the lack of erasability. This limitation keeps read-only (and even write-once) optical disk systems out of many markets, but it can be a distinct advantage for data distribution.

- The CD file size is not convenient for computer applications. Each ECC block contains 672 data bytes; because these blocks are interleaved, at least 1344 bytes of data must be read before any piece of data can be decoded. Most computer systems and applications are optimized for file sizes that are exact powers of 2—256, 512, or at most 1024 bytes.

- The EDAC for CD is partly cosmetic, relying on interpolation and even blanking. In general applications, this strategy is unacceptable because any errors can lead to the loss or (even worse) the alteration of critical data.

- Because the disk rotates CLV, the motor speed must be changed for radial access, and the access time is relatively long. The required rotation rate is 200 rpm at an outer radius and about 500 rpm at the inside. A delay of about 1 second is required to make such a speed adjustment; this is at least as long as the radial seek time.

The CDROM system is an extension of the CD system that solves the deficiencies in data reliability and format. The disk has the same physical parameters as a CD, including disk dimensions, track pitch, CLV layout, mark lengths, raw data capacity, etc. The raw data is encoded using the EFM modulation code and CIRC error-correction code. However, instead of audio data, a secondary digital information channel is encoded. This channel, which has a rate of 1.4 Mbit/s, includes file identifiers, user data, and additional redundancy for an additional level of error correction. The new ECC is also cross-interleaved, but is not identical to the CD CIRC. The secondary ECC and data format use up another 15% overhead from the data channel. The ECC is organized so that occasional uncorrectable errors in the CIRC decoding are spread across many code groups at this level. The CDROM is organized in blocks of 2352 bytes each, of which 2048 bytes (2k) are user data. This data file takes up the space that otherwise would contain 588 digital audio samples, or 13 ms of music. Because it is buried within the CD file structure, access to any one of these data files requires that much more information be read and decoded. The net data capacity of a CDROM disk is 540 Mbytes. The user (or rather the disk preparer) has complete freedom in the kind of digital information on the disk—text, graphics, facsimile images, tabulated data, computer software, etc.

If CDROM is to be useful for general data distribution, the hardware and data format must be widely understood and accepted. Standardization has been a challenge, but agreement has been reached on a long list of details, including the drive characteristics, disk dimensions, and most data format issues. In early 1986 a group of industry experts met as an informal standardization committee (called the High Sierra group) and issued a complete proposal for the CDROM file structure and disk format. This proposal is now the basis for very active international standardization activities (see standards document ECMA/TC15/86/16 [1986]).

CDROM disks are now being prepared and manufactured by many companies. Once the desired data are properly formatted on magnetic tape, the disks are readily manufactured at existing plants using standard CD technology. CDROM drives are now offered by a number of vendors; a wide variety of configurations, interfaces, and performance are available. Figure 2.3 shows a compact unit from Denon that includes an SCSI interface, which supports communication with many microcomputer systems. Other available drives are described by Tiampo (1987). A number of periodicals already support the burgeoning CDROM market and other read-only optical recording applications. A list of these is included in the references to this chapter.

2.3   Other Read-only Formats

In the future we may see read-only optical disks in a variety of sizes and formats. Many of these will be readable on multifunctional disk drives. The additional ability to play read-only disks would be desir-

Figure 2.3 *This* CDROM *drive from Denon, model DRD-251, includes an SCSI computer interface. Photo courtesy of Denon America, Inc.*

able on any write-once or erasable system, because it enhances the capability for efficient replication and distribution of data. The addition of a read-only capability is straightforward; it is only a matter of accommodating a slightly different readout signal in the data areas. (Most optical disk drives have a separate optical/electronic channel for the preformatted information between the user files anyway.)

The evolution of read-only optical disk systems should be expected to parallel that of other optical disk systems. In the future, we may see the development of high-performance read-only formats that provide rapid data access using constant disk rotation, high-performance actuators, and lightweight heads. Rapid access will be especially important for intensive data-base applications such as expert systems. Higher data rates will be important for the retrieval of high-resolution images.

Another direction for drive evolution is the integration of various read-only formats into a single drive unit. The Pioneer CLD–1010 pictured in Figure 2.4 is such a drive. It can play four types of disks: CD, CD-V, 8" laser videodiscs, and standard 12" laser videodiscs. Because the basic readout techniques and the required head design are similar in each case, the only significant design challenge in the multifunctional read-only drive is the incorporation of several decoding channels—FM demodulation for video, EFM digital decoding for CD, and circuitry for various other digital channel codes and error-correction codes.

Figure 2.4 *This multifunctional read-only disk drive, model CLD-1010 from Pioneer can play four types of disks. Photo courtesy of Pioneer Electronics (USA) Inc.*

CD-V

In our discussion of the optical videodisc (Chapter 1, Section 1) we saw that the videodisc signal frequencies extend beyond 11 MHz, much higher than those for CD systems (1.4 MHz). The wider bandwidth is possible because the marks are scanned at a much higher velocity: 1.2 m/s for CD vs. greater than 14 m/s on a 300-mm videodisc. If the videodisc channel can be processed a bit more efficiently (say, 10% more), it is possible to use the additional bandwidth to add a digital sound-track to the video programs. In the Compact Disc Video, or CD-V, format proposal, a CD channel is added below the FM-encoded video along with the usual analog stereo signals. The audio SNR is increased significantly, from less than 70 dB (analog) to 90 dB (digital).

CD-V programming—but not much of it—can be fit on a CD-sized disk. As with the CD format, the capacity is maximized by operating at a fixed scan velocity. But it is necessary to scan at 12 m/s to recover a full-bandwidth video signal. At the outer radius of a CD (58 mm), the required rotation rate is at least

$$f_{min} > 12 \text{ m/s} /(2 \cdot \pi \cdot 58 \text{ mm}) = 34 \text{ rps}; \qquad (2.3)$$

at smaller radii, the rotation rate must be even higher. Because of drive and media limitations, CD-type systems cannot operate at rates much higher than 50 rps. Therefore, the entire CD recording zone cannot be used for video. In the CD-V product concept, the inner third of the data area, which is not useful for video, is used for additional, unaugmented audio according to the standard CD format. The 120-mm CD-V disk holds up to 5 minutes of video with a digital soundtrack and at least 20 more minutes of plain audio.

It should be clear from this product definition that CD-V is primarily aimed at entertainment markets; a disk could hold one music video plus a few more related songs. Larger-format products using the same composite channel have also been proposed. An 8" disk can hold 20 minutes of video (per side) and a 12" disk can hold up to 60 minutes per side. Such disks are primarily useful for elaborate, music-oriented entertainment programs.

CD-I

The Interactive Compact Disc, or CD-I, is a combination of the CD system and video technology that begins from a premise which is the opposite of CD-V. Instead of adding digital audio to a videodisc, it adds digital display information such as text and graphics to a CD. The CD channel is used directly, but the data blocks can contain a digitized audio signal, or text, or graphic images (but not sophisticated animation). Because of the limited bandwidth of the CD channel (1.4 Mbit/s), a CD-I system cannot produce motion video. Even low-resolution digital images require about 100 kbytes per frame, and motion sequences require 30 frames per second (a total of more than 24 Mbit/s). High-resolution color pictures can be presented on CD-I, but they must be held in a frame store for continuous, still-frame viewing.

The C&D bits which are part of the CD format could be used to supply information simultaneously with a digital soundtrack. C&D information is carried in a channel that is entirely independent of the audio channel and its ECC. At an overhead of 4%, the C&D channel rate is $0.04 \cdot 1.4$ Mbit/s = 70 kbit/s. This is fast enough to generate a new video image every few seconds. However, a standard format whereby the C&D redundancy could be used for graphics, data, or text has not yet been developed.

The applications for CD-I are new but growing rapidly. A few of the imaginative possibilities are:

- *entertainment*—interactive games and stories that include the branching software;

- *expert systems* with responses that include audible and graphical advice;

- *business*—catalogs that include exhaustive specifications, diagrams, pictures, and even sales pitches; and

- *training*—textual and graphical instructional material combined with a soundtrack, data, and the software for sequencing the presentation and judging responses. Training applications account for most of the attention received by CD-I to date.

Both the CD-I and CD-V formats were developed at Philips and then presented to the marketplace as possible de facto standards, just as the CD format was presented. However, these formats have not yet been widely accepted, probably because the technology appears to be in a state of flux and because appropriate product applications are not defined well enough.

DVI

RCA has developed a read-only optical disk system that is particularly effective for video imagery. The Digital Video Interactive (DVI) technology combines advanced image-compression techniques and unique decoding hardware to create a full hour of digitized video from a single CDROM disk.

The optical drive and media in the DVI system are not unique; the single-sided, 120-mm disk and drive have the same performance characteristics (raw capacity, data rate, access time, etc.) as the standard CD system. The DVI innovations are the techniques for digitizing, compressing, and decompressing video programs. A standard, studio-quality video frame contains 512 × 400 picture elements. Three bytes of information are required to describe the color of each pixel accurately. Therefore, a high-quality digitized TV frame contains over 600 kbytes of information. The television refresh rate (in the NTSC system used in the United States) is 30 frames per second, so a standard-resolution digital television signal requires a channel rate of about 20 Mbyte/s. Current standards for digital video transmission require 20 Mbyte/s for composite video and over 30 Mbyte/s for RGB signals. But the CD system operates at a raw data rate of only 0.15 Mbytes/s. In principle, the rate could be boosted by spinning the disk faster (as in CD-V), but this would reduce the playing time to very much less than the desired 60 minutes (and put impossible burdens on the drive's mechanical systems). In fact, a 700 Mbyte data base could store only half a minute of real-time, digitized video. So, how does DVI manage to fit so much more onto the disk? The answer is that video imagery does not really use the full digital information channel. Colors and shades of brightness tend to change slowly across the image, so the color of a particular pixel can be encoded by just a few bits that represent the change from neighboring pixels. In those images that contain high-frequency, high-contrast components, the accuracy of the color rendition is sel-dom important to the human viewer. This means that an individual video frame can be represented using much less than 600 kbytes. In addition, most video programming is relatively static: The image does not change much from frame to frame. The data required to represent a frame can be further reduced by storing only the frame-to-frame changes. Finally, the DVI system that RCA initially demon-strated displayed a reduced resolution of 256 × 200 pixels, one fourth of the usual detail. Combining all these techniques, RCA found that a pleasing video display could be maintained with only about 6 kbytes per frame—a compression ratio of 100×. See Leen-hardt (1987) for a description of a DVI demonstration.

The DVI image compression can be produced by standard comput-ing techniques when the video programming is prepared prior to disk mastering; speed is unimportant at this stage. But very fast, sophisti-cated hardware is required for readout. The DVI system includes a complete digital frame store (a full 1 Mbyte of dynamic RAM, which is continuously clocked out to produce the real-time TV signal) and decompression circuitry to translate the compressed data for each frame into overall changes to the stored image. Although the input data rate from the DVI disk is low, all the circuitry must operate at very high data rates to keep updating the digital TV signal.

The kind of compression exemplified by DVI must be distin-guished from the facsimile compression techniques described in Chapter 3, Section 2, because video compression is accompanied by the loss of (it is hoped, insignificant) data. Facsimile compression, on the other hand, occurs without the loss of any image information. Both types of compression are efficient only if the original digital image truly has a low information content.

MAJOR CONCEPTS

- The audio Compact Disc is the prototype for read-only optical disk systems. It incorporates most of the features required in any optical disk system: servo systems, compact head, a digital channel, advanced error correction, and a very large capacity of 700 Mbytes/disk (Figure 2.1 and Table 2.1).

- CDROM is an adaptation of the Compact Disc for general distribution of information. A second layer of error-correction coding reduces the capacity slightly to 540 Mbytes per disk.

- Read-only optical storage is ideal for a wide variety of applications, from audio entertainment to digital video and database distribution.

REFERENCES

Bouwhuis, G., J. Braat, A. Huijser, J. Pasman, G. van Rosmalen, and K. Schouhamer Immink, *Principles of Optical Disc Systems,* Adam Hilger, Ltd., Boston (1985). Chapter 7 by K. Immink includes a discussion of data encoding in the CD system.

ECMA, "Volume and file structure of CDROM for information interchange," document #ECMA/TC15/86/16 (1986). This is a final proposal to the International Standards Organization (ISO) for the CDROM data format.

Irving, G., "The use of optical disk in libraries," *Legal Reference Services Quarterly,* **6,** 33 (1986). The predicted future for optical disk systems in reference libraries, including a discussion of relevant economic factors.

Lambert, S., and S. Ropiequet, *CD ROM. The New Papyrus,* Microsoft Press, Redmond, Washington (1986). A detailed review of the CDROM concept and its most promising applications. Includes descriptions of CD technology applied to CDROM.

Leenhardt, C., "The General Electric/RCA DVI or digital video interactive," *Memoires Optiques,* **39,** 20 (1987). A description of the DVI proposal and its current status.

Tiampo, J., "Drives . . . market driven," *CD-ROM Review,* **2,** no. 4, 18 (1987). A buyers guide to available CDROM drives.

━━━━ PERIODICALS

CD Data Report, Langley Publications, Inc. A monthly newsletter specifically for the CDROM industry.

CD-ROM Review, CW Communications/Peterborough, Inc. A bimonthly publication specializing in CDROM applications, software, and hardware.

Optical Information Systems, Meckler Publishing Corporation. A bimonthly periodical primarily covering read-only optical recording technology and applications.

Optical Memory News, Rothchild Consultants. A monthly newsletter covering a wide variety of optical recording topics, ranging from new technology to business news and market intelligence.

Memoires Optiques, ARCA Editions Press. A monthly newsletter that covers a wide range of optical recording products and markets from a European viewpoint.

CHAPTER 3

Write-Once Systems

3.1 Real-time Recording

The total output power of a diode laser in an optical recording system is not very great, but the power density of the optical stylus is impressively high. Fifteen mW focused to a diameter of 1 μm results in an average power density of $2 \cdot 10^{10}$ W/m^2! Light absorbed by a surface at such a high power density can cause rapid alteration or damage by a variety of mechanisms. Actually, the fact that the energy arrives in the form of light is usually of secondary importance, because the dominant mechanisms are almost always thermal (as described in Chapter 13). Depending on the surface material's thermal properties and its light-absorption efficiency, a 15-mW optical stylus could raise the temperature by hundreds or even thousands of degrees in less than a microsecond.

The surface alterations or damage caused by an optical stylus pulsed at moderate power are as small as the stylus. They may also be permanent and highly visible. Write-once optical recording systems take advantage of the small mark size to achieve great areal information density. Mark permanence (irreversibility) allows archival data storage. High optical contrast makes the readout functions of a write-once drive as easy to perform as in a read-only system. Other recording characteristics important or essential in practical write-once media are: immediate real-time marking, so that the data can be read without delay or special processing; a sharp recording threshold, so that repeated readout at reduced laser power will not alter the medium; and fidelity, so that mark sizes and shapes repeatably correspond to the areas of laser exposure.

A few of the many types of write-once recording mechanisms are illustrated in Figure 3.1.

a. *Ablative* recording in thin metal films. Because of differences in surface energy between the film and the substrate, some materials would thermodynamically prefer to bead up or form voids (Kivits, deBont, Jacobs, and Zalm, 1982). In order for holes to open, the film must be melted locally by the recording laser; therefore, a sensitive ablative recording medium should have a low melting point. This is why tellurium, bismuth, selenium, and alloys with a low melting-point received early attention as write-once materials. Recording requires more than just a melted region, because the continuous film is in a local energy minimum; a hole of some minimum size must be created by other means before surface-tension forces can take over the dynamics and create a stable void. Merangoni forces (a surface-tension gradient due to the surface-temperature gradient) could open the initial hole if the heating and cooling occur slowly. But for high-speed recording, actual vaporization of the film surface usually dominates the initial hole-opening dynamics, hence the term *ablative* recording.

b. *Dye/polymer* recording. Marks formed in light-absorbing organic films also look like holes, but there are major differences between ablative recording in metal films and in organic mate-

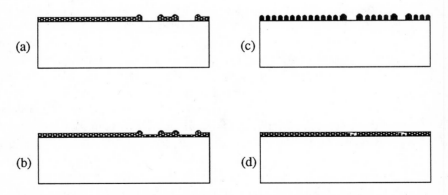

Figure 3.1 *Several examples of write-once recording materials and their recording mechanisms are: a) ablation of a thin metal film; b) ablation of a plastic film; c) coalescence of an island film; d) crystallization of a metastable amorphous film.*

rials. Because the thermal conductivity of organic materials is much lower than that of metals, extremely high temperatures can be reached, and material ablation is the dominant process. In addition to vaporizing and removing a measurable amount of material, the ablation provides a back pressure that pushes molten material out of the mark (Wrobel, Marchant, and Howe, 1982). The fact that surface tension has little to do with mark formation in organic materials is demonstrated by the residual layer of recording material in the bottom of the pit. The net surface energy is actually increased by the recording process.

c. *Coalescent* and *textured* media. The optical properties of a surface sometimes depend critically on its texture. Burroughs developed a recording layer that was a thin film of Au, vacuum deposited in the form of small, isolated islands (Apfel, 1983). In this form, the film absorbs light strongly. But heat causes the islands to coalesce into larger clumps, reducing the net absorption. The write-once TeO_x media made by Mitsushita operates in a similar fashion: Very small Te islands embedded in an oxide matrix "melt" upon laser heating and coalesce as larger Te crystals that have increased reflectance. Yet another example of a recording medium that changes its shape is the Plasmon™ disk described in Chapter 13, Section 2; here the heat of recording allows a textured, reflective surface to flatten out, increasing its reflectance.

d. *Phase-change* media. Some materials can exist stably in two or more structural phases, which display different optical properties. The heat of recording anneals the recording material from a metastable phase to a more favorable state. For example, chalcogenide materials (see Chapter 4, Section 3) may be deposited as amorphous films, then locally annealed during recording to the crystalline phase, which is usually more reflective. No material motion is required for phase-change recording except on the atomic scale. In principle, this is the cleanest of the write-once mechanisms, but it can also be hard to control—thermodynamically-favored phase change could occur at inappropriate times and places due to high storage temperature, contaminants, or autocatalytic reactions.

These examples serve to indicate the diversity of physical mechanisms that can be exploited for optical recording. For a review of

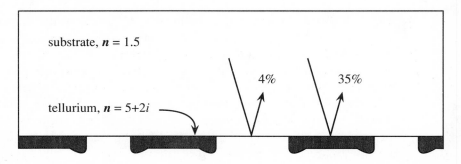

Figure 3.2 *Note the reflectance variations resulting from ablation of a Te film.*

optical recording physics see Wrobel (1983). The designs of actual recording media are considerably more complex than just a recording layer on a substrate. Common design features that increase media sensitivity and stability are described in Chapters 13 and 14.

The readout technique for write-once media is rather straightforward, much simpler than the readout process for replicated read-only media described in Chapter 5, Section 4. Almost all write-once media form marks that have a high reflectance contrast. Consider the venerable tellurium media coated on a transparent optical disk substrate as illustrated in Figure 3.2. Pits marked in the recording layer are visible because they are much less reflective ($\sim 4\%$) than the unmarked film ($\sim 35\%$). The reflectance coefficients for a thick (opaque) film are

$$r_p = [n_f^2 \cdot \cos\theta - n_0 \cdot (n_f^2 - n_0^2 \cdot \sin^2\theta)^{1/2}] / [n_f^2 \cdot \cos\theta + n_0 \cdot (n_f^2 - n_0^2 \cdot \sin^2\theta)^{1/2}]$$

and

$$r_s = [n_0 \cdot \cos\theta - (n_f^2 - n_0^2 \cdot \sin^2\theta)^{1/2}] / [n_0 \cdot \cos\theta + (n_f^2 - n_0^2 \cdot \sin^2\theta)^{1/2}] \tag{3.1}$$

where θ is the incidence angle, p and s refer to the polarization state of the light, and n_f and n_0 are the (complex) indices of refraction of the film and the incident medium. This interaction of light at a planar interface is derived in elementary electromagnetism texts such as Jackson (1975). For $\theta = 0$, Eq. (3.1) simplifies to

$$r = (n_0 - n_f)/(n_0 + n_f) \tag{3.2}$$

By symmetry, the normal-incidence reflectance is independent of the polarization. The corresponding reflectance (the fraction of the incident illumination reflected from the surface) is

$$R = |r|^2 \tag{3.3}$$

Crystalline tellurium has a refractive index $n_f \cong 5 + 2i$ at near-infrared wavelengths ($\lambda \cong 800$ nm). The complex value indicates that tellurium has the high absorption coefficient characteristic of metals. Inserting this value into Eq. (3.2), we find that the reflectance from unmarked areas of a tellurium disk is about 35% for illumination through the substrate ($n_0 = 1.5$). The effect of a writing pulse on this kind of medium is to open a (it is hoped, clean) hole in the metal film. Substituting for the refractive index of air ($n_f = 1$), we find that the reflectance of the recorded marks is 4% (see Figure 3.2). The recorded marks can be easily detected because the reflected light intensity (converted to an electrical signal by a photodetector) drops abruptly when the optical stylus crosses a recorded mark.

The Matsushita write-once material provides an example of write-once readout with the opposite contrast. Figure 3.3 illustrates a TeO_x recording layer (tellurium sub-oxide) which is a glassy TeO_2 matrix encapsulating very small tellurium particles. (Microencapsulation effectively protects the Te against corrosion.) The refractive index of this composite material is about $3.1 + 1.2i$, leading to an initial media reflectance of 18% (substrate incident). The heat from a recording pulse causes the Te microcrystals to melt. Although the composite film is not macroscopically deformed in the recording process, on a microscopic level, the Te particles tend to merge and then re-

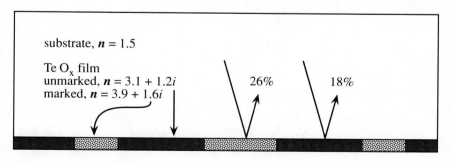

Figure 3.3 *Note the reflectance variations due to coalescence in a tellurium sub-oxide film.*

crystallize after cooling. As a result of crystallization and coalescence, the material's composite refractive index increases to about $3.9 + 1.6i$. Therefore, the recorded marks have a reflectance of 26%, significantly higher than that of the background.

The data signals recovered from TeO_x media have a polarity opposite to that of signals from metallic Te media. However, it is possible to alter the optical contrast of any type of recording medium by proper media design. In Chapter 13, Section 2 we will discuss a trilayer configuration that reverses the polarity of signals from an ablative Te disk.

These two kinds of Te-based write-once media also illustrate variations in the meaning of real-time recording. Hole-opening in standard tellurium media is a very fast process, taking less than 1 μs. Therefore, the data are available to be read or verified almost immediately after the recording laser pulse. The DRAW technique described in Chapter 11, Section 4, which is a powerful method for guaranteeing recording fidelity, relies on this immediate visibility of the recorded pattern.

The marks formed in a TeO_x medium, on the other hand, might not be immediately visible. The melted tellurium regions initially solidify in an amorphous state, and have about the same refractive index as the unmarked film. Eventually (within 100 ms) the amorphous regions recrystallize and the marks become visible. This kind of TeO_x is a real time recording material in the sense that it develops itself, but it cannot support DRAW or even rapid verification (see Chapter 11, Section 3). After discovering and studying this phenomenon of delayed development, Matsushita improved TeO_x with the addition of Pd, resulting in extremely rapid recrystallization for DRAW and more limited particle coalescence for lower media noise (Ohta, Kotera, Kimura, Akahira, and Takenaga, 1986).

3.2 12″ Disks and Drives

The first significant market for optical recording products (not just read-only) was created by the introduction of 12″ write-once systems. These systems were designed to take advantage of the pre-existing videodisc technology for drives and substrates and to exploit the media advantages of high storage density, removability, and data

Figure 3.4 *The LD®1200E 12″ optical disk drive is a good example of a 12″ write-once system. Used with permission of Laser Magnetic Storage International Company (LMS), a joint venture of Philips and Control Data Corporation.*

permanence. A good example of these systems is the 12″ drive of LMSI, pictured in Figure 3.4. LMSI was originally a partnership of Control Data and Philips, formed to combine their respective technical strengths in computer systems and optical recording. However, the 12″ write-once systems are principally used in new, hybrid applications, not as standard computer peripherals.

Table 3.1 is a summary of the performance characteristics of the LMSI drive. The performance specifications of other 12″ systems are quite similar. When judging specifications like those listed in Table 3.1, it is important to recognize that they do not always give a clear picture of system performance. True measures of performance must take into account not only the drive and media capabilities but also their mutual interactions and the influence of the use strategy (i.e., software). These various interactions go by the generic name of *sys-*

TABLE 3.1 The LD® 1200E 12″ Optical Disk System

Disk diameter	306 mm, glass substrate air sandwich
Data capacity	1 Gbyte/side
Access time	150 ms
Data rate	262 kbytes/sec
Drive size	19″ rack-mountable
EDAC strategy	Reed-Solomon ECC and read-during-write verification technique

tems issues. One illustration from a systems study of the LMSI LD®1200E drive (NTIS, 1986) will demonstrate the importance of systems considerations and the need to treat specifications (even honest ones) with skepticism. Figure 3.5 shows the measured rate of data transfer as a function of the file size. The specified rate of 262 kbytes/s is exceeded, but only for files larger than 100 kbytes. The measured dependence is a very close fit to the relationship

$$T = F/[100 \text{ ms} + F/(300 \text{ kbytes/s})], \qquad (3.4)$$

where T is the transfer rate and F is the file size. The interpretation of Eq. (3.4) is that the drive can read and record very long files at a rate approaching 300 kbytes/s (exceeding the specified transfer rate), but an additional overhead of 100 ms is imposed every time the drive is accessed. The significance of this delay depends strongly on how the drive is used in a given application.

The overall performance characteristics of 12″ write-once systems explain their mixed acceptance in the marketplace. As promised, the disk capacity is very large. Because of their powerful error-correction codes, the systems are suitable for the storage of general digital infor-

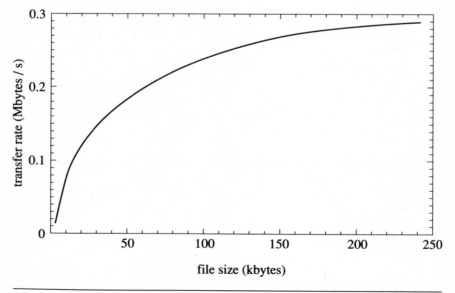

Figure 3.5 *Transfer rate versus file size for the LD®1200E system is illustrated here.*

mation. However, they do not fit easily into conventional computer systems because the drive is an unusual size, the effective data rate is much lower than standard memory devices for minicomputers and mainframe computers; and most importantly, the access time is much too long to compete with magnetic disk drives. The performance characteristics compare favorably with magnetic tape, so these systems are sometimes used as back-up devices. The archival character of write-once media does not conflict in principle with the requirements for back-up applications, but practical limitations arise because most existing computer systems were designed on the assumption that the storage medium can be rewritten. For short-term back-up, the net cost of write-once disks might exceed reusable tape, even though the initial cost per Mbyte is less.

The several extant 12″ write-once optical disk systems look similar on the outside, but they are not compatible. Disks with data written on one system cannot be read on a system from a different manufacturer. Points of incompatibility include different media dimensions (such as thickness), different recording and readout characteristics, and different data formats. Originally, a major perceived advantage of optical recording was that removability should lead to interchangeability. It should be possible to prepare a data base using one system and ship it for use at a distant site by another system. But available write-once systems do not yet really support this kind of information sharing.

Fortunately, significant new applications have developed for large write-once systems. The most important are archival document storage, image storage, and very large on-line data bases. Document storage is described in the balance of this section. Image storage is also well suited to new, high-density storage systems, because the storage requirements for each picture can be enormous (at least 1 Mbyte for a decent image—see Chapter 2, Section 3); a few errors would not endanger the overall picture integrity (easing the perceived risk of new technology), delays for image processing and data transfer of large files makes access time relatively unimportant, and the market for image storage systems is increasing rapidly. Large on-line data bases are another burgeoning market that is driving optical recording technology. The needs for very large capacity are so great that compromises with access time and other performance characteristics are acceptable. Optical disk juke-boxes which address such needs are described in Section 3.4.

Quite a number of document storage systems have been developed around 12″ optical disk drives. Figure 3.6 illustrates one (the KIMS system 3000 from Kodak) that has a data capacity of 2.6 Gbytes per disk (counting both sides of the disk). This is claimed to be sufficient for 60,000 document pages.

In order to appreciate fully the usefulness of optical disks for document storage, we need to understand how much information a document contains and how it is digitally encoded. The simplest form of document is a text file, such as the output of a word processor in which each character is equivalent to 1 ASCII byte. A page contains about 3 kbytes of information: 40 lines × 80 characters (give or take some bytes for control characters, blank lines, etc). A 1-Gbyte disk can hold up to 300,000 document pages of this sort, enough to outlast the lifetime of even the most prolific writer. However, digital text files with no figures are not the most common or most important class of document. Most documents are distributed in a typed or printed form. They may contain hand-written sections (such as signatures), drawings, or even halftone photographs. Under ideal circumstances it may be possible to apply optical character recognition

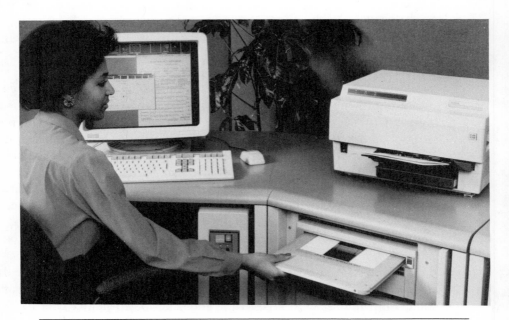

Figure 3.6 *This document storage system using a 12″ write-once optical disk has a data capacity of 2.6 Gbytes per disk. Photo courtesy of Eastman Kodak Company.*

and substitute an ASCII byte for each typed or printed character. It may even be possible to create a document-specific font by looking for repeating elements. But this level of sophistication and machine intelligence is not yet widespread. In any case, a complete document-encoding system must also handle drawings and pictorial data such as signatures.

Line-scanners, those used to encode documents for facsimile transmission, are the best practical examples of how to digitize documents. They are classed according to their resolution on the scanned page, quantified by the number of picture elements, or *pels,* per inch. One hundred pel/inch refers to 100 scan lines per inch, with 100 picture elements per inch along each line. One hundred pel/inch was once thought to be satisfactory for some applications, but 200 pel/inch has now become the facsimile standard. For higher quality images, 300 and 400 pel/inch are frequently required. High resolution is particularly important for the replication of oriental text characters or halftone images (like photographs in books and newspapers). Figure 3.7 illustrates the appearance of 10-point type with 100, 200, and 300 pel/inch digitization.

Figure 3.7 *The resolution in digitally scanned text depends on how many pel/inch are used.*

Digitized documents are represented by one bit per picture element, 0 for white and 1 for black. This high contrast is not appropriate for images, but it is widely accepted for text. Even analog means for document copying (electrophotography, microfilm, etc.) are usually optimized for resolution and contrast, not gray-scale rendition. Graphs, drawings, and signatures can also be adequately represented in this way. But facsimile copies of photographs and similar images are often unpleasing unless they have gone through a halftone process that converts gray tones into regular patterns of very small black-and-white dots. Even then, the resolution required to prevent aliasing (moire patterns resulting from under-sampling) is surprisingly high; at less than 400 pel/inch, halftones coarser than a 100-line screen show severe aliasing, and finer halftones lose the appearance of a gray scale. And of course, a facsimile representation does not convey color information.

The raw digital content of an $8\frac{1}{2}'' \times 11''$ page is over 10^5 bytes at 100 pel/inch, increasing to nearly 2 Mbytes at 400 pel/inch. Compared to a comparable text file (3 kbytes), this is an astounding inefficiency. Fortunately, we have some simple techniques for paring away much of the redundant information. From Figure 3.7 we may note that the picture elements are not completely independent; rather, they are strongly correlated with their neighbors. At 300 pel/inch, it is unusual to find sites with less than eight white or four black elements in any direction. And between lines, we would expect to find extremely long runs with thousands of consecutive white pels. Much of this redundancy can be reduced by encoding the data with a data compression code like the Huffman code, which describes the data in terms of the number of consecutive black or white elements, rather than bit by bit.

Some examples from the Modified Huffman code are illustrated in Table 3.2. Note that the code rules are different for white and black runs. This is because the code was optimized for the run distributions measured from typical documents at 200 pel/inch resolution, and the lengths of black runs from typed or printed characters are distributed quite differently from the white spaces. The code words that describe very short runs are longer than the runs themselves. But for the smallest *typical* run lengths (>4 pels), the code words are shorter, and *very* long runs are coded *very* efficiently. For 200 pel/inch document facsimiles, the Huffman code usually yields $5\times$ to $15\times$ compression compared to a bit-by-bit representation; a crude

TABLE 3.2 The Modified Huffman Code, Code Word Examples

RUN LENGTH	WHITE RUNS	BLACK RUNS
0	00110101	0000110111
1	000111	010
2	0111	11
3	1000	10
4	1011	011
5	1100	0011
6	1110	0010
10	00111	0000100
20	0001000	00001101000
30	00000011	000001101000
64	11011	0000001111
128	10010	000011001000

average for the compression is $10\times$. At higher resolution, the data-compression ratio is increased further: $13\times$ at 300 pel/inch; and $15\times$ at 400 pel/inch. Increased compression is possible because the typical lengths of white and black runs are longer when viewed with higher resolution, and the number of runs per line is fixed. Even more compression could be achieved using a code that is optimized for the specific document type and resolution. In fact, "adaptive encoders" can be built which continuously monitor the run-length statistics and modify the code rules to optimize the compression.

The Huffman code takes advantage of redundancy along a horizontal scan line, but in Figure 3.7, strong correlations from line to line are also evident. The relative element address designate, or READ code, is a two-dimensional compression code that takes advantage of line-to-line similarities by coding one line according to the standard Huffman rules and then coding only the line-to-line changes for several more lines. Typical data compression with the READ code is $14\times$ at 200 pel/inch.

Assuming an average $14\times$ compression ratio at 200 pel/inch, a typical document page can be stored in 30 kbytes. A 1-Gbyte optical disk could store up to 40,000 pages. Thus document storage is a particularly appropriate early application for optical recording because of the existing need for increased capacity and more compact storage, and because the error rate is not particularly critical (psychologically easing the acceptance of a new technology).

It is important to note that document data compression is accomplished without *any* loss of information. Decoding is a reversal of the encoding process which exactly reproduces the raw data. The only unpleasant price for facsimile data compression is an increased sensitivity to errors. For example, one digital error in a document coded with the READ code can blank out several complete scan lines (surprisingly, this does not normally make a document illegible). Document data compression is possible only because of the redundancy built into text images. If each bit of facsimile data corresponded to an actual bit of *information,* the bits would not be spatially correlated, and run-length encoding would actually increase the amount of data, rather than compressing it. In other words, data compression is not appropriate for most forms of digital information.

3.3 $5\frac{1}{4}''$ Disks and Drives

The second wave of optical recording products are the $5\frac{1}{4}''$ write-once optical disk systems. The $5\frac{1}{4}''$ full-height drive is sized to fit standard slots in microcomputers and related equipment. Vigorous activities within the national and international standards organizations (ANSI, ECMA, and ISO) began for the $5\frac{1}{4}''$ systems long before products were introduced; the intent was to provide for data interchange between different models of media and drives. By the end of 1986, general agreement had been reached on a number of media characteristics, such as disk diameter (130 mm), center hole (magnetically permeable hub with a 4-mm I.D.), substrate thickness and optical properties, and the case design. However, technical disagreements over the data format prevented the development of a true standard. Instead, two parallel definitions are being promulgated, with the expectation that the market will eventually make a clear choice between them. The *continuous/composite* proposal uses grooves for tracking and each sector of data is recorded as a contiguous block. The *sampled servo* proposal does not use grooves for tracking; instead, tracking signals are generated using many discrete tracking pads which are distributed throughout the data areas. Chapter 7, Section 2 and Chapter 10, Section 2 describe these two track-sensing schemes. At present there is still no overwhelming technical reason to prefer one approach over another.

Figure 3.8 *One commercially available write-once system is the LaserDrive®510 $5\frac{1}{4}''$ optical disk drive. Storage International Company (LMS), a joint venture of Philips and Control Data Corporation.*

The lack of agreement on a common format is an unfortunate impediment to the $5\frac{1}{4}''$ optical recording market. Nevertheless, a number of write-once systems are now commercially available. Figure 3.8 shows the LaserDrive®510 system from LMS. This system uses the sampled servo tracking method. Its basic specifications are listed in Table 3.3.

Further confusion was dealt into the $5\frac{1}{4}''$ market by the introduc-

TABLE 3.3 Two $5\frac{1}{4}''$ Optical Disk Systems

	LASERDRIVE®510	IBM 3363
Substrate	130-mm polycarbonate, metal hub	130-mm polycarbonate, molded 15-mm I.D.
Cartridge	ANSI/ISO standard	$135 \times 145 \times 9.2$ mm
Data capacity (per surface)	327 Mbytes	200 Mbytes
Access time	75 ms	>100 ms
Data rate	600 kbytes/s	250 kbytes/s
Drive size	$5\frac{1}{4}''$ full-height form-factor	Packaged as a stand-alone subsystem
EDAC strategy	Long-distance Reed-Solomon ECC	Long-distance Reed Solomon ECC

tion of the IBM 3363 system. The design of this system contradicts all the international standards proposals. The disk has no hub; it has tracking grooves but does not use the continuous/composite data format; and the case design is unique. It is quite conceivable that the IBM drive will be more than just a spoiler for $5\frac{1}{4}''$ optical disc standardization; if it becomes popular enough in the marketplace, it could spawn a new, de-facto standard. But the acceptance of the IBM 3363 system may be hampered by performance characteristics that are more conservative than those of any other $5\frac{1}{4}''$ system. These characteristics are compared with the LMSI system in Table 3.3.

Like the IBM drive, most write-once optical disk drives are configured as stand-alone subsystems, not integrated inside a microcomputer enclosure. They are used primarily in applications for which on-line capacity is the dominant requirement. Hard-disk backup is the biggest application; the existing competition for back-up comes from cartridge tape drives, which are still rather expensive and which have much slower access speeds than any optical disc drive. Other applications include customized data bases and document storage at the personal level; a disk with a capacity of only 200 Mbytes could still hold about 6000 facsimile pages, enough for most individual users. Future product evolution in this form-factor will probably concentrate on further capacity increases. A capacity of 1 Gbyte/surface has been achieved on one surface of a 130-mm disk in a technology demonstration.

3.4 Optical Disk Juke Boxes

A number of special data storage applications require memories that can store large, slowly evolving data bases. Insurance company files, major financial record systems, and scientific computing centers are examples of systems that contain vast amounts of information that must be quickly accessible at all times. Provided that the required retrieval speed is not too fast and that existing data files do not need to be revised too frequently, a juke-box arrangement of write-once disks and drives could be a nearly ideal storage system. A juke box consists of a library of disks next to one or (preferably) more drives with a picker mechanism that can retrieve, load, and unload the disks from the drives. The juke box can be thought of as a large drive that has a capacity many times greater than that of a single optical drive and a very slow access time (but still much faster than that of a tape drive).

Every 14″ optical disk system ever developed was designed with a juke-box application in mind. For instance, the first major optical recording systems were mass-storage juke boxes delivered to the USAF by RCA. The 14″ system developed by Kodak is another current example. Figure 3.9 illustrates the juke box, or *optical disk library,* that integrates multiple Kodak disks and drives.

The Kodak double-sided 14″ disk has a capacity of 3.4 Gbytes of user data per side. For a disk already spinning on a drive, the access time is not remarkably fast; file access can take up to 400 ms. But the usual access-time specification is not particularly important in a juke box. A typical data request will require that a new disk be retrieved, mounted, and spun up. So the motions of the picker mechanisms, not the optical head, limit the effective access time. In the Kodak juke-box system, the required time averages 12 sec.

The basic configuration for the 6800 optical disk library includes one drive, one disk-loading mechanism, and storage for 50 disks.

Figure 3.9 *The model 6800 optical disk library from Kodak is an example of a juke box. Photo courtesy of Eastman Kodak Company.*

Figure 3.10 illustrates how this juke box can optionally be configured for a wide range of applications. The basic unit (A) can be augmented by additional drives (C), space for 100 additional disks (D), or both (B). The combination of A and D is optimized for mass stor-

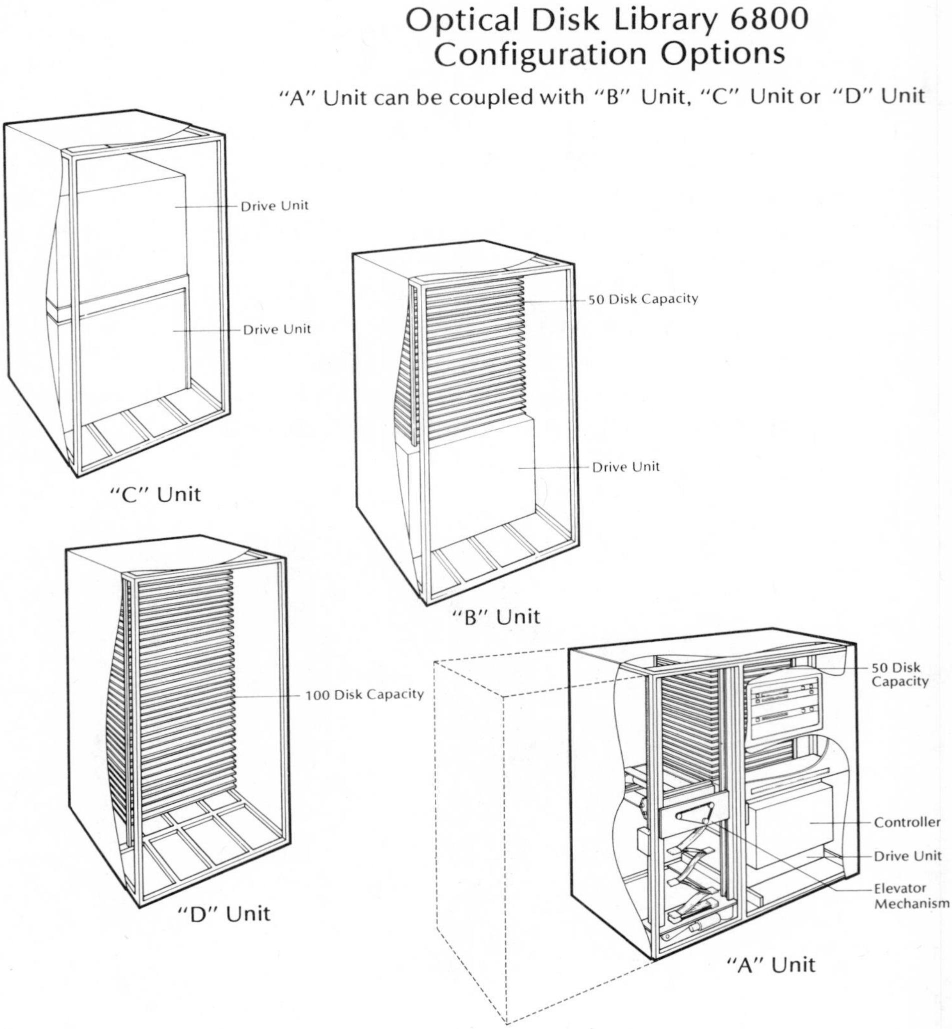

Optical Disk Library 6800
Configuration Options

"A" Unit can be coupled with "B" Unit, "C" Unit or "D" Unit

Figure 3.10 Configuration options for the Kodak 6800 optical disk library make the system suitable for a wide range of mass-storage applications. Courtesy of Eastman Kodak Company.

age capacity. On 150 disks, the system has a total capacity exceeding 1 terabyte.

Smaller disks and drives can be integrated into juke-box systems just as easily as large ones. A number of 12″-based juke boxes are on the market. Juke-box systems based on 130-mm ($5\frac{1}{4}$″) disks have also been designed. Since any given computer request is likely to address an unmounted disk, there is no particular advantage to a higher per-disk capacity. The important trade-offs in designing a juke box are the volumetric storage efficiency of the disks and the ease and speed with which they can be handled, loaded, and spun. Large and small optical disks have approximately the same thickness and are capable of the same data density, so the volumetric density is nearly independent of disk size. For a given juke-box capacity, large disks are easier to store and access because fewer are needed. On the other hand, smaller disks can be transported and spun more quickly.

To enhance the volumetric storage efficiency, the optical disks in a juke box are usually stored without surrounding cases. In many systems each disk is held in a carrier frame that grips the disk around the perimeter but does not increase its effective thickness (similar to the carrier designed for capacitive videodiscs). Bare disks can be contaminated by excessive exposure to dust, so the juke box should maintain a relatively clean interior environment.

If a juke box is designed around large disks, the drive(s) will have more spinning capacity. But this is important only if (1) there are enough drives to keep a significant fraction of the data base spinning, or (2) only a small part of the data base sees frequent use. Small-format drives, on the other hand, are significantly cheaper, and a large number of small drives might be preferable to one or two larger drives. In any case, more than one drive is required in an optimized juke-box design, because there should be enough drives so that the picker mechanisms operate continuously without waiting on spin-up, access, file transfer, and spin-down activities.

In order to maximize the picker speed, the juke-box system should keep track of disk utilization and arrange the disks so that the most current or most popular disks occupy the most convenient slots. Older disks which are seldom requested are eventually ejected from the system and replaced by blank disks ready for new data. Presumably the older disks are destined for storage in a vault (just like magnetic tape, except that the optical disk vault need not be quite so large and no retensioning is required). At the busy end of the file-usage hierarchy, there are always data files that are so active that they cannot be efficiently stored on a write-once medium. So the juke box must also be connected to a moderately large high-performance memory (i.e., high-performance Winchester drives). Eventually, juke-box arrangements using erasable optical disks may simplify the overall system design.

3.5   Optical Tape and Optical Card

Tape

Figure 3.11 illustrates the concept of an optical tape drive, a system optimized for total storage capacity rather than for data rate or access time. Data are organized in short tracks that run across the width of the tape. A beam deflection device repetitively scans the optical stylus across the tape, and the tape is transported from reel to reel to access new tracks. This recording format has been demonstrated in the high-speed photographic film recorders mentioned in Chapter 1, Section 1. Conventional write-once materials and optics would increase the potential storage density of optical tape by about $100 \times$ and also eliminate any need for post-processing.

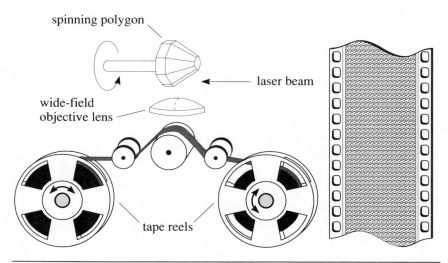

Figure 3.11 *This hypothetical optical tape system organizes data in short tracks running across the width of the tape.*

There are several devices available for scanning the optical stylus across the tape. Figure 3.11 illustrates a spinning polygon, which deflects the laser beam across a large, well-corrected projection lens. If the polygon has n facets, the stylus makes n scans for every rotation of the polygon. In streaming applications (recording or readout), the tape is pulled past the head slowly, but the velocity of the optical stylus is high because of the rapid beam deflection. Just as in high-performance magnetic tape drives, the tape could be transferred from reel to reel at much higher velocity during access operations.

A particularly ingenious optical tape drive design has been demonstrated by Vogelgesang and Hartmann (1988). They were able to implement tape access using a fixed optical head (no beam deflector or coarse head actuator). The reel of tape is stored inside a large-diameter reference drum and one loop of tape is wrapped helically around the outside of the drum. For each revolution of the drum, the head scans one long track, which is skewed at 0.7° to the length of the tape. As the drum rotates (at high speed), the reel of tape is driven with a slight differential motion so that the tape slides about 150 μm around the drum for every revolution, resulting in a track pitch less than 2 μm.

The practical design of an optical tape system involves tradeoffs between data density, data rate, and the several mechanical components. Consider a system in which the tape's recording zone has a width of 12 cm, a bit length of 2 μm (across the tape), and a track pitch of 4 μm. Compared to optical disk systems, these are low densities; but tape formats always entail such performance compromises, because tape positioning is less accurate than disk positioning and because a large objective lens with a wide field of view usually has limited resolution. In this example, each track could contain 6000 bits of recorded information, possibly enough to carry 512 bytes of user data plus ECC and format overhead. The density of user data is 125 kbytes per mm along the tape. For a streaming data rate of 10 Mbit/s (raw), the polygon must scan 1700 tracks/s, but the tape velocity is just 7 mm/s. If an eight-sided polygon is used in the scanner, it needs to spin at about 200 rps.

In an optical tape system proposed (but not yet demonstrated) by DocData, an entire short track is written or read simultaneously by an array of 256 diode laser sources. The DocData tape has a width of about 12 mm and a thickness of 12.5 μm. The tape is intended to be permanently housed in a case, 110 mm × 56 mm × 15 mm.

The case would be completely sealed to inhibit corrosion and prevent dust contamination from the outside. The read/write laser sources are focused on the tape with a spacing of 4 μm; therefore each track has a length of only 1 mm across the tape. The tape is mechanically repositioned beneath the head to access any of ten longitudinal bands. At a track pitch of 10 μm, the raw data density averaged along the length of the tape would be 30 kbytes/mm.

Even though the areal data density on optical tape is not high (by optical disk standards), the total capacity and volumetric data density are very large. Suppose a reel of optical tape has a diameter D, a tape thickness δ, and a data density ρ (bytes/mm). The total data capacity of the reel is ρ times the length of tape, or

$$\text{capacity} \cong 0.25 \cdot \pi \cdot D^2 \cdot \rho / \delta. \qquad (3.5)$$

The proposed DocData case holds a reel with D $\cong$ 50 mm, so the total raw data capacity is about 5 Gbytes (an impressive amount of data stored in a box the size of an audio cassette).

The difficulties of optical tape systems are due partly to their peculiar performance characteristics and partly to some unsolved technical difficulties. Data retrieval is very slow, especially if the drive handles the tape gently to avoid damage. Slow access coupled to the usual write-once limitations, makes optical tape a poor substitute in most magnetic tape applications, though it may be of interest for high-speed data logging or remote data acquisition.

The technical problems of optical tape are related to media damage and dust contamination. It is difficult to protect the recording surface of a tape from abrasion, because each layer tends to slide against the next layer as the tape is wound and unwound. Protective layers can be applied, but they increase the tape's thickness and stiffness. When δ increases, the volumetric data density decreases. And if the tape is stiff, it must be wound onto an oversized reel; then the volumetric efficiency and the access rate are reduced. For a realistic tape thickness, the substrate cannot provide much dust protection because it is not thick enough and because the numerical aperture of the objective lens is too small. (See Chapter 12, Section 3 for an explanation of this point.)

As late as 1986, at least three companies were planning imminent introduction of optical tape systems. However, by mid-1987 most of these efforts had reverted to research.

Cards

In the late 1970's, OMEX developed a high-density optical storage system in which the media units were 4″ × 4″ glass plates (Burns, 1979). Each plate was divided in a rectilinear fashion into 1040 bands per card (0.1 mm wide), 44 sectors per band (2.3 mm long), and 8000 user bytes per sector. As in the case of optical tape, each band was made up of short, closely spaced tracks; the track pitch was about 2 μm, and the information density along the tracks was about 1 bit/μm. The overall data density on an OMEX card was about $3 \cdot 10^5$ user bit/mm². This SlideStore system was designed for optimal volume storage density (uniformly filled slides packed tightly into a storage volume) and mechanical simplicity. The system used a relatively slow X-Y stage to access files and move from track to track, a wide-field objective lens, and an acousto-optic modulator to deflect the optical stylus along the 100-μm track length. Drawbacks to the SlideStore system were slow access within the card and (especially) a premature application of technology before the necessary optical components, media, electronics, etc., were readily available.

The current conception of the optical card is personified by the Drexon® Laser Card from Drexler Technology. These credit-card-sized units are intended to store up to 2.6 Mbytes of user data each. Figure 3.12 illustrates this product. Chemically, the write-once

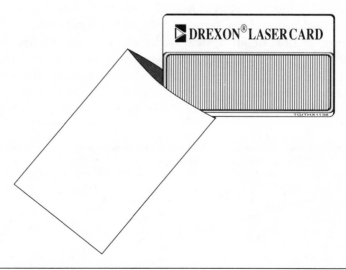

Figure 3.12 *The Drexon® Laser Card is a credit-card sized optical card.*

Drexon® medium is related to photographic film. At the recording surface is a silver-rich gelatin layer created by physical development of a chemically fogged photographic emulsion. Like developed black-and-white photographs, the recording layer is chemically quite stable. Most of the card's thickness is a transparent layer that provides a measure of protection from the inevitable dust and scratches. But scratches and handling damage remain the most serious drawbacks for optical card systems. One appealing characteristic of this particular manufacturing process is that a format pattern can be exposed into the card by contact-printing during the manufacturing process. ROM cards for data distribution can be manufactured in the same way. A higher capacity (at least 5 Mbytes) is possible on ROM cards.

Optical card readers and reader/writers have been developed especially for use with the Laser Card (Pierce, 1988). The design of a card reader/writer is considerably simpler than that of most optical disk drives. The head can use a half-aperture design that does not need a beam splitter (see Chapter 6, Section 4). The tracks are widely spaced with a pitch of 10–15 μm. Track access and scanning are both relatively slow and involve simple linear motion. Performance specifications for the model LC-303 optical card reader/writer from Nippon Conlux are listed in Table 3.4.

A more complicated, aggressive optical card system has been proposed by Optical Recording Corporation. The tracks on this card have a close-pitched, arcuate form; the recorded surface looks rather like a section of an optical disk. To scan the tracks, the proposed card reader rotates the objective lenses around the card instead of rotating the card. The optical head has four objective lenses, visited sequentially by the laser beam so that the tracks are actually 90° arcs. With a track pitch of 2 μm and an in-track density of 1 bit/

TABLE 3.4 The Nippon Conlux Optical Card Reader/Writer

Data capacity	2.6 Mbytes/card
Access time	< 500 ms
Data rate	10 kbytes/sec
Drive size	10.6″ × 10.6″ × 4.3″
EDAC strategy	Reed-Solomon ECC, net error rate $< 10^{-10}$

μm, this optical card system could store a raw capacity of 100-200 Mbytes on a recording zone of 40 × 80 mm. Such a high-capacity optical card system will require media with much greater resolution and sensitivity than the Drexon media. Several companies are developing cards based on the conventional write-once recording materials used in optical disks.

MAJOR CONCEPTS

- Many physical mechanisms can contribute to marking of optical recording media. Most of these mechanisms are driven by heat. The recording laser is really just an intense, local heat source (Figure 3.1).

- Marks in write-once media are visible as regions of altered reflectance, either greater or less than the unmarked areas (Figures 3.2 and 3.3).

- Archival storage of scanned (digitized) documents is a major application for write-once optical disk systems. A typical page scanned with high resolution takes up about 30 kbytes of storage.

- In a juke-box arrangement, an optical disk drive is linked to a disk library to provide automated access to a very large data base, up to 1 terabyte.

- Optical tape systems can achieve extremely high volumetric storage densities, but at a cost of reduced access speed and data integrity.

REFERENCES

Apfel, J., "The optical model of a trilayer incorporating an island metal film recording layer," *SPIE Proceedings,* **420,** 104 (1983). The optics of coalescent recording in thin, discontinuous gold films.

Burns, L., "SlideStore—A laser mass memory for image storage," *SPIE Proceedings,* **200,** 79 (1979). The OMEX optical recording system, which used 4" × 4" slides rather than disks.

Hunter, R., and A. Robinson, "International digital facsimile coding standards," *Proceedings of the IEEE,* **68,** 854 (1980). Basic description of Huffman and READ facsimile codes.

Jackson, J., *Classical Electrodynamics,* John Wiley & Sons, Inc., New York (1975). Chapter 7 describes the interaction of light waves at planar interfaces.

Kivits, P., R. de Bont, B. Jacobs, and P. Zalm, "The hole formation process in tellurium layers for optical data storage," *Thin Solid Films,* 87, 215 (1982). The basic physics of ablative recording in metal films.

NTIS, "Evaluation of the OSI LD1200 optical disk drive," NTIS document PB87–153441 (1986). An evaluation of OSI's 12″ optical disk system from the perspective of system performance.

Ohta, T., K. Kotera, K. Kimura, N. Akahira, and M. Takenaga, "New write-once media based on Te-TeO$_2$ for optical disks," *SPIE Proceedings,* 695, 2 (1986). A description of Matsushita's improved TeO$_x$ write-once material.

Pierce, G., "Development of the Drexler optical card reader/writer system," *SPIE Proceedings,* 899, 31 (1988). A description of read/write hardware for optical cards designed by SRI.

Rothgordt, U., G. Aaron, and G. Renelt, "One-dimensional coding of black and white facsimile pictures," *Acta Electronica,* 21, 21 (1978). An introduction to the concept of run-length encoding.

Vogelgesang, P., and J. Hartmann, "Erasable optical tape feasibility study," *SPIE Proceedings,* 899, 172 (1988). A novel optical tape drive design that requires no beam deflection.

Wrobel, J., "The physics of recording in write-once optical storage materials," *SPIE Proceedings,* 420, 288 (1983). A review of physical processes responsible for laser marking of various materials.

Wrobel, J., A. Marchant, and D. Howe, "Laser marking of thin organic films," *Applied Physics Letters,* 40, 928 (1982). The basic physics of ablation and flow in organic recording layers.

CHAPTER 4

Erasable Optical Disk Systems

The principal obstacle to the growth of the optical recording market is that read-only and write-once systems are not fully functional replacements for any existing recording systems. Their most obvious limitation is the lack of data erasability. By "erasability" we do not mean simply the ability to remove prior information (data can easily be "wiped out" on write-once media), but the ability to locally reverse information-carrying marks from one state to another. Erasability also implies that the recording medium can undergo an unlimited number of such write/erase or write/re-write cycles. (For most applications, a million cycles is close enough to infinity.) In many back-up and archiving applications, especially those using magnetic tape, erasure and rewriting is infrequent and theoretically unnecessary. Yet, the assumption that the medium is erasable is built into both the operating system and the mind of the data processing manager. Write-protected disks and privileged files (with read-only access) are supported, but neither situation is comparable to read-only or write-once recording. Write-once systems that lack the feature of erasability must create their own markets, no matter what other advantages they may offer. Conversely, if the functionality of an optical recording system can be rounded out by the addition of erasability, it should find many ready-made market opportunities.

In this chapter we describe systems based on magneto-optical and phase-change media, the two most promising approaches for erasable optical recording. Other intriguing methods of erasable optical recording have been demonstrated, but not with sufficient success to justify product development in the foreseeable future. At the low-technology end, erasable recording in spin-coated organic materials has been demonstrated by Gupta and Strome (1986). Such media may be attractive from the point of view of media cost and corrosion resistance. However, the recording mechanism is not truly reversible because it involves material flow; therefore unlimited cycles of recording and erasure are not possible. At the opposite end of the technical spectrum is the work at IBM on *spectral-hole burning*. This method (see Lenth, Macfarlane, Moerner, Schellenberg, Shelby, and Bjorklund, 1986) could result in extremely high data density, 100 to 1000 times greater than conventional optical recording. The development of spectral-hole burning is hampered by such major limitations as cryogenic operating conditions, lack of a recording threshold (which limits the number of readout cycles), and the special need for a wavelength-tunable laser. But because of continued progress, such as the development of recording materials with a nonlinear optical response (Moerner, Macfarlane, and Lenth, 1987), spectral-hole burning continues to be promising for the distant future.

4.1   Magneto-optical Systems

The concept of high-density data recording in magneto-optic films dates back at least to 1957, when Williams, Sherwood, Foster, and Kelly suggested that a magnetic memory could be designed using a MnBi storage layer and a magneto-optical readout system. The idea was further elaborated in 1958 by Mayer, who realized that recording could best be accomplished using the thermo-magnetic effect (Curie-point writing) and that a beam-addressable system was possible. (He suggested using a focused electron beam for recording; recall that lasers were not demonstrated until 1960.) A 1959 patent by Burns presaged true optical recording by suggesting that the light output of a CRT could be used for thermo-magnetic recording. However, this idea was impractical; it required critical preheating of the media to a temperature just below the Curie point, because a CRT is not a very intense light source.

Like all practical optical recording methods, M-O recording relies on a sharply thresholding thermal effect. At room temperature (and below) the recording layer is very resistant to changes in its magnetic domain structure. This stability is described in terms of the coercivity, the applied magnetic field required to change the magnetization.

For example, a coercivity of 2 kilo-oersted (kOe) means that the magnetic pattern cannot be switched or altered by an applied field smaller than 2 kilogauss (kG). The coercivity of an M-O material typically exceeds several kOe at temperatures under 100°C. However, all magnetic materials have a characteristic temperature, called the Curie temperature or T_{curie}, above which the magnetic structure is disordered and the coercivity disappears. In typical M-O recording materials, T_{curie} is approximately 200°C. If a region of the recording layer is heated above T_{curie}, it loses all memory of its prior magnetization. As it cools back through T_{curie}, the film assumes a magnetization determined by a residual magnetic field, usually applied by an external bias magnet.

Ideally, the only remanent effects of the heat applied to an M-O recording film are changes in magnetization—which are perfectly and infinitely reversible. Some M-O materials may be damaged through chemical or thermal mechanisms that are independent of the magnetics. But in general, reversibility is much more reliable in M-O materials than in other types of erasable optical media where melting and structural changes are intrinsic to the recording process.

Conventional magnetic storage materials (i.e., on flexible or rigid magnetic disks) have coercivities of a few hundred Oe. This coercivity is sufficient to ensure unlimited magnetic stability, with the usual caveat against exposure to high external fields. Under operating and storage conditions, an M-O recording material has much higher coercivity; therefore, the recorded M-O patterns are just as stable and even less susceptible to damage from external fields. In conventional magnetic media, the magnetic domains are oriented parallel to the plane of the film (longitudinal magnetization). Recently, some magnetic recording systems have used materials in which the domains are oriented perpendicular to the plane (vertical magnetization). Figure 4.1 illustrates these two types of magnetic domains. The demagnetization field from in-plane domains tends to oppose the magnetization of neighboring, oppositely magnetized domains. But the demagnetization field from a perpendicular domain reinforces the magnetization of neighboring domains. To the extent that demagnetization is important, vertical magnetic media can support a somewhat higher recording density than conventional longitudinal media. Practical M-O recording films possess vertical magnetic anisotropy, so that the magnetic domains are always oriented vertically (either "up" or "down"). In this sense, M-O recording is the techno-

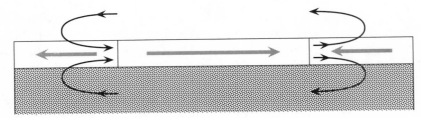

longitudinal magnetization

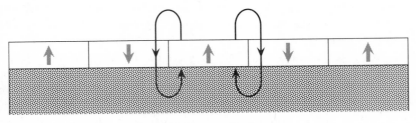

vertical magnetization

Figure 4.1 *This figure shows a comparison of demagnetization fields within longitudinally and vertically magnetized media.*

logical successor to vertical magnetic recording and it enjoys the same potential advantage of intrinsically high data density.

In conventional magnetic recording systems, data readout is a matter of inductively sensing the fringing fields that emerge from the recording film and enter the magnetic head (which must be positioned *very* close to the media surface). When the fringing fields are weak, as with thin-film media or vertical magnetic media, inductive readout is more difficult. M-O readout, on the other hand does not rely on fringing fields. Rather, it utilizes the Kerr magneto-optic effect, which senses the magnetic field within the surface layers of the recording medium. In qualitative terms, the Kerr effect is a slight rotation of the polarization of a beam of light as it is reflected from a magnetized surface. The rotation angle depends on the details of the optical interaction within the M-O material. It is also proportional to the net magnetization parallel to the direction of light propagation. If the magnetization is reversed (i.e., by recording or erasure) the Kerr angle is reversed. Unfortunately, practical M-O media produce very small Kerr rotations, usually much less than one degree. The slight rotation results in a very small optical signal, but a variety of readout techniques have been developed to enhance the signal and differentiate it from the major types of noise. These techniques are described in Chapter 8, Section 4, in connection with head design.

Figure 4.2 illustrates how the magneto-optic Kerr effect can be used to sense either longitudinal or vertical magnetic domains. In these situations, the polarization rotation is called the longitudinal and polar Kerr effect, respectively. In each case, the sense of rotation depends on whether the magnetization is aligned parallel to or opposite to the incident light direction. The light need not be incident in a direction precisely parallel to the magnetization. A focused beam can be used to sense the magnetization in a small spot, provided that the light rays are predominantly parallel to the magnetization. Note that a more tightly focused beam (forming a smaller optical stylus) can be used with the polar Kerr effect, because the media surface does not get in the way. In thin magnetic films, shape anisotropy usually stabilizes longitudinal domains and inhibits vertical magnetization. But some materials possess sufficient intrinsic *vertical magnetic anisotropy* to overcome shape anisotropy and ensure that the recording layer supports only vertical domains and produces a polar Kerr effect.

The Faraday effect can be used for M-O readout as an alternative to the Kerr effect. The Faraday effect is a rotation of the polarization of the light that is transmitted through the recording layer. For thick recording films, the Faraday angle may be much greater than the Kerr angle. However the transmittance of a thick M-O film is so small that the overall signal (transmittance × rotation) is small. The

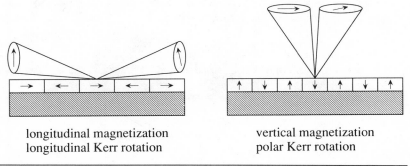

longitudinal magnetization
longitudinal Kerr rotation

vertical magnetization
polar Kerr rotation

Figure 4.2 *The Kerr effect can be used to sense longitudinal and vertical domains.*

Faraday signal is sometimes greater than the Kerr signal for an optimized film thickness, but actual systems use the reflective Kerr effect because the convenience of placing all the optics on the same side of the recording medium is a conclusive advantage.

Observation and readout of marks on a magneto-optic medium is illustrated in Figure 4.3. The marks are not visible in an ordinary viewing system, such as a bright-field microscope. Only the surface structure of the substrate can be seen—for example, the grooved profile shown in the figure. To image the marks, we must illuminate them with polarized light (aligned horizontally in the figure) and then view them through an analyzer, which is another polarizer aligned nearly perpendicular to the incident polarization. The contrast of the marks (whether they appear brighter on a dark background or dark on a brighter background) depends on the sense of the Kerr (or Faraday) rotation and on whether the analyzer is aligned slightly clockwise or counterclockwise from the null position. An optical head detects M-O marks in a similar fashion, using a polarizer and analyzer combination.

Test systems for evaluating M-O media have been commercially available since 1985 (e.g., Nakamichi's model OMS series). However, M-O drives useful as computer peripherals or in other data-storage applications have only recently become available. Several

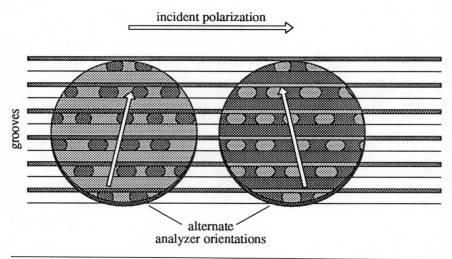

Figure 4.3 *Contrast in Kerr-effect readout depends on the analyzer orientation.*

companies have demonstrated or introduced M-O drives in 1989. Table 4.1 lists some of the characteristics of a full-height $5\frac{1}{4}$" drive announced by Sharp (Nishioka, 1987).

To evaluate the Sharp system, it may be important to consider both the total disk capacity and the capacity per side. The total disk capacity (380 Mbytes) may be a relevant quantity if the system is used for archival purposes (as a back-up device) or if the volume storage density is an important feature (in a juke box). But the Sharp system has only one optical head, so only one side of the disk can be accessed at a time; and two-sided media cannot be used to full advantage in single-sided drives. This kind of two-sided disk could even be a liability if data from both sides are needed simultaneously. If the two sides were distributed as separate units, they could be accessed simultaneously on two drives. But a two-sided disk must be ejected and reinserted with each data call. The situation is quite different for a two-sided disk designed for a two-headed system. In this case, both sides of the disk are accessible simultaneously. In order to be compatible with a two-headed drive, the two halves of the disk must be formatted oppositely (one clockwise, the other counterclockwise). In this two-sided design, both sides would not be readable on a simpler single-headed drive unless the spindle rotation can be reversed.

TABLE 4.1 Announced Performance Characteristics of a $5\frac{1}{4}$" M-O Drive from Sharp

Disk diameter	130 mm
Data capacity	190 Mbyte/surface
	2-sided disk
Access time	150 ms seek time
	33 ms latency (readout)
	CAV operation
	>183 ms average access time (read)
	>250 ms average access time (write)
Data rate	>1.2 Mbit/s sustained
	2.4 Mbyte/s over a SCSI interface
Drive size	full-height $5\frac{1}{4}$" form factor
EDAC characteristics	$<10^{-4}$ BER
	$<10^{-12}$ net error rate
	Error protection provided by a high-level ECC and by fencing of large defects

The areal data density is lower in proposed M-O systems than in write-once systems. The overhead for formatting and error correction is comparable, but the intrinsic signal quality in M-O systems is not quite as good as in write-once systems. As a consequence, first-generation M-O systems have somewhat lower data densities and data rates.

The recording and readout rate shown in Table 4.1 is rather low compared to that of existing magnetic systems. But the data rate is not always critical to the overall system performance, especially for applications that handle small files. Instead, the most significant indication of slowness is the access time. Both the seek time and the latency are comparable to those of existing write-once drives, and much slower than those of typical (or even low-end) magnetic Winchester drives. Advances in drive design may soon produce M-O and write-once drives that rival Winchesters in seek time and latency. However, current M-O technology suffers from an additional disadvantage vis-a-vis conventional magnetic technology: Each recording operation must be preceded by a separate pass to erase the addressed sector. This adds one full rotation time, tripling the average latency. Methods for direct overwrite (single-pass or simultaneous erase and write) in M-O systems are presently attracting a lot of attention. See Section 4.4 for some proposed overwriting techniques.

The net error rate claimed for M-O systems is the same as for all other types of optical recording systems. This is largely a reflection of a common user requirement that all systems must meet. It is reasonable to suppose that the raw error distributions in all classes of optical disks will be similar, especially if the errors are due primarily to substrate defects and particulate contamination. Since they use similar or even identical error correction codes, all optical disk systems should provide comparable levels of protection against uncorrectable errors. However, erasable optical disk systems have one major advantage in the area of defect management. Write-once disks can be prequalified only by indirect or sampled testing. But 100% of an erasable disk can be tested prior to its use in a certification step (see Chapter 11, Section 4). This allows the manufacturer of disks to reject disks that have serious defects or to fence out any sector on the disk which contains a dangerous number of defects. Fencing of an erasable optical disk is even more effective than the usual fencing of magnetic disks because of the high-powered ECC.

4.2 M-O Recording Materials

Among M-O recording materials, the early favorite was MnBi. The earliest magneto-optic materials had Curie points well below room temperature (making reliable data storage problematical). But MnBi can be prepared in a crystalline form with a Curie point of $T_{curie} \cong$ 200°C, high enough for data stability and low enough for acceptable recording sensitivity, given current limitations on available laser power and substrate stability. Chen (1968) presented a detailed study of M-O marking and readout on MnBi thin films. MnBi films also exhibit a fairly large Kerr effect, 0.7°, and a very large Faraday effect, 73 deg/μm. Other early M-O recording materials are described in a survey by Lee (1973). These materials were generally polycrystalline. They had a grainy optical appearance and the magnetic domains were irregular in shape, following crystallite boundaries. For these reasons, the readout noise level from early M-O recording materials was very high. Once it was understood, the poor signal-to-noise ratio (SNR) of polycrystalline films discouraged further work on M-O systems.

Erasable optical recording received an important boost with the discovery at IBM of a new class of M-O materials, the rare-earth/transition-metal (RE/TM) alloys (Choudari, Cuomo, Gambino, and McGuire, 1976). The rare-earth elements include gadolinium, terbium, dysprosium, etc., from the lanthanide section of the periodic table. The useful transition metals are iron and cobalt. The rare-earth components, which usually comprise about 20 atomic % of the composition, help to create compatible, amorphous alloys and impart vertical magnetic anisotropy. The transition-metal components provide the dominant magneto-optical interaction and create most of the Kerr effect. The M-O interaction is strong only by comparison with other known materials; the Kerr rotation from an RE/TM film is typically less than 0.4°. But fortuitously the effect reaches a maximum in the near-infrared, $\lambda \sim 800$ nm, the wavelength range for practical optical disk readout (see the discussion of diode lasers in Chapter 6).

The amorphous character of RE/TM recording materials is advantageous for several reasons. Readout and recording noise caused by crystallite boundaries is eliminated. The magnetic properties can be readily engineered over a wide range, because uniform amorphous films can be created over a wide composition range. Amorphous films are usually more elastic than their crystalline counterparts, so damage is less likely during the thermal cycle associated with recording. The absence of grain boundaries usually makes amorphous films less susceptible to corrosion than crystalline films of the same composition. And because amorphous films have lower electrical resistivity, smaller eddy currents are generated during high-frequency magnetic switching.

RE/TM alloys are ferrimagnetic, meaning that the rare-earth and transition-metal components form magnetic sublattices that contribute oppositely to the net magnetization, as illustrated in Figure 4.4. The magnetization of each sublattice decreases with increasing temperature and eventually vanishes above T_{curie}. But the rates of decrease differ. Usually the opposing magnetizations exactly cancel at some temperature below T_{curie} which is called the compensation point, T_{comp}. The compensation point can be either greater than or less than the ambient temperature, T_a. At T_{comp}, there is no net magnetization, and the ferrimagnetic material cannot interact with any external magnetic fields. Therefore, at temperatures near T_{comp} the coercivity, H_c, is very high and magnetic domains are very stable.

In the usual Curie-point recording process, the laser heats the me-

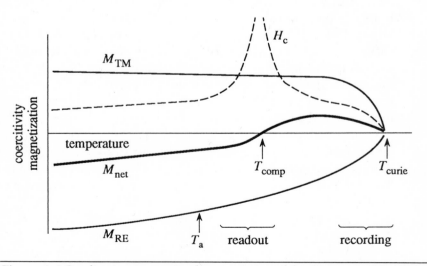

Figure 4.4 *Qualitative magnetic characteristics of ferrimagnetic RE/TM materials are shown here.*

dium above T_{curie} and the necessary thermal threshold is due to the sharp drop in coercivity near T_{curie}. The magnetic bias field that determines the residual magnetization pattern can be fairly small in this case. It need only overcome demagnetization and any stray fields.

With ferrimagnetic materials, it is possible to perform M-O recording without heating the medium to T_{curie}. Just above T_{comp}, the coercivity drops very rapidly. If the bias field is strong enough, the optical stylus need only heat the recording film above T_{comp} to the temperature at which the coercivity equals the bias. However, this technique of *compensation-point recording* is usually not very practical because of the difficulties of maintaining a constant bias field, ensuring a constant value of T_{comp}, and correcting for a wide range of T_a. The signal from compensation-point recording is generally noisier than from Curie-point recording. The compensation point can be adjusted to improve Curie-point recording. When T_{comp} is somewhat higher than T_a, the coercivity is very high at T_a (enhancing data stability during storage) and especially at the slightly elevated temperatures encountered during low-power readout (enhancing data stability during extended readout).

The compensation point of an RE/TM alloy depends primarily on the concentration of the RE component. Figure 4.5 shows curves of net magnetization versus temperature for three TbFe compositions. The film with 23 atomic % Tb has a value of T_{comp} well above room temperature. Because of a reduced contribution from the RE sublattice, films with less Tb have lower compensation points; at 19 atomic % Tb, T_{comp} is below room temperature (off the graph). Conversely, Tb-rich films have higher values of T_{comp}. In fact, if the Tb composition exceeds approximately 26 atomic %, there is no compensation point, because in some sense T_{comp} is greater than T_{curie}. Amorphous RE/TM materials can be prepared with a wide range of composition without local phase separation; thus their magnetic properties can be easily adjusted.

In practical recording materials, the compensation point should be kept well below the Curie point; otherwise, the medium might respond in a confused way to Curie-point recording. During the recording process, the new domain structure is frozen in as heated regions of the film cool through a temperature just below T_{curie} where the bias magnetic field equals the coercivity. At that moment, the net magnetization of the film is aligned with the applied field. However, the alignment of the transition-metal sublattice can be either parallel

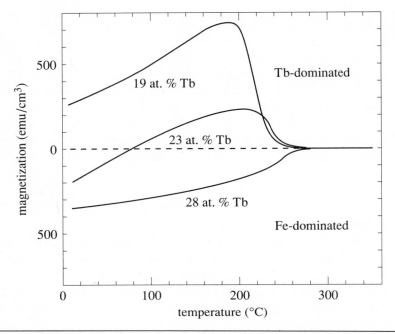

Figure 4.5 *These representative magnetization curves for TbFe show that the compensation point depends strongly on the composition.*

or anti-parallel to the applied field, depending on which sublattice dominates the net magnetization. If T_{comp} is much less than T_{curie}, the transition-metal sublattice dominates the magnetization as the film cools; therefore, the transition-metal magnetization in the recorded marks will be parallel to the applied field. If the rare-earth concentration is high enough (e.g., 28% in Figure 4.5), no compensation point exists and the rare-earth sublattice dominates at all temperatures. In such a film, the transition-metal magnetization of recorded marks is always aligned opposite to the applied bias field. The Kerr rotation angle and the signal contrast (dark marks on a brighter background, or vice versa, as shown in Figure 4.3) depend on the direction of the transition-metal magnetization. Therefore, RE/TM recording films with and without a compensation point display opposite signal contrasts. A recording film with an intermediate composition ($\sim 26\%$) is very undesirable because the contrast could reverse during operation due to slight variations in the composition, the bias field, or other recording conditions. This effect is seen as a dramatic increase in noise and a reduction in signal amplitude. A slightly higher rare-earth concentration is also undesirable because aging (oxidation of the rare-earth component) could shift the effective composition into the intermediate, confused range.

For Curie-point recording, the optical stylus must heat the recording film by $T_{curie} - T_a$ everywhere in the recorded mark. The required laser power is proportional to this temperature difference; therefore, T_{curie} controls media sensitivity. High sensitivity is important to permit high recording rates. But if the medium is too sensitive, it might not tolerate enough readout power without data damage. As shown in Figure 4.5, the Curie point is essentially independent of the RE/TM composition ratio, but it does depend on the choice of the TM component. Fe-based RE/TM films usually have a value of T_{curie} less than 200°C. But T_{curie} is much higher in Co-based films, up to 300°C. When an RE/TM recording material is formulated, the ratio of Co to Fe is adjusted to produce the desired media sensitivity.

Because it affects the value of T_{comp}, the RE/TM composition ratio also affects the net magnetization. This changes both the coercivity of the material and the internal demagnetization fields. In a useful recording material, the coercivity should exceed the demagnetization field at all temperatures, or else neighboring domains will interfere with each other. A high demagnetization field near T_{curie} would make the recording process dependent on the local magnetization conditions and less strongly dominated by the bias field. Furthermore, a high demagnetization field at T_a could compromise the data stability. Figure 4.6 illustrates the dependence of demagnetization and coercivity on film composition. The solid and dashed lines are the demagnetization fields and coercivity, respectively, plotted in equivalent units. Compared to RE-poor films ($T_{comp} < T_a$), RE-rich films have both higher coercivity and lower demagnetization, and hence, greater magnetic stability during and after recording. Therefore, the compensation point should not be too low. We noted previously that high noise levels also result if T_{comp} is too close to T_{curie}. In one study, minimum noise was obtained from compositions with $T_{comp} \sim T_{curie} - 70°C$ (Nagato, Kawamoto, Sato, and Yorozu, 1988). As a general prescription, practical M-O recording materials should be formulated with T_{comp} intermediate between T_a and T_{curie}.

The recording mechanism for M-O media is truly and indefinitely reversible. Nevertheless, the recording layer can be damaged by a

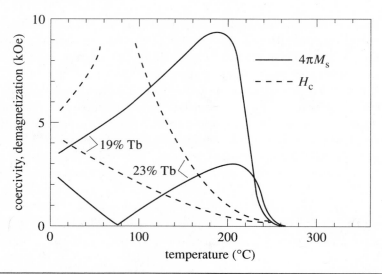

Figure 4.6 *A comparison of the coercivity and the demagnetization fields for TbFe films is shown here.*

laser pulse of too high a power or too long a duration. As we will see in a detailed discussion of the exposure process (Chapter 5, Section 3), the center of the recorded mark is heated to temperatures much higher than the edge of the mark, approximately twice as high. To be truly erasable, the M-O material must survive temperatures of about $2 \cdot T_{\mathrm{curie}} - T_a$ without any kind of damage. Inadvertent hole-melting has not been a serious problem with M-O materials because the melting point is very high, but still the simultaneous requirements of high sensitivity and a high read-out power can be accommodated only when T_{curie} is approximately 200°C. Partial annealing of the film (into a crystalline structure or a relaxed amorphous structure without vertical anisotropy) can occur during the recording process if the Curie point and the recording temperature are especially high. Such annealing can be a slow process that slowly renders the material useless after thousands of erasure cycles.

Temperatures approaching 1000°C are achieved during the marking of some write-once media. However M-O media cannot be heated this efficiently because the recording film and protective layers conduct heat too well. Lateral heat diffusion and some vertical diffusion into the substrate keep the scanned surface from heating up so rapidly (see Chapter 13, Section 3). The high thermal diffusivity poses a potential performance problem: If the track pitch is too small, during recording the optical stylus can inadvertently heat neighboring tracks to the point that partial writing or erasure occurs. If the heat diffuses farther than the radius of the optical stylus, thermal diffusion (rather than the magnetic properties of the medium or the size of the stylus itself) might determine the lower limit on the mark size. The effects of thermal diffusion can be reduced by recording with short pulses or at a high scanning velocity, but at the cost of even more laser power.

Table 4.2 is a recapitulation of the desirable materials properties

TABLE 4.2 Basic Requirements for an M-O Recording Material

INTRINSIC CHARACTERISTIC	PURPOSE
Amorphous structure	Optically smooth surface to reduce background noise; amorphous magnetic structure so that the domains are smooth
High melting point or annealing temperature	Media stability after many write/erase cycles
Low thermal conductivity	Prevent thermal spreading for high sensitivity and minimum mark size
$T_{curie} \cong 200°C$	High recording sensitivity
High coercivity near room-temperature	Data stability
Rapid drop in coercivity near T_{curie}	Sharp recording threshold, high readout power, and wide system tolerances
Vertical anisotropy	Vertical magnetization to produce the polar Kerr effect
High intrinsic M-O interaction at $\lambda \sim 800$ nm	Large Kerr effect for diode laser readout
Moderate absorption coefficient	Efficient absorption, moderate reflectance, high sensitivity, and enhanced signal
Chemical stability	Media lifetime and corrosion resistance

for a high-performance M-O recording film, including a few points not discussed above. Vertical anisotropy is an absolutely essential material requirement; without it, shape anisotropy would favor in-plane magnetization. For many materials, the source of anisotropy is poorly understood. Seemingly minor changes in film composition or deposition conditions can change the anisotropy greatly. Vertical anisotropy dominates the magnetic character of RE/TM materials in part because the ferrimagnetic balance reduces the net magnetization and shape anisotropy. A moderately high absorption coefficient (the imaginary part of the refractive index) is important so that most of the incident recording beam will be coupled into the thin film. If the absorption coefficient were too high, the bare M-O film would reflect too much of the light, but a multi-layer structure can always be designed to couple the light back into the absorptive layer (see Chapter 13, Section 2). Chemical stability is a particular weakness characteristic of RE/TM materials because the RE components react so readily with oxygen and moisture. Chapter 14, Section 4 describes barrier layers that must be added to make up for this deficiency. Since the list of ideal characteristics for M-O recording materials is very long, it is unlikely that any one material will be optimal in every respect. Nevertheless, a number of interesting compositions have been studied and many research groups continue to develop new compositions. See Bloomberg and Connell (1988) and Bell (1986) for in-depth reviews of known materials for magneto-optical (and other erasable optical) recording.

The magneto-optical Kerr and Faraday effects arise when the recording film has different refractive indices for clockwise and counterclockwise circularly polarized light. For example, a magnetized TbFeCo film could have refractive indices close to $n_{cw} = 3.1 + 3.4i$ and $n_{ccw} = 3.0 + 3.3i$. If the (vertical) magnetization is switched, these values are reversed. Applying Eq. (3.2), we can calculate the corresponding reflectance coefficients for normal incidence: $r_{cw} = 0.71 + 0.24i$ and $r_{ccw} = 0.70 + 0.25i$ (for air-incidence, $n_0 = 1$). If the film is illuminated by linearly polarized light, the reflected beam is a combination of the incident polarization and a small perpendicular component. The reflection coefficients corresponding to the polarization components are:

$$r_\parallel = \underline{r} \text{ and } r_\perp = \underline{r}k \, e^{i\kappa}, \tag{4.1}$$

where

$$\underline{r} \equiv |r_{cw} + r_{ccw}|/2 \text{ and } ke^{i\kappa} \equiv i(r_{cw} - r_{ccw})/(r_{cw} + r_{ccw}). \qquad (4.2)$$

When r_{cw} and r_{ccw} are nearly equal in magnitude ($R_{cw} \cong R_{ccw}$) and differ only in phase, $\kappa \sim 0$ and the reflected light is linearly polarized. This condition is sometimes called circular birefringence. In general, however, the reflectance is also polarization dependent ($R_{cw} \neq R_{ccw}$, called circular dichroism) and $ke^{i\kappa}$ is a complex number. In this general case the reflected beam polarization is elliptical. The factors k and κ defined in Eq. (4.2) correspond respectively to the orthogonal reflectance ($R_\perp = k^2 R_\parallel$) and its phase shift relative to the incident mode reflectance. For the TbFeCo example mentioned above, the reflectance coefficients corresponding to the incident and orthogonal polarizations are $r_\parallel = 0.75$ and $r_\perp = 0.013 + 0.03i$; the corresponding reflectances are $R_\parallel \cong 56\%$ and $R_\perp \cong 0.02\%$. Obviously, measuring intensity of the orthogonal polarization component is not an effective means of detecting the Kerr rotation. Ellipsometric techniques should be used instead.

$R_\parallel$ and $R_\perp$ do not tell enough about M-O readout; they do not tell whether the reflected beam is linearly or elliptically polarized or what the direction or degree of polarization rotation is. The general polarization characteristics for readout of a magneto-optic film are illustrated in Figure 4.7. The input beam is linearly polarized, with the

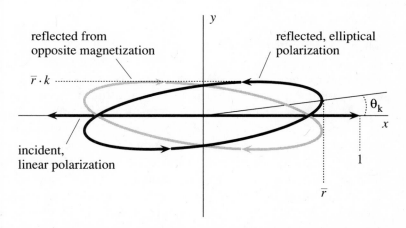

Figure 4.7 *The magneto-optic Kerr effect rotates the polarization and/or makes it elliptical.*

E-field always oriented along one axis. In general, the reflected light is elliptically polarized and its E-field oscillates around an elliptical contour. (The oscillation is very rapid, occurring at the optical frequency $f = c/\lambda \sim 4 \cdot 10^4$ cycles/s.) If the magnetization is reversed, the major axis of the ellipse is rotated and the sense of rotation is reversed. The angle formed between the incident polarization and the major axis of the ellipse is the Kerr rotation angle,

$$\tan(2\theta_k) = -2k \cos \kappa / (1 - k^2)$$

$$\theta_k \cong k \cos \kappa. \qquad (4.3)$$

The quantitative degree of Kerr rotation is always small, 0.3° for our TbFeCo example. Even so, the Kerr rotation is the best available indicator of the underlying magnetization pattern. The ellipticity of the reflected polarization is defined as the ratio of the minor axis to the major axis;

$$\epsilon \cong k \sin \kappa \qquad (4.4)$$

in the limit of small θ_k. In Chapter 8, Section 4, we will see that the magneto-optical signal can be optimized by making $\kappa = 0$ and eliminating the ellipticity term. If the phase error in our example ($\kappa = 40°$) is compensated, the Kerr angle is increased to 0.4°.

4.3   Phase-change Systems

The most promising alternative to magneto-optics for erasable optical recording (the one that has received the most technical attention) is phase-change recording. Many materials can exist in several different crystalline phases. Although only one phase is energetically favored, alternate structures can inhabit local minima so that a considerable activation energy is required to switch them to the ground state. Often the material can be switched from one metastable phase to another by appropriate thermal conditioning. If the temperature is kept low enough, the new structure is essentially permanent.

Ovshinsky (1970) described how amorphous/crystalline phase switching can be used for optical data storage. He demonstrated such switching behavior in a variety of semiconductor-based materials, especially chalcogenides (glasses based on the chalcogen elements S, Se, and Te). Other classes of phase-change optical recording materials exist, including some that switch between two different crystalline phases. For example, a silver/zinc alloy has been investigated as a phase-change material because it can be thermally cycled between two crystalline structures with strikingly different colors, gray and pink (Minemura, Andoh, and Maeda, 1988).

The typical phase-change optical recording material is a multicomponent alloy that has a stable, compatible, crystalline phase and a metastable amorphous phase with different optical properties. Write-once optical recording in such materials was described in Chapter 3, Section 1. For write-once operation, the material is prepared as an amorphous film; the heat of recording anneals the marked areas irreversibly to the energetically favored crystalline phase. However, in an erasable phase-change system, annealing is the technique for erasure; the erase beam heats the data track to a temperature just below the melting point long enough to recrystallize and erase any amorphous marks.

Recording is accomplished by locally melting the recording material and then cooling it quickly enough to quench it in the amorphous phase. Quenching occurs most readily when the cooling is extremely rapid. The maximum cooling rate is determined primarily by the film thickness and the thermal constants of the film and substrate. In general, the time required for heat to diffuse a distance l is

$$\tau \sim l^2/\kappa \qquad\qquad (4.5)$$

where κ is the thermal diffusivity (see the discussion around Eq. (13.7). For a recording film thickness of 100 nm, a thermal diffusivity of 10 $\mu m^2/\mu s$, and a mark width of 1 μm, the time for the temperature to drop significantly by lateral thermal diffusion within the recording layer is about 0.1 μs. If the substrate diffusivity is 0.1 $\mu m^2/\mu s$ (an appropriate value for plastics), the time for heat to diffuse one film thickness (~ 0.1 μm) into the substrate is also about 0.1 μs. The film cannot be cooled any faster than this, therefore, any erasable phase-change material must be quenchable with a cooling time as long as 0.1 μs.

The various thermal effects in phase-change materials are illustrated in Figure 4.8. Quenching occurs only when the material is melted (to induce an amorphous structure) and then cooled rapidly. Annealing begins to occur whenever the material is above a critical temperature, denoted by T_g. The annealing rate usually increases dramatically at higher temperatures. When the heating is slight or of

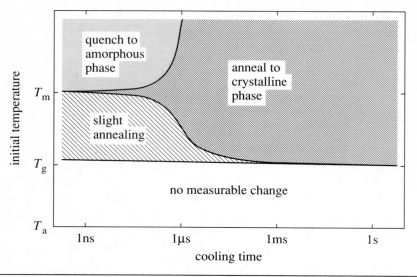

Figure 4.8 *The state of a phase-change material depends on its thermal history.*

short duration, each thermal cycle might only partially recrystallize the amorphous marks. In some early demonstrations of erasable phase-change recording, multiple passes with the optical stylus at moderate power were used to effect complete erasure. As in all optical recording, readout is performed with much less laser power than that required for erasure and recording. The readout illumination still heats up the recording film somewhat; but if the readout temperature is kept below T_g, repeated reads will not cause slow recrystallization (erasure) of data marks. Rapid, single-pass erasure is possible only if the annealing rate is high at temperatures slightly below the melting point, but the requirement of data stability dictates that the threshold temperature must be much higher than the ambient, $T_g >> T_a$. These two requirements are mutually compatible only if the annealing process has a high activation energy.

The basic materials requirements for a reversible phase-change optical recording material are summarized in Table 4.3. High thermal conductivity must be avoided for the usual reasons: poor thermal efficiency (low recording sensitivity) and thermal effects on the mark resolution. But very low conductivity could make it more difficult to cool and quench the material for recording. Likewise, a low melting point increases the recording sensitivity; but if the melting point is

TABLE 4.3 Basic Requirements for an Erasable Phase-Change Material

INTRINSIC CHARACTERISTIC	PURPOSE
Refractive index change	Optical contrast between crystalline and amorphous regions
Moderate thermal conductivity	Rapid cooling and quenching vs. high sensitivity
Low melting point	High sensitivity
Rapid annealing below T_{melt}	Single-pass erasure
High activation energy for annealing	Sharp erasure threshold, data stability
Compatible alloy or compound	No phase segregation after melting
Density compatibility	Low internal stress
Rigid media structure	Inhibit cumulative deformation from cycling

too low, there may not be a wide enough power range for reliable erasure. In addition, a low melting point increases the risk of (irreversible) hole formation during recording.

Since phase-change materials are generally mixtures of several elements, chemical compatibility in the crystalline phase has been a serious problem. The repeated melting/quenching/annealing cycles in an erasable system tend to encourage phase segregation of more stable compounds if the original alloy is not perfectly compatible. Substantial diffusion can take place each time the material is melted. Phase cycling also exacerbates thermal mismatch between the recorded and erased phases. If the two material forms do not have the same density, the recording process will induce strain within the film, which could eventually damage the film or force material to flow away from the data tracks. Physical restraint is used to minimize cycling damage. Figure 4.9 shows a phase-change material overcoated with a rigid restraining layer that inhibits material flow and hole formation during recording. The issues of long-term stability and reversibility are a fundamental challenge for phase-change materials. In M-O recording, the switching is purely electronic, but in phase-change recording each cycle involves actual atomic motion. Eventually, a noticeable phase separation or material flow will accumulate.

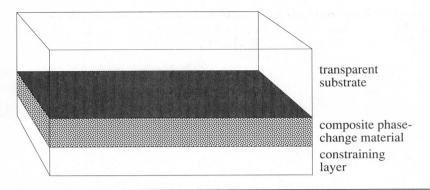

transparent
substrate

composite phase-
change material

constraining
layer

Figure 4.9 *Some design features can prevent deformation of phase-change media.*

In 1982, Matsushita publicly demonstrated a real-time video recorder based on an erasable optical disc (Takenaga, Yamada, Ohara, Nishiuchi, Nagashima, Kashihara, Nakamura, and Yamashita, 1983). The optical disk was based on a phase-change material similar to the TeO_x composite material that Matsushita had previously introduced for write-once recording (see Chapter 3, Section 1). By adding small quantities of Sn and Se, they were able to stabilize the amorphous phase of Te (increase T_g above T_a). The actual recording material (a TeSeSn chalcogenide) was embedded as very small particles within a glassy TeO_2 matrix. The matrix served to stabilize the material against phase separation and cycling damage. As many as 10^6 record/erase cycles of a single track were demonstrated with minimal changes in signal level, noise level, and error rate. However, in spite of considerable research and promising demonstrations, erasable phase-change recording is not yet a practical reality. The critical difficulties appear to be with media manufacturing. The basic materials requirements can be met simultaneously, but so far the specific media formulations do not have adequate manufacturing latitude.

4.4 Overwriting

From a systems perspective, the one advantage that erasable phase-change recording has over M-O recording is that straightforward techniques are available for phase-change overwriting. In M-O recording, the conventional recording and erasure processes require oppositely oriented bias fields. Two passes beneath the head are required to update any data, dramatically increasing the average latency. The inability to overwrite can nearly double the average access time in an otherwise high-performance system.

Single-pass erasure and recording has been demonstrated in phase-change media using the dual-beam technique illustrated in Figure 4.10. Separate laser beams are focused simultaneously by the optical head onto the data track during recording. The first spot has a long, narrow shape (3 to 10 μm in-track and 1 μm cross-track). With a steady, unmodulated output it uniformly heats the data track long enough to anneal it. The second spot is a conventional (nearly round) optical stylus, which is pulsed to record new marks. The separation between the spots is just sufficient to separate the two laser beams so that they can be focused through the same objective lens. Sanyo has recently proposed a three-source laser with beams that are separately optimized for readout, erasure, and recording. The optics required to image a multi-source laser are discussed in Chapter 8, Section 5.

The two-beam approach is straightforward but not easy to implement. The separate beams must be kept in careful alignment, simultaneously in focus on the same track, and then isolated for readout. The shape and quality of the erase beam must be carefully maintained to prevent inadvertent or incomplete erasure.

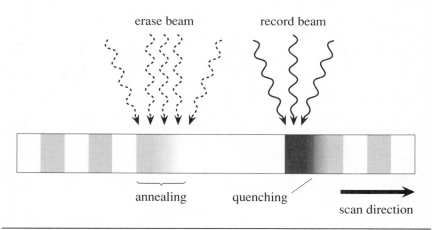

Figure 4.10 *Pre-erasure of a phase-change medium using a two-beam head is shown here.*

If the phase-change material could be optimized for both rapid erasure and reliable recording, a simple single-beam method for overwriting with a standard optical head could be realized. Phase-change recording materials designed for this purpose have been developed at Hitachi (InSeTe) and Matsushita (GeSbTe); see Yasuoka, Ojima, Terao, and Nishida (1987). The annealing rate at elevated temperatures is so high in these materials that, during the recording scan, each point on the track is either erased or marked, depending on the level of laser power. As shown in Figure 4.11, complete annealing occurs during one scan past the optical stylus if the laser heats the medium to a moderate temperature. But if the laser is pulsed high enough to melt the film, the subsequent cooling time (less than half the scan time) is short enough to partially quench the amorphous mark, preventing complete recrystallization. Obviously, the materials properties are critical to this single-beam overwrite technique. The material must be designed for the specific data rate and scan velocity of the system; for instance, the limited range of velocities encountered at different radii at constant rpm might cause incomplete erasure at the outer radius (where the scan time is shorter) and/or poor signal contrast at the inner radius (where the cooling time is longer). Incomplete erasure, lack of a distinct threshold be-

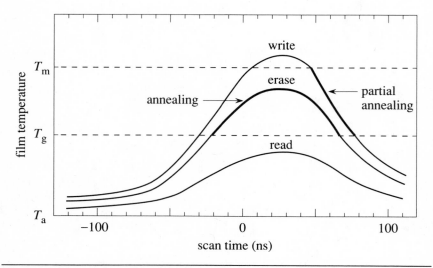

Figure 4.11 *Different thermal cycles for single-beam overwrite in a phase-change medium are shown here.*

tween the erase and record power levels, and tight tolerances on media composition are a few of the practical difficulties for the single-
beam phase-change overwrite method.

Because direct overwrite is considered to be such a valuable feature
for erasable optical recording, considerable research has gone into
developing such techniques for magneto-optical recording. In conventional M-O recording, the laser is pulsed while the bias field
(which determines the magnetization of the recorded marks) remains
constant. An obvious way to overwrite is to reverse the roles of the
laser and the bias field in the recording process (Lewicki and Guisinger, 1971). The laser beam is held continuously at the writing
power level while the bias field is switched to form marks of alternat-
ing magnetization. This modulated field method will work with any
M-O material, but it requires a more intricate drive design. The recording method is illustrated in Figure 4.12. Each point along the
track undergoes the same thermal cycle as it scans beneath the laser
stylus, differing only with distance from the track center. During recording, there is a small region at the trailing edge of the optical
stylus where the temperature exceeds T_{curie}. This region is completely
demagnetized, with no memory of the previous magnetization distribution. As the medium moves out from under the laser stylus, it
cools back below the Curie point and a magnetization parallel to

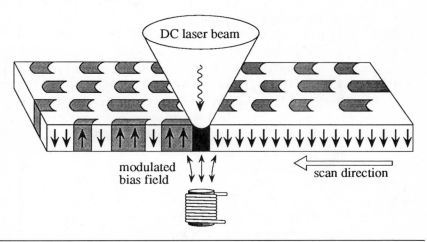

Figure 4.12 *Overwriting with a modulated bias field creates crescent-shaped domains.*

the applied bias is frozen in. When the bias field is switched, the magnetization reverses along an arc-shaped region at the trailing end of the stylus where the film temperature is just lower than T_{curie}. The resultant domain pattern along the track has the asymmetrical appearance shown in Figure 4.12. In a demonstration of this concept, Araki et al. (1985) used a modulated bias field and an unmodulated laser beam to record a track 2 μm wide. The track was a succession of crescents or chevron-shaped marks just 0.45 μm long.

In addition to its overwriting characteristic, the modulated field recording method has at least three intrinsic advantages over ordinary M-O recording. Design constraints on the laser and laser driver circuit are simplified, because the beam need not be modulated at such high frequencies. Marks can be recorded at a higher in-track density because the minimum mark size is determined by the bias switching rate and the sharpness of the recording threshold, just as in ordinary magnetic recording. (Note that the size of the laser stylus still limits the readout resolution.) And recording nonlinearities due to thermal diffusion is eliminated because every point along the track has the same thermal history. The latter advantage means that drifts in recording power or media sensitivity do not cause any peak shift. However, these advantages are countered by the practical difficulty of applying the large modulated bias field. Because of its high inductance, a large electromagnet cannot be switched very rapidly. Until recently, demonstrations of the modulated field technique have been limited to frequencies less than 1 MHz and data rates of about 1 Mbit/s. In order to switch at a higher rate, the coil size and inductance must be reduced. One design approach is to embed the coil in the kind of aerodynamic "flying head" used in magnetic disk drives (Ojima, 1988). This approach revives the danger of head crashes, a danger that optical recording was supposed to eliminate. However the head/media spacing in this case can be much greater than in Winchester drives: switching rates above 10 MHz can be achieved with a coil spacing as large as 50 μm. A relatively thick protective film can be coated over the recording layer to provide a measure of mechanical protection.

Two other techniques for M-O overwriting have been proposed which require specially designed media. The first such technique relies on the demagnetization properties of certain ferrimagnetic RE/TM alloys. Shieh and Kryder (1986) showed that in some materials (with $T_a < T_{comp} << T_{curie}$) recording and erasure can both be accomplished without any external bias field. In a uniformly magnetized film, the demagnetization field is always directed so as to oppose the existing magnetization and to support reverse magnetized domains. As illustrated in Figure 4.13a, when a laser pulse heats a region of the recording film to the point of negligible coercivity, the demagnetization field causes it to switch, even if no external bias field is applied. This characteristic of demagnetization has been known since the earliest work in M-O recording. It is also responsible for the enhanced stability of small domains in vertically magnetized films. Historically, the trouble with relying on the demagnetization field for recording has been that an applied bias was still required for erasure; if the medium was designed to provide a high enough demagnetization field for reliable recording, a correspondingly higher bias field was required to counter it during erasure.

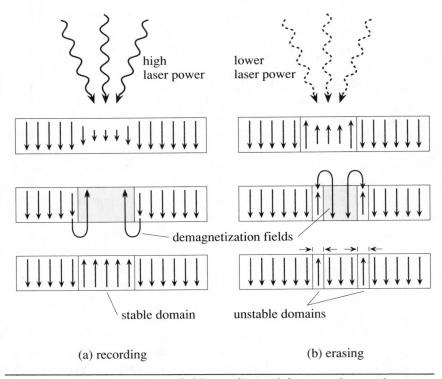

(a) recording   (b) erasing

Figure 4.13 *Demagnetization fields can be used for recording and erasure as shown here.*

The novel aspect of Shieh and Kryder's discovery was that a lower-power pulse does not form a stable mark but can erase a reversed domain if it is present. Figure 4.13b shows how erasure might be accomplished by a laser pulse at reduced power. In isolation, the pulse would not form a stable domain. However, within an existing domain it leads to a magnetization re-reversal surrounded by a thin annular region that is no longer magnetically stable. The re-reversal is enhanced if the compensation point is intermediate between T_{curie} and T_a, because then the demagnetization fields from outside the existing mark do not interfere. In the proposed recording method, mark locations are precisely identified on the medium (e.g., by encoded timing constraints). During recording, the laser is pulsed at each location, either at high power to form a reversed domain or at reduced power to erase a mark that might be present. If no mark is present, the erase pulse has no permanent effect. Potential problems with demagnetization recording include the difficulties of accurately identifying the mark locations each time (erasure would be incomplete if the erasure pulse arrived significantly off-center), preventing the formation of large, unerasable domains, and manufacturing media with close compositional tolerances. In principle, the mark positions could be located by a "read before write" method using a readout stylus that precedes the recording stylus. (Contrast this with the DRAW technique discussed in Chapter 11, Section 4.)

The second media-based method for M-O overwriting also relies on demagnetization effects, but only for erasure. It is based on the peculiar properties of a two-layer M-O media structure demonstrated by Nikon (Saito, 1987) following earlier suggestions from IBM (Bell, 1986). The lower layer has a high magnetization and low coercivity. It must either be thermally isolated or have a relatively high T_{curie}. Only the upper layer is magneto-optically visible, so it is the actual memory layer. It has a higher coercivity and a lower T_{curie} than the lower layer. The lower layer serves as a magnetic reference as illustrated in Figure 4.14. The drive has two permanent bias magnets, one with a high field and one with a much weaker field. Each point on the recording surface rotates past the stronger, reference magnet before it passes by the head. The strong bias field uniformly orients the reference layer, but does not disturb the high coercivity memory layer. The weaker magnet is positioned opposite the optical head with its field oriented opposite to the reference magnet. For recording, the laser is modulated between high and moderate power

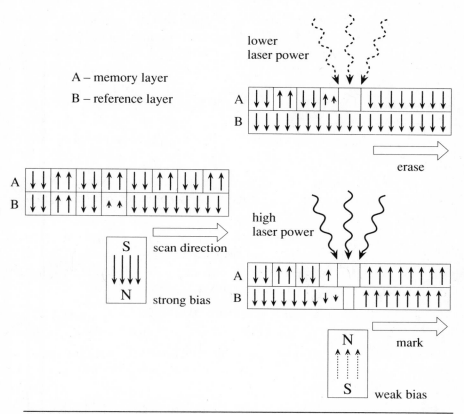

Figure 4.14 *Recording and erasure using a magnetic reference layer are shown here.*

levels. At the high power level, both the memory and reference films are heated above T_{curie}, so the final mark magnetization is determined by the second bias magnet. But where the laser exposure is reduced, only the memory layer is heated above T_{curie}. The field from the reference layer dominates the bias in these regions, reversing the recorded magnetization and forming M-O marks.

The hardware required for the two-layer recording technique is not difficult to design or implement. The materials properties required by each media layer can be engineered in RE/TM alloys. However, it may prove difficult to manufacture the complex disk structure with sufficient control of the individual film thicknesses and compositions. In addition, the performance of a two-layer overwrite system is temperature dependent. Precise control of the recording power is required even under ideal conditions; if the ambient temperature changes, the power settings must be compensated accordingly.

MAJOR CONCEPTS

- In M-O media, magnetic domains are created where the recording layer is locally heated above its Curie point.

- M-O readout relies on the magneto-optic Kerr effect. The media must be magnetically anisotropic so that the domains are oriented vertically.

- The practical materials for M-O recording are amorphous alloys of rare-earth and transition metals, such as TbFe. The materials properties are compositionally dependent, but not critically so (Figures 4.5 and 4.6).

- The Kerr rotation angle from RE/TM alloys is typically less than $0.5°$; consequently, the readout signals are very small.

- Reversible phase-change materials are the principle alternative to M-O materials for erasable optical recording.

- Phase-change recording and erasure are accomplished by different thermal cycles. Marks are recorded by melting a small area and then rapidly freezing it in an amorphous state. Erasure results from slower heating, which anneals the media back to a polycrystalline condition (Figure 4.8).

- The performance of erasable phase-change media depends critically on composition.

- Methods for direct (single-pass) overwrite are a major goal of current R&D for erasable optical recording.

REFERENCES

Araki, S., A. Asayama, and H. Kobayashi, "Magneto-optical writing system with the pulse magnetic field," *IEEE Translation Journal on Magnetics in Japan,* **TJMJ-1,** 691 (1985). A demonstration of modulated field M-O recording.

Bell, A., "Erasable self biasing thermal magneto-optic medium," European

Patent #86111465.0 (1986). Overwriting using a two-layer magneto-optic recording medium.

Bell, A., "Materials for high density optical data storage," *CRC Handbook of Laser Science and Technology, Volume V,* ed. M. Weber, CRC Press, Boca Raton (1986). A detailed review of materials issues for optical recording, especially useful for its treatment of M-O and phase-change materials.

Bloomberg, D., and G. Connell, "Magnetooptical recording," *Magnetic Recording, Volume III,* eds. C. Mee and E. Daniel, McGraw Hill, New York (1988). A comprehensive review of M-O materials and recording physics.

Burns, L., and E. Keizer, "Magnetic recording system," U.S. Patent #2,915,594 (1959). Curie-point recording using the focused image of a CRT as the modulated heat source.

Chen, D., J. Ready, and G. E. Bernal, "MnBi thin films: physical properties and memory applications," *Journal of Applied Physics,* **39,** 3916 (1968). The M-O recording and readout characteristics of MnBi.

Choudhari, P., J. Cuomo, R. Gambino, and T. McGuire, "Beam addressable film using amorphous magnetic material," U.S. Patent #3,949,387 (1976). The discovery of RE-TM materials for magneto-optic recording.

Gupta, M., and F. Strome, "Erasable laser recording in an organic dye-binder optical disc medium," *Journal of Applied Physics,* **60,** 2932 (1986). A demonstration of (limited) erasability in a simple organic medium.

Lee, K., "Magnetic thin films for optical storage," *Journal of Vacuum Science and Technology,* **10,** 631 (1973). A materials survey of early candidates for M-O recording.

Lenth, W., R. Macfarlane, W. Moerner, F. Schellenberg, R. Shelby, and G. Bjorklund, "High-density frequency-domain optical recording," *SPIE Proceedings,* **695,** 216 (1986). Persistent spectral hole burning used for high-density optical recording.

Lewicki, G., and J. Guisinger, "Thermomagnetic recording and magneto-optic playback system," U.S. Patent #3,626,114 (1971). An early patent covering field-modulated M-O recording.

Mayer, L., "Curie-point writing on magnetic films," *Journal of Applied Physics,* **29,** 1003 (1958). The basic principles of Curie-point recording.

Minemura, T., H. Andoh, and Y. Maeda, "Reversible color changes in sputter-deposited Ag-Zn alloy films," *J. Appl. Phys.,* **63,** 4632 (1988). Reversible recording in AgZn by cycling between two crystalline phases.

Moerner, W., R. Macfarlane, and W. Lenth, "Frequency domain optical storage: the importance of photon-gated materials," *Topical Meeting on Optical Data Storage, Technical Digest Series 1987,* **10,** 151 (1987). Nonlinear materials for spectral-hole-burning which have a recording threshold.

Nagato, K., A. Kawamoto, T. Sato, and Y. Yorozu, "Compositional dependence of recording noise in amorphous rare-earth—transition-metal magneto-optical discs," *J. Appl. Phys.,* **63,** 3856 (1988). Recording noise is minimized when $T_{comp} \sim T_{curie} - 70°C$.

Nishioka, Y., "Rewritable magneto-optical disc drive unit," *JEE,* September 1987, 74 (1987). A description of Sharp's $5\frac{1}{4}$" magneto-optic system.

Ojima, M., T. Nakao, H. Sukeda, N. Ohta, H. Yasuoka, T. Nishida, and M. Terao, "High speed overwritable optical disc," *SPIE Proceedings,* **899,** 154 (1988). A review of direct overwrite techniques for both M-O and phase-change media, including a discussion of a flying bias coil.

Ovshinsky, S., "Method and apparatus for storing and retrieving information," U.S. Patent #3,530,441 (1970). The concept of data storage in phase-change materials, specifically those which switch reversibly between amorphous and crystalline states.

Saito, J., M. Sato, H. Matsumoto, and H. Akasaka, "Direct overwrite by light power modulation on magneto-optical multilayered media," *International Symposium on Optical Memory 1987, Technical Digest,* 9 (1987). Nikon's demonstration of direct overwrite on a two-layer M-O medium.

Shieh, H., and M. Kryder, "Magneto-optic recording materials with direct overwrite capability," *Applied Physics Letters,* **49,** 473 (1986). Method and materials for recording and erasing magneto-optic marks without an external bias field.

Takayama, S., T. Niihara, K. Kaneko, Y. Sugita, and M. Ojima, "Magnetic and magneto-optical properties of Tb-Fe-Co amorphous films," *Journal of Applied Physics,* **61,** 2610 (1987). A description of how film composition affects the critical properties of RE-TM films.

Takenaga, M., N. Yamada, S. Ohara, K. Nishiuchi, M. Nagashima, T. Kashihara, S. Nakamura, and T. Yamashita, "New optical erasable medium using tellurium suboxide thin film," *SPIE Proceedings,* **420,** 173 (1983). A description of the first effective material for erasable phase-change optical recording.

Williams, H., R. Sherwood, F. Foster, and E. Kelly, "Magnetic writing on thin films of MnBi," *Journal of Applied Physics,* **28,** 1181 (1957). The first proposal of high-density data storage with magneto-optic readout.

Yasuoka, H., M. Ojima, M. Terao, and T. Nishida, "Novel 1-beam-overwriting method for phase change erasable disk," *International Symposium on Optical Memory 1987, Technical Digest,* 21 (1987). Demonstration of a phase-change material which anneals quickly enough for single-beam overwriting.

PART II

OPTICAL HEAD TECHNOLOGY

The term *head* refers to that part of the drive that actually marks the recording medium and/or to the transducer that reconstructs the signals. For the sake of cost and performance, we are primarily interested in dual-function heads that both write and read. Home phonograph recorders, that were popular earlier in this century, had a simple type of dual function head—a stylus with a voice-coil actuator. For recording, weight was added to the stylus so that it would cut grooves into a soft, plastic disk in response to audio signals transduced by a voice-coil. With the weight removed, the stylus would simply follow the groove pattern, regenerating the audio signal in the same voice-coil. Parallels can be drawn between modern recording heads and this old device: Readout generates much smaller signals than those we must provide for recording; repeated readout presents some risk of wear for both the recorded pattern and the head; and head positioning is crucial for accurate recording and readout.

Magnetic heads are at least as simple as the phonograph example. Standard ring heads are composed of a magnetically soft ring core with a narrow gap, a small coil wrapped toroidally around the core, and a support that properly references the core to the medium. Other magnetic head designs are also simple. However, optical heads are much more complex. Their complexity is the reason why optical drives are more difficult and more expensive to build than magnetic drives.

The heart of an optical head is a diffraction-limited optical stylus: not a material object, but a spot of light that probes the media surface for information (at low intensity) or serves as an intense, local heat source to mark the surface (at high intensity). In Chapter 5 we develop the basic optical concepts necessary to describe the optical stylus, to understand how it is formed, and to interpret the readout signals it produces. In Chapter 6 we describe laser diodes, the light source that has made optical recording more than an academic curiosity. In Chapter 7 we describe tracking and focusing techniques used to control the relative head/media position with submicron precision. In Chapter 8 we present a variety of optical-head layouts and explain the basic optical engineering concepts behind the designs.

CHAPTER 5

The Optical Stylus

5.1   The Diffraction Limit

The surface curvature of a lens is designed to image light from one point onto another. The objective lens in Figure 5.1 collects light rays that emerge from points on the *conjugate image plane* and focuses them onto corresponding points on the *object plane*. When a light ray leaves a medium with an index of refraction n_1 and enters another with index n_2, its angle of incidence (the propagation direc-

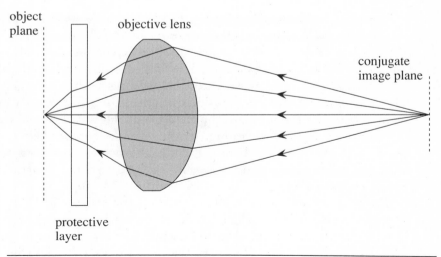

object
plane

objective lens

conjugate
image plane

protective
layer

Figure 5.1 *Light rays are focused by an objective lens.*

tion measured from a line perpendicular to the interface) is refracted from θ_1 to θ_2 according to Snell's law:

$$n_1 \sin \theta_1 = n_2 \sin \theta_2. \qquad (5.1)$$

The two surface curvatures of an ideal objective lens are designed to refract the rays from a point on the image plane as they pass through the lens so that they all converge exactly to a focus on the object plane. The lens might be designed for an *infinite conjugate;* in this case the incoming rays are parallel and the beam is said to be collimated. If the objective lens is intended to focus the light through a transparent protective layer (substrate or overcoat) it must be modified to compensate for the additional refraction at the air/substrate interface; in a sense, the transparent substrate acts as a functional part of the objective lens.

An objective lens can be described in terms of its diameter, $\mathscr{D}$, and its focal length, f, defined as the distance between the lens and the focus at the object plane for an infinite conjugate (parallel beam). The performance of a lens is not independently affected by either of these dimensions. Instead it depends directly on a dimensionless quantity called the *numerical aperture*. The numerical aperture is defined by

$$NA \equiv n \sin \theta_{max} \qquad (5.2)$$

where θ_{max} is the incidence angle of a light ray focused through the margin of the lens and n is the refractive index of the medium. From Snell's law (Eq. 5.1) we can see that the NA is independent of the medium in which it is evaluated, whether inside or outside of the protective layer. It is possible to design lenses with NA larger than 1, i.e., oil immersion microscope objectives for which $n > 1$ everywhere between the lens and the focal point. However, these are impractical for optical recording, where intimate contact between the head and media is anathema. Practical objective lenses for optical recording have NA in the range 0.4 to 0.6, meaning that the marginal incidence angle (in air) is in the range 24° to 37°.

From the point of view of ray-tracing, or geometrical optics, it appears that a beam of light could be focused to an infinitesimally small spot. If so, we could form an optical stylus of arbitrarily small size and high intensity. However, photons are not particles; the wave nature of light gives rise to diffraction effects that prevent the formation of spots much smaller than the wavelength.

In the scalar diffraction limit, light waves can be described in terms of a scalar function, the electric field amplitude. Given a light source emitting steadily at a fixed frequency ω (or fixed wavelength $\lambda = 2\pi c/(\omega n)$) the field is the product of a time-invariant, spatially varying amplitude times a periodic phase term: $E(x)e^{i\omega t}$, where x is a vector describing the location in space and t represents time. Spatial variations in the phase of the wave are indicated by the varying, complex values of E. For example, a homogeneous plane wave is described by $E(x) \propto e^{-2\pi i x \cdot \eta / \lambda}$, where η is a unit vector in the direction of propagation. In terms of the electric field, the electromagnetic energy density is $|nE|^2$. The intensity of a plane wave (power per unit area in the direction of propagation) is

$$I = cn|E|^2. \tag{5.3}$$

In the remaining discussions of this chapter, the speed of light, c, appearing in Eq. (5.3) will be subsumed in the units of E, so that $I = n|E|^2$. We will also assume that the optical situations all occur in air where $n = 1$. The resulting equations will remain valid for light focused within transparent materials, provided that they are evaluated using the vacuum wavelength of light rather than the (shorter) wavelength interior to the materials.

The propagation of scalar waves can be explained by Huygens' principle, which states that every point on a wavefront is the source of a spherical wave. The field at any point is the coherent sum of contributions from every point on a previous wavefront or surface:

$$E(x) = \int_{\text{previous surface}} dA \cos \psi \exp[-2\pi i |X-x|/\lambda] E(X)/(|X-x|\lambda) \tag{5.4}$$

where X represents points on the surrounding surface and dA is the corresponding area element oriented at an angle ψ to the line between X and x.

From the point of view of diffraction, the function of an objective lens is to alter the phase profile of the incoming beam so that the wavefronts are spherical surfaces centered on the focal point (the intersection of the optical axis with the object plane). For an infinite conjugate, the object plane is a distance f from the lens. Choose as the surface of integration in Eq. (5.4) the pupil sphere, a sphere of radius f centered at the focal point, and identify points on the sphere by rectilinear aperture coordinates $u \equiv X/f$ and $v \equiv Y/f$ where $X = (X, Y)$. In terms of these coordinates, the lens aperture is defined by $u^2 + v^2 \leq NA^2$. The field $E(X)$ can be divided into amplitude and phase parts, $\sqrt{\vartheta}\,(u, v\,)e^{i\phi(u, v\,)}$. Here, ϑ is the input beam intensity at the aperture and ϕ is the distribution of (hopefully small) phase errors or aberrations created by the optical system. In the Fraunhofer zone near focus on the object plane, the distance $|X - x|$ is essentially constant and equal to f. Eq. (5.4) may be approximated as

$$E(x, y, z) = \mathscr{D}/(2\lambda NA) \quad \iint du \, dv \, \sqrt{\mathscr{I}} \exp[i\,\phi \qquad (5.5)$$
$$- 2\pi i(xu + yv + zw)/\lambda],$$
$$u^2 + v^2 \leq NA^2$$

where $x = (x, y, z)$ and $\omega^2 \equiv 1 - u^2 - v^2$. At the nominal focus $(x = y = z = 0)$ the integral simplifies further to

$$E_0 = \mathscr{D}/(2\lambda NA)\iint du \, dv \sqrt{\mathscr{I}} \exp^{i\phi}. \qquad (5.6)$$

The central spot irradiance, $I_0 \equiv |E_0|^2$, is maximized at a value of

$$I_{\max} = |\mathscr{D}/(2\lambda NA)\iint du \, dv \sqrt{\mathscr{I}}|^2 \qquad (5.7)$$

when ϕ is constant across the aperture. This condition is achieved only when the light source is perfectly coherent and the optics (objective lens, protective layer, etc.) are free of aberrations. The overall lens quality is often specified in terms of *waves of aberration* (rms or peak-to-peak). Specific types of aberration are also quantified in *waves of spherical,* etc. A more descriptive characterization of the focused spot is the Strehl ratio, $I_0/I_{\max}$. This is the ratio of the maximum irradiance in the actual spot to the irradiance that could theoretically be achieved at perfect focus without any aberration. Formerly, an optical system was said to be *diffraction-limited* if it met Marechal's criteria: Strehl ratio > 0.8. But with the advent of sophisticated optical systems and coherent laser beams, a more critical definition is required. For applications such as optical recording, a system is said to be diffraction-limited if the Strehl ratio is greater than 0.9.

For a given amount of power, P, focused through the aperture, the central spot irradiance is maximized when the aperture is unapodized, or uniformly illuminated ($\vartheta = 4P/\pi \mathscr{D}^2$). This ideal irradiance value (from Eq. 5.7) is

$$I_{\max} = \pi PNA^2/\lambda^2. \qquad (5.8)$$

If the focused spot also had a flat, circular irradiance profile, its diameter would be $2[P/(\pi I_{\max})]^{1/2} = 2\lambda/(\pi NA)$. However, this is not an accurate approximation to the spot shape. Evaluating Eq. (5.5) on the object plane, $z = 0$, we obtain the field profile

$$E(r) = \pi \mathscr{D}/(\lambda NA) \int_0^{NA} d\rho\rho\sqrt{\mathscr{I}} \cdot J_0(2\pi r\rho/\lambda). \qquad (5.9)$$

Substituting a uniform beam intensity profile, we can simplify this to

$$E(r) = 2(\pi P)^{1/2}/(\lambda NA) \int_0^{NA} d\rho\rho J_0(2\pi r\rho/\lambda) \qquad (5.10)$$

$$= (P/\pi)^{1/2} J_1(2\pi rNA/\lambda)/r,$$

where r is a radial coordinate in the object plane and J_0 and J_1 are the usual Bessel functions of the first kind. The irradiance pattern is

$$I(r) = (P/\pi)[J_1(2\pi rNA/\lambda)/r]^2. \qquad (5.11)$$

Figure 5.2 is a plot of this distribution, which is the famous Airy pattern. It is an accurate expression for the spot formed by focusing a coherent, collimated beam of uniform intensity such as the light from a distant point source. The secondary rings that surround the central peak are a striking characteristic of the Airy pattern, but they

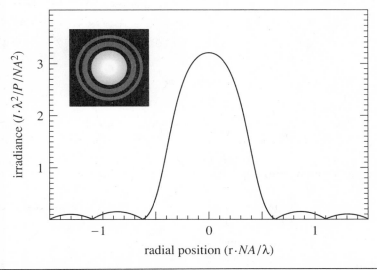

Figure 5.2 *The Airy profile describes the spot formed by focusing a beam of uniform intensity.*

have little practical importance. As long as the system is free of serious aberration (or defocus), the rings are very faint and contain no more than a few percent of the total power. The central core of the Airy pattern extends out to the first null of J_1, a diameter of 1.2 λ/ NA—twice as far as our previous estimate. Of course, the effective size of the spot is significantly smaller; the full-width-at-half-maximum (f.w.h.m.) of the spot is just $s = 0.6\lambda/NA$. For $\lambda = 0.8$ μm and $NA = 0.5$ the diameter is $s \simeq 1$ μm. It is perhaps fortuitous that the same factors that minimize the spot size (small λ and large NA) also maximize the irradiance (Eq. 5.8). Consequently, a system can be designed for both high resolution (high data density) and high spot intensity (high data rate).

The diffraction theory is necessary for an accurate understanding of the tightly focused optical stylus. But simple ray-tracing provides correct results far from focus. Figure 5.3 is a qualitative attempt to match a diffraction-limited spot, like that described by Eq. (5.11), with the cone of light converging from the objective lens. Away from focus, the diameter of the irradiance pattern, s, cannot increase at a rate faster than $ds/dz = \tan \theta$. If the minimum diameter is of the order λ/NA, then the depth of focus is of the order λ/NA^2. This qualitative fact is the basis of an important design consideration. A high NA is desirable for the formation of a small, intense optical

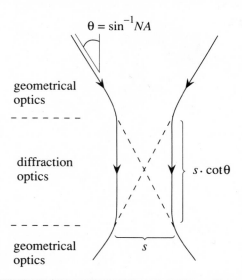

Figure 5.3 *Depth of focus for a diffraction-limited spot is shown here.*

stylus, but it also requires much tighter position tolerances, especially for focus. It would be much simpler to reduce the stylus size by reducing the wavelength (if shorter-wavelength lasers were available).

The basic propagation expression for scalar diffraction, Eq. (5.4), is not entirely self-consistent. It is accurate only when the wave components come from similar directions (when the vectors $X - x$ in the integral are nearly parallel). Therefore, the scalar-diffraction description of a focused spot is rigorous only in the limit of small *NA*. Scalar addition is not sufficient to describe how the components in a tightly focused beam combine, because the wave normal from one component may not be perpendicular to the electric field from another component wave. In a complete theory, light waves are represented by a vector field. Vector diffraction theory can be used to calculate the focused spot intensity in the general case. Although the mathematical analyses are of little interest here, a few results may be appropiate. Table 5.1 compares spot-size calculations based on the scalar diffraction approximation with an exact physical optics solution (Geyer, 1980, private communication). Note that the scalar diffraction approximation of the optical stylus is quite accurate when $NA < 0.65$.

In addition to affecting the size of the optical stylus in high-performance systems, vector diffraction can also affect the appearance of small marks. Dil and Jacobs (1979) have shown that the scalar diffraction theory does not accurately estimate the apparent size and phase contrast of very small features. For instance, groove dimensions (depth and width) are overestimated when the polarization is parallel to the groove or underestimated when the polarization is perpendicular. These vector effects depend on the wall angles or as-

TABLE 5.1 Calculations of Spot Size (f.w.h.m) Using Scalar and Vector Diffraction Theories[*]

| *NA* | SCALAR DIFFRACTION | VECTOR DIFFRACTION | |
		$r\|E$	$r\bot E$
0.50	1.16λ	1.14λ	1.08λ
0.65	0.90	0.88	0.80
0.85	0.68	0.64	0.56
0.95	0.62	0.56	0.42

[*]*assuming a Gaussian beam with a fill-factor $\alpha = 2$*

pect ratio of the mark features (see Bouwhuis, 1985). The error is usually slight for marks recorded in an optical disk drive, but it may be quite significant for the small pits on a CD or videodisc or the preformat patterns made by a high-performance mastering machine.

5.2 Truncation of a Gaussian Beam

The Airy pattern described in Section 5.1 is formed when the aperture of the objective lens is uniformly illuminated by a coherent beam. However, a laser beam normally does not have a uniform intensity profile. The intensity at the edge of the aperture will be less than at the center, and the lens will not collect and focus all of the light. An approximately uniform intensity is achieved if the beam is expanded to be much larger than the aperture, but in this case, most of the light is lost outside the aperture. This is a very inefficient way to focus a laser beam. In general, the size and irradiance of the optical stylus are affected by both nonuniform beam intensity (a condition called apodization) and loss of light outside the aperture (beam truncation).

Usually a collimated laser beam can be accurately described by a Gaussian intensity profile. (See the description of laser diodes in Chapter 6, Section 2.) For a circular Gaussian profile, the intensity pattern is

$$\mathcal{I}(\rho) = \mathcal{I}_0 \exp(-\alpha\rho^2/NA^2), \qquad (5.12)$$

where ρ is a radial coordinate at the aperture, normalized as in the previous section, $\rho^2 \equiv u^2 + v^2$. We will refer to the parameter α as the *apodization* factor. If the maximum beam intensity on the optical axis is ϑ_0, then the marginal intensity is $\vartheta_0 e^{-\alpha}$. The f.w.h.m. of the beam is $\mathcal{S} \equiv 2\rho$, where ρ satisfies $\exp(-\alpha\rho^2/NA^2) = 1/2$, or

$$\mathcal{S} = 1.67NA/\sqrt{\alpha}. \qquad (5.13)$$

The *fill factor,* defined as the ratio of $\mathcal{S}$ divided by the aperture diameter ($2NA$), is $0.83/\sqrt{\alpha}$. When α is very large, the aperture does not really truncate the beam and the lens is said to be under-filled. When α is near zero, the lens is illuminated quite uniformly, but only by the central core of the beam. So the power, P, available to form the optical stylus is much smaller than the total power of the beam, $\mathcal{P}$.

Given these definitions and a few equations from the previous section, we can calculate in detail how the truncation of a Gaussian beam affects the optical stylus. The fraction of available optical power that enters the lens is a simple function of the apodization factor. Dividing an integral of Eq. (5.12) over the aperture by an integral over the entire beam, we obtain

$$P/\mathscr{P} = 1 - e^{-\alpha}. \tag{5.14}$$

The total power is related to the beam intensity and aperture diameter through

$$\mathscr{P} = \pi \mathscr{I}_0 \, \mathscr{D}^2/4\alpha. \tag{5.15}$$

Using Eqs. (5.12) and (5.15) and evaluating Eq. (5.7), we find that the central spot irradiance from an ideally focused Gaussian beam is

$$I_{max} = 4\pi \mathscr{P} NA^2 [1 - e^{-\alpha/2}]^2 / (\alpha \lambda^2). \tag{5.16}$$

Figure 5.4 is a graph of this irradiance as a function of α. As expected, the focused spot is very weak when α is small, because most of the light is lost outside the aperture. The irradiance is also small when α is very large. This is because the lens is severely under-filled

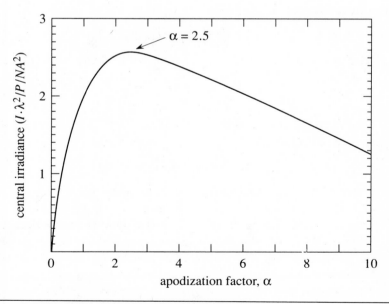

Figure 5.4 *Central irradiance of a focused spot as a function of the apodization factor is graphed here.*

and the effective NA is small. The maximum irradiance is achieved when $\alpha \cong 2.5$. In this case the beam intensity has dropped at the edge of the aperture to about 10% of the central maximum, and only 10% of the total beam power is lost. The most efficient way to use a laser beam to form an optical stylus is to match the beam size to the lens aperture according to this prescription (e.g., by beam expansion or by choice of the lens diameter). Note that the irradiance falls off sharply for small α and slowly for large α; for this and other reasons, an over-filled lens (or excessively truncated beam) will perform more poorly than an under-filled lens.

5.3   The Gaussian Spot Approximation

An over-filled lens creates a focused spot described by the Airy pattern, as described in Section 5.1. This condition exists in typical read-only heads. But in recording systems, the objective lens is under-filled and a slightly different spot shape results. Given a Gaussian beam with very large α, the limits of integration in Eq. (5.5) can be changed to ∞ to good approximation. The field distribution at a perfect focus ($z = 0$) is

$$E(r) = \pi \mathscr{D} \sqrt{\mathscr{I}_0} NA \exp[-2\pi^2 NA^2 r^2/(\alpha\lambda^2)]/(\alpha\lambda). \qquad (5.17)$$

Substituting for ϑ_0 from Eq. (5.15), we find the corresponding irradiance profile:

$$I(r) = 4\pi \mathscr{P} NA^2 \exp[-4\pi^2 NA^2 r^2/(\alpha\lambda^2)]/(\alpha\lambda^2). \qquad (5.18)$$

A Gaussian spot profile can be described in terms of its variance, σ^2, and total power, P :

$$I(r) = P \exp[-r^2/(2\sigma^2)]/(2\pi\sigma^2). \qquad (5.19)$$

Think of σ as the rms radius of the focused spot. The f.w.h.m. is $s = 2.35\sigma$. Comparing Eqs. (5.18) and (5.19), we see that a Gaussian beam focused through an under-filled lens forms a Gaussian spot with $\sigma = \lambda(\alpha/8)^{1/2}/(\pi NA)$ and total power $P \cong \mathscr{P}$. An inspection of Eq. (5.5) explains why a Gaussian beam can form a Gaussian spot. Apparently a positive lens is a device that converts the field at the aperture into its Fourier transform at the object plane. Since the Fourier transform of a Gaussian distribution is another Gaussian distribution, a Gaussian beam will form a Gaussian spot if it is not distorted or truncated by the aperture (or by aberration or defocus).

For calculational purposes, it would be convenient if the optical stylus could always be described in such a simple functional form. We have already seen that a uniform irradiance profile is not a good approximation for a focused spot. However, a Gaussian profile is a fair approximation to the focused spot for any degree of truncation.

A spot with a Gaussian profile has just two free parameters. Its radius, σ, is constrained by the irradiance and total power. Evaluating Eq. (5.19) at $r = 0$ and substituting the general expressions for P and I from Eqs. (5.14) and (5.16), we obtain the following estimate:

$$\sigma^2 \cong \alpha(1 + e^{-\alpha/2})/[8\pi^2(1 - e^{-\alpha/2})](\lambda/NA)^2. \qquad (5.20)$$

Another estimate of σ can be made by fitting the Gaussian profile to I_0 and the second derivative d^2I/dr^2 (both derived with some effort from Eq. 5.5):

$$\sigma^2 \cong \{4\pi^2[1 + 2/\alpha - 1/(1 - e^{-\alpha/2})]\}^{-1/2}(\lambda/NA)^2. \qquad (5.21)$$

These independent estimates of σ disagree by less than 5% for any value of α, suggesting that the spot profile indeed has a nearly Gaussian shape.

Figure 5.5 is a plot of Eq. (5.20). The minimum spot size is achieved when the aperture is totally over-filled; but optimum truncation ($\alpha = 2.5$, as defined in Section 5.2) produces an acceptably small spot:

$$\sigma \cong 0.25\lambda/NA \qquad (5.22)$$

or

$$s \cong 0.59\lambda/NA.$$

Exact spot profiles can be calculated by numerically integrating Eq. (5.5). Such calculations confirm that a Gaussian approximation (defined by Eq. 5.16 and Eqs. 5.20 or 5.21) is extremely accurate. Out to a radius of 2σ, the relative error is less than 15% for any value of α. At larger radius, the Gaussian approximation does not duplicate the faint Airy-like diffraction rings that appear for any finite value of α.

The Gaussian approximation is generally valid when the optical system is of high quality and the stylus is in focus. In some cases the

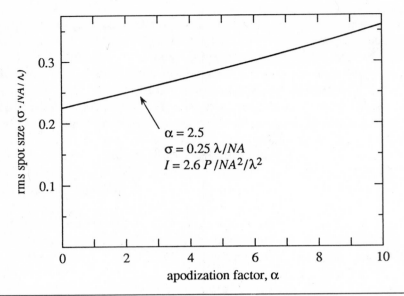

Figure 5.5 *Dependence of spot size on the apodization factor is graphed here.*

profile is elliptical (see Chapter 6, Section 2), but even then, a bivariate Gaussian profile is usually a good approximation:

$$I(x,y) = P \exp[-x^2/(2\sigma_x^2) - y^2/(2\sigma_y^2)]/(2\pi\sigma_x\sigma_y) \qquad (5.23)$$

which is a generalization of Eq. (5.19). The simple results of Section 5.4 are still valid for this profile, provided the appropriate σ is chosen for each direction.

Depth of Focus

We can use the Gaussian spot model to approximate the depth of focus of the optical stylus. Consider a stylus focused in free space as a Gaussian beam. In the absence of apertures or lenses, an aberration-free Gaussian beam retains the Gaussian form as it propagates, although the beam size changes. If σ_0 is the minimum rms radius at the beam waist (e.g., the object plane), the beam size elsewhere is given by

$$\sigma/\sigma_0 = \{1 + \lambda^2 z^2/(16\pi^2\sigma_0^4)\}^{1/2}, \qquad (5.24)$$

where z is the distance from the beam waist along the optical axis (Kogelnik and Li, 1966). Since the power in the beam is independent of z, the central intensity is just inversely proportional to the area of the spot, $I_0(z) \propto \sigma_0^2/\sigma^2$. The depth of focus is arbitrarily defined as the range over which the Strehl ration $[I_0(z)/I_0(0)]$ is greater than 80%. With this definition, Eq. (5.24) yields a focal range of $\pm 6.3\sigma_0^2/\lambda$. If the objective lens is optimally filled Eq. (5.22), the total depth of focus is

$$\Delta z \cong 0.8\lambda/NA^2. \qquad (5.25)$$

Eqs. (5.22) and (5.25) are accurate and convenient approximations for the size of the optical stylus. For typical parameters $\lambda = 0.8\ \mu m$ and $NA = 0.5$, the stylus diameter is $s \cong 0.94\ \mu m$ and the depth of focus is $\Delta z \cong 1.7\ \mu m$.

Optimum NA

Most useful optical recording media have very sharp recording thresholds. That is, they cannot be marked unless the irradiance or exposure (irradiance times pulse duration) exceeds some threshold. Usually the threshold is due to thermally activated mechanisms within the recording material. In the ideal case, there exists a threshold irradiance, I_{crit}, such that a mark forms whenever I_0 exceeds I_{crit}, and the mark shape corresponds precisely to the region where $I(x) \geq I_{crit}$. In some cases, marking corresponds physically to a critical exposure, where the accumulated energy per unit area exceeds a threshold. If the pulse-length is constant, an I_{crit} can still be defined which corresponds to the critical exposure.

Suppose we need to create a mark of given radius, r. Further assume that the pulse length is so short that any motion of the media beneath the optical stylus can be neglected. We call this *static marking*. If the spot irradiance profile is Gaussian, the incident power required to form a mark of radius r is given by Eq. (5.19):

$$P = P_0 \exp[r^2/(2\sigma^2)], \qquad (5.26)$$

where $P_0 \equiv 2\pi\ \sigma^2 I_{crit}$ is the threshold recording power, below which no mark of any size can form. The required power changes with the spot size, according to the derivative

$$dP/d\sigma = P(2/\sigma - r^2/\sigma^3). \qquad (5.27)$$

The necessary power is minimized when $dP/d\sigma = 0$, or

$$\sigma = r/\sqrt{2}, \qquad (5.28)$$

a result first reported by Maydan (1971). If we need to make static marks of radius r, the most efficient objective lens has a numerical aperture

$$NA \cong 0.35\,\lambda/r. \qquad (5.29)$$

In most optical recording systems the requisite spots are smaller than 1 μm in diameter, so Eq. (5.29) mandates an NA higher than 0.6, an impractically high value for most applications, considering the shallow depth of focus and the difficulties of lens design.

The LaBudde Model for Static Marking

Most optical disk recording is not *static*. At a scanning velocity of 10 m/s (for instance, 1800 rpm at a radius of 53 mm), the stylus covers 1 μm of the track in 100 ns, and the assumption of static marking could be valid only for extremely short recording pulses. However, static marking can be a valid description of low-data-rate recording on optical cards. It is also applicable in simple test equipment designed to screen and characterize recording media. Such static-testing devices often consist simply of a microscope with a laser beam merged with the illuminator.

The Gaussian stylus approximation yields a simple prediction of the readout signal as a function of recording power for static marking in thresholding materials. This model was developed and validated by LaBudde, Labudde, and Hazel, (1985). In a static power-series experiment, a series of marks are created at various recording powers (but with a fixed pulse length). The readout contrast of each mark is measured by centering the stylus on the mark (at a lower, readout power), detecting the total light reflected back through the objective lens, and comparing this light level with the reflectance observed from unmarked areas.

Given a highly thresholding recording process, the critical irradiance (or critical exposure) corresponds to a local reflectance change from R to $R + \Delta R$. Suppose that all the light reflected from the surface is re-collected by the objective lens. (This is a good approximation if the media surface remains smooth or if the lens is very underfilled.) The signal contrast corresponding to a mark of radius r_m is the fraction of the light reflected at the mark location minus the fraction reflected without a mark,

$$S = \int_0^{r_m} dr\ 2\pi r\ I(r)\Delta R\ /\ \int_0^{\infty} dr\ 2\pi r\ I(r) \qquad (5.30)$$

$$= \Delta R[1 - \exp(-r_m^2/2\sigma^2)].$$

Substituting for r_m from Eq. (5.26), we obtain the simple expression

$$S = \Delta R(1 - P_0/P), \qquad (5.31)$$

which is valid for $P > P_0$. In other words, the optical contrast of a mark, as sensed by the optical stylus that recorded it, is a linear function of P^{-1}. If the power series data is plotted in terms of S vs. P^{-1} (as in Figure 5.6), the intercept at $S = 0$ gives the threshold power, P_0, and the projected intercept at infinite power is the local reflectance change, ΔR.

If a recording material is susceptible to several kinds of physical changes, its recording behavior can be characterized by multiple thresholds. As a hypothetical example, a phase-change recording material with $R = 20\%$ could undergo a reflectance increase to R_1

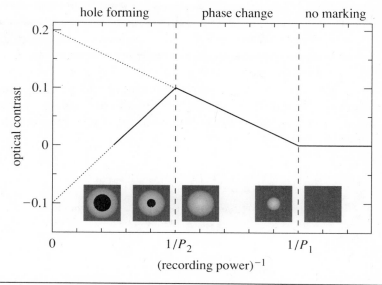

Figure 5.6 *Readout contrast versus recording power in a hypothetical phase-change medium with two thresholds is shown here.*

$= 40\%$ at a threshold of P_1. At a much higher threshold, P_2, it may begin to melt, forming holes of low reflectance, $R_2 = 10\%$. We can easily generalize Eq. (5.31) to accommodate multiple thresholds. For the case of two thresholds we have,

$$
\begin{aligned}
S &= 0 & P &< P_1 & (5.32)\\
&= (R_1 - R)(1 - P_1/P) & P_1 &< P < P_2 \\
&= (R_1 - R)(1 - P_1/P) + (R_2 - R_1)(1 - P_2/P) & P_2 &< P.
\end{aligned}
$$

Figure 5.6 illustrates a static power-series for this example. Note that the plot is still piece-wise linear, with breaks in the slope occurring at each threshold as the center of the mark takes on a new appearance. Projected intercepts at $1/P = 0$ can still be used to estimate the relative reflectance, $R_i - R$, associated with each marking process.

The Scanned Marking Limit

In most optical recording situations, the scanning velocity is not negligible. The time for a point on the media to scan past the optical stylus is often much shorter than the laser pulse. At the opposite extreme from static marking is the approximation of scanned marking in which the pulse length is effectively infinite. Static marking occurs when the laser pulse is short compared to the scan time, $\tau << s/v$, where s is the f.w.h.m. of the stylus and v is the scan velocity; scanned marking occurs when $\tau >> s/v$. For typical parameters, $s = 1~\mu\text{m}$ and $v = 10~\text{m/s}$, the scanned marking approximation is valid for any recording pulse much longer than 100 ns.

In scanned marking, the cumulative exposure (energy per unit area) is not proportional to the stylus irradiance; rather, it is proportional to a line integral through the irradiance profile. The exposure at any point on the recording surface from a single, long pulse of a Gaussian stylus is given by:

$$
\mathcal{E}(x,y) = I_0 \int_{-\infty}^{x} du \exp[-(u^2 + y^2)/(2\sigma^2)]/v \qquad (5.33)
$$

$$
= \exp[-y^2/(2\sigma^2)][1 - \psi(x/\sigma)]P/[(2\pi)^{1/2}\sigma v]
$$

where

$$
\psi(\omega) \equiv \int_{\omega}^{\infty} du \exp(-u^2/2)/(2\pi)^{1/2}
$$

is an error function representing the tail of the Gaussian distribution and x and y are coordinates relative to the center of the stylus at the time when the pulse began. The media is considered to be moving in the $-x$ direction.

For $x >> \sigma$, far from the end of the mark, the error function is negligible and the exposure distribution depends only on the distance from the center of the track:

$$\mathscr{E}(x,y) \cong \exp[-y^2/(2\sigma^2)] \, P/[(2\pi)^{1/2}\sigma v], \text{ for } x >> 0. \qquad (5.34)$$

(Actually, $x > \sigma$ is far enough from the end of the mark for reasonable accuracy.) The maximum exposure is reached along the center of the track,

$$\mathscr{E}_{max} \equiv \mathscr{E}(x,0) = P/[(2\pi)^{1/2}\sigma v], \text{ for } x >> 0. \qquad (5.35)$$

Near the end of the mark, at the point centered under the stylus when the recording pulse began, $\psi = 1/2$, and the exposure is

$$\mathscr{E}(0,0) = \mathscr{E}_{max}/2. \qquad (5.36)$$

As in the previous discussions, suppose that the recording medium has a thresholding behavior, so that marking occurs wherever a critical exposure, $\mathscr{E}_{crit}$, is exceeded. Eq. (5.35) gives us the minimum power for recording a mark of any size:

$$P_0 = (2\pi)^{1/2}\sigma v \mathscr{E}_{crit}. \qquad (5.37)$$

This expression combined with Eq. (5.34), tells us the power required to make a mark with some desired width, w:

$$P_w = P_0 \exp[w^2/(8\sigma^2)]. \qquad (5.38)$$

Differentiating with respect to σ, we find that the power required to make a long mark of fixed width is minimized when the stylus size is $\sigma = w/2$, the optimum objective lens numerical aperture is

$$NA \cong 0.5 \, \lambda/\omega, \qquad (5.39)$$

and the power is $P = 1.65P_0$. Note that this optimization differs from the criteria for efficient static marking ($\sigma = r/\sqrt{2}$), which we derived previously (see Noguchi, 1982).

Yet another prescription for the optimum recording conditions arises from considerations of recording distortion. Ideally, we would like to record marks with lengths that exactly match the recording pulse length (length = τ/v). If the critical exposure contour includes the point $(x = 0, y = 0)$ where the stylus turns on, then symmetry ensures that it will also include the point that is centered beneath the optical stylus when the recording pulse finally ends. For long recording pulses, this condition is achieved when $P = 2P_0$ (Eq. 5.36). At recording powers less than twice the threshold, the marks will be shorter than the recording pulses; at higher recording powers, the marks will be slightly longer. This prescription for minimizing mark distortion does not depend on the assumption of a Gaussian stylus profile; any symmetric profile would give the same result as long as the recording threshold is simply a critical *exposure*. A useful generalization from the various recording models is the rule that the optimum recording power is nearly twice the threshold and that the exposure at the center of a mark is about twice the exposure at the edge.

5.4 Readout Signals

Information recorded by the optical stylus can also be read out by the stylus because the marks are optically different from the unmarked background, or land. Figure 5.7 illustrates several adjacent tracks of marks. The marks may have different shapes, (hopefully) corresponding to different recording pulse lengths. However, all the marks should have the same, uniform reflectance. If the land reflectance is R_0, the land reflectance coefficient is $r_0 = \sqrt{R_0}$. The mark reflectance can differ in amplitude, phase, or both; the general form of the mark reflectance coefficient is $r = re^{i\phi}$. Most write-once media form marks that are much lighter or darker than the land, $r \ll r_0$

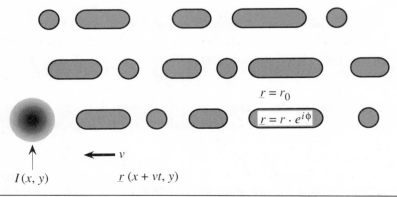

$r = r_0$

$r = r \cdot e^{i\phi}$

$I(x, y)$ $\leftarrow v$ $r(x + vt, y)$

Figure 5.7 *Scanning recorded marks with the optical stylus is shown here.*

or $r >> r_0$. In such cases the phase difference, ϕ, does not influence the readout much. On the other hand, the pits in read-only disks and the preformat features molded into optical disk substrates differ from the land areas only in phase.

The optical stylus is composed of light rays (or superpositions of plane waves) that are incident on the recording surface over a range of incident angles, from $0°$ to $\sin^{-1}(NA/n)$. It is sometimes important to realize that both the land and mark reflectance coefficients depend on the incidence angle. For instance, a finely tuned antireflection trilayer (Chapter 13, Section 2) might have $R_0 \sim 0$ at normal incidence but a much higher reflectance for marginal rays. The reflectance coefficients can also be polarization-dependent; examples include M-O marks, which exhibit Kerr rotation, and narrow tracking grooves, in which vector diffraction effects are important.

During readout, the optical power focused in the stylus is held constant while a track scans beneath it at a fixed velocity, v. At any instant, the total amount of light reflected from the surface is just an integral of the stylus irradiance profile times the reflectance pattern on which it is focused. Some or all of the reflected light is re-collected by the objective lens and relayed to the photodetectors, which generate an electrical current proportional to the amount of light received. The variety of possible readout schemes includes full-aperture detection, in which a single detector is arranged to collect all the light that emerges from the objective lens; point detection, in which a smaller detector collects only the light that returns on the optical axis; and split-aperture detection, in which two detectors collect the light from opposite halves of the aperture. The signals from point detection and full-aperture detection approximately measure the amount of reflected light. The signal from split-aperture detection is the difference of the two detector photocurrents; this net signal may be positive or negative, indicating that the reflected light has been deflected (or rather, diffracted) in the forward or reverse directions.

It is tempting to model the dynamic readout of data using the same simplifying assumptions that underlie the LaBudde static marking model (Section 5.3). If a full-aperture detection scheme is used, it might be reasonable to assume that the amount of light incident on the detector at any time is equal to the amount reflected from the recording surface. This is a fairly good approximation when the incident beam under-fills the aperture and if the reflected light is not scattered to large angles by diffraction. Under these conditions, we can describe the time-dependent readout signal as a convolution of the optical stylus with the reflectance pattern,

$$S(t) \propto \int\limits_{0}^{\infty}\int\limits_{0}^{\infty} dx \; dy \; I \, (x, y) R(x + vt, y). \qquad (5.40)$$

Calculations using this simple readout model are particularly easy when the stylus profile is a simple, separable function like the Gaussian approximation. Figure 5.8 illustrates the readout signal predicted for a track of dark marks of varying length. The model explains several basic characteristics of full-aperture readout. Although the marks have sharp boundaries, the corresponding slopes on the readout signal cannot be sharper than the profile of the stylus. And the readout pulses that correspond to short marks (or short spaces) can have lower amplitudes than the pulses from long marks, because a substantial fraction of the illumination falls outside the small marks. This is a manifestation of the *resolution limit,* due to the finite size of the optical stylus.

The model of readout as a convolution of the stylus with the disk reflectance pattern is intuitively appealing, and it yields qualitatively useful results when the mark contrast is primarily due to a change in R. However, when the marks are very small, and especially when a

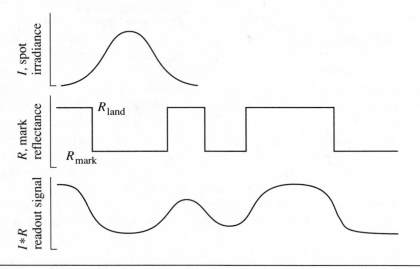

Figure 5.8 *A simplistic model of readout as a convolution of the stylus with the reflectance pattern is illustrated here.*

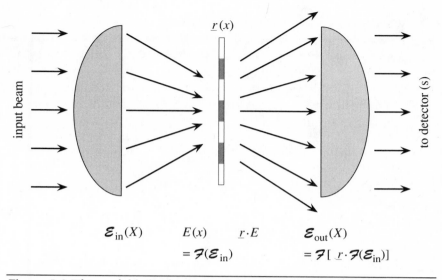

Figure 5.9 *This unfolded schematic of the readout system illustrates the principles of the diffraction theory of readout.*

phase difference, ϕ, dominates the optical contrast, the readout theory must account for diffraction effects. Figure 5.9 illustrates the readout process from the point of view of scalar diffraction. In the figure, the optical path has been unfolded to distinguish the two functions of the objective lens. First, the objective lens serves to focus the incident beam. The beam can be represented by a field distribution $\mathscr{E}_{in}(X)$ at the aperture. $\mathscr{E}$ is a complex number, incorporating both the intensity distribution of the beam and any aberrations of the ideal phase profile. The lens serves to convert the incident field into its Fourier transform, E, at the object plane (which is assumed to be coincident with the media surface). Upon reflection from the surface, the field of the outbound light is reduced in amplitude and/or altered in phase; this is represented by a point-by-point multiplication of E times the complex reflectance coefficient r. Finally, the objective lens re-collects the light and relays to the readout detectors a return beam, $\mathscr{E}_{out}$, which is a Fourier transform of the reflectance-modified optical stylus. If the media reflectance is uniform (e.g., in a large, unmarked land area), the return beam is identical to the incident beam:

$$
\begin{aligned}
\mathscr{E}_{out} &= \mathscr{F}(E(\mathbf{x}) \cdot \underline{r}) \\
&= r_0\, \mathscr{F}^2[\mathscr{E}_{in}\mathbf{X})] \\
&= r_0\, \mathscr{E}_{in},
\end{aligned}
\tag{5.41}
$$

where $\mathscr{F}$ is the Fourier transform operator described by Eq. (5.4). But in general, the reflected beam differs in its irradiance pattern and phase profile as well as in its total power. Frequently a significant amount of the reflected light is scattered completely outside the aperture of the objective lens by diffraction at the recording surface.

The field in the readout beam can be described as the Fourier transform of the reflected field:

$$\mathscr{E}_{\text{out}}(X) = \mathscr{F}[E(x)\,\underline{r}] \qquad\qquad (5.42)$$
$$= \mathscr{F}[E(x) * \mathscr{F}(\underline{r})],$$

where $*$ represents a two-dimensional convolution operation,

$$f(x, y) * g(x, y) \equiv \int\limits_{-\infty}^{\infty} \int\limits_{-\infty}^{\infty} d\xi\, d\psi\, f(\xi, \psi)\cdot g(\xi - x, \psi - y).$$

Or alternatively, the stylus can be viewed as a Fourier transform of the input beam, $E(x) = \mathscr{F}[\mathscr{E}_{\text{in}}(X)]$, so that

$$\mathscr{E}_{\text{out}}(X) = \mathscr{E}_{\text{in}}(X) * \mathscr{F}(\underline{r}), \qquad\qquad (5.43)$$

since the Fourier transform is its own inverse. In words, the reflected beam at the aperture is exactly equal to the incident beam (as truncated by the aperture) convolved with the Fourier transform of the reflectance pattern. This is an extremely powerful result for readout modeling, because a convolution is much easier to compute than the corresponding Fourier transforms.

As a particularly illustrative application of the diffraction theory of readout, consider the modulation transfer function, or MTF, of the readout system. For our purposes, the MTF is defined as the dependence of the readout signal level on the period of the track pattern for a sequence of identical marks spaced uniformly along the track with period p. The Fourier transform of the track reflectance pattern is a sum of Dirac delta functions (diffraction orders) at locations $n\lambda\mathscr{D}/(2p\cdot NA)$ across the aperture where $n = 0, \pm 1, \pm 2$, etc. (see Chapter 7, Section 2). The convolution of Eq. (5.43) describes a readout beam that looks like the superposition of a series of images of the apertured input beam. The relative phases of the diffraction orders (and their corresponding aperture images) depend on the orientation of the track under the optical axis (the center of the stylus), but their locations and amplitudes are constant. Therefore, time variation of the readout beam only occurs by interference between the orders where they overlap. Figure 5.10 shows representative MTFs for full-aperture and point detection systems. Note that point detection yields a signal only when $p > \lambda/NA$; otherwise, the $\pm 1^{st}$ orders are diffracted to such an extent that they miss the center of the aperture entirely. Full-aperture detection has twice as much resolution.

When $p < \lambda/(2NA)$, all the diffraction orders except $n = 0$ miss the aperture entirely and no readout signal can be produced by any readout scheme. Note that the Gaussian spot approximation is not particularly helpful in this context. The Fourier transform of a Gaussian is another Gaussian, so Eq. (5.40) would predict that there is always some overlap between the diffraction orders. If so, the MTF would only approach zero asymptotically for $p < \lambda/(2NA)$. But in reality, the MTF always has an absolute cutoff at this resolution limit.

The chapter bibliography includes several references to the diffraction theory of optical disk readout, ranging from a detailed derivation of the theory (Hopkins, 1979) to an intuitive explanation (Korpel, 1978) and a computational model (Marchant, 1982). In this section we will conclude with just a few of the phenomena explained by the readout theory. The interested reader should refer to the references for details.

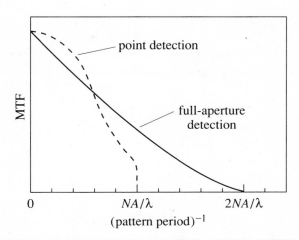

Figure 5.10 *These representative MTFs for two detector configurations show that point detection yields a signal only when $p > \lambda/NA$.*

The first readout example, illustrated Figure 5.11, describes the full-aperture readout of replicated pits in typical read-only disks. These pits are molded with a depth of about 120 nm, so the reflective phase shift, as viewed through the substrate, is $\phi = 4\pi n$ 120 nm$/\lambda \cong \pi$ for a refractive index of 1.5 and a wavelength of 800 nm. A phase contrast of π radians maximizes the readout signal from full-aperture detection. The light reflected from such pits has the opposite phase of the light reflected from the land areas. As a pit edge scans beneath the optical stylus, destructive interference greatly reduces the light reflected back through the lens; the light is lost because it is strongly diffracted and scattered away at large angles. Figure 5.11 shows that an intensity dip corresponds with the edges of each pit. When the pits are narrow compared to the width of the spot, (cross-track) scattering continues to occur as the pit passes beneath the stylus. The readout waveform corresponds qualitatively to a cross section of the track. But if the pits are wide compared to the stylus, the beam will be only slightly diffracted when it is reflected from within a long pit. Therefore, full-aperture detection of wide (phase) pits can produce confusing readout waveforms.

Figure 5.12 illustrates readout signals from split-aperture detection, when the aperture is divided perpendicular to the scanning direction. The amplitude of the difference signal is maximized when $\phi = \pi/2$ radians. In fact, marks optimized for full-aperture readout ($\phi = \pi$) yield no signal through a split-aperture system. The signal from split-aperture readout looks qualitatively like a derivative of the track cross section. In the absence of any mark, the two detectors produce identical currents and the net signal is zero. But the leading edge of a mark diffracts the reflected light preferentially toward one

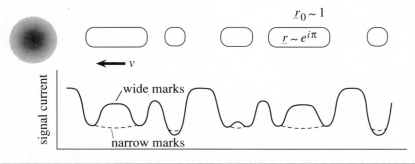

Figure 5.11 *A readout signal from phase-pits with $\phi \sim \pi$ is shown here.*

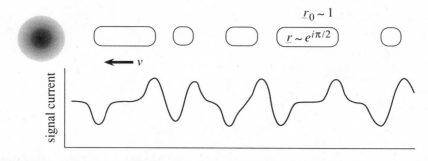

Figure 5.12 *The split-detector difference signal from the readout of phase pits is maximized when* $\phi \sim \pi/2$.

detector, creating a signal pulse; the trailing edge of the mark diffracts the light toward the other detector to create a signal pulse of the opposite polarity. The peaks of these pulses accurately identify the edges of the marks. It is sometimes noted that split-aperture detection has a low MTF at low spatial frequencies, when p is large. This is because very long marks produce only two short pulses, one at each end, so the average signal power is low. The peak-to-peak signal amplitude is constant (and quite high) at low spatial frequencies. The MTF extends to the same resolution limit for split-aperture readout as for full-aperture readout.

5.5 Aberration

In Section 5.3 we saw that a small amount of defocus increases the size of the focused spot and reduces its irradiance, but it does not change its essentially Gaussian profile. However, other kinds of aberration can produce qualitatively different spot profiles, especially when combined with some defocus. Figure 5.13 illustrates the cause and appearance of spherical aberration. *Spherical aberration* refers to any type of phase error that is symmetrical around the optical axis, so that ϕ is a function only of $\rho \equiv (u^2 + v^2)^{1/2}$ in Eq. (5.5). In geometrical terms, the result is that rays that pass through the aperture at different radii are focused at different points on the optical axis. In Figure 5.13 the marginal rays are focused farther from the lens than the paraxial rays. Somewhere between the paraxial and

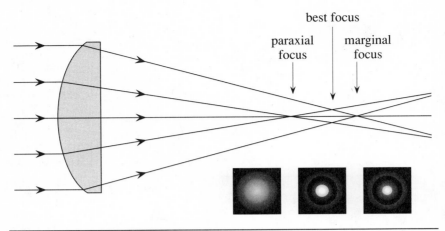

Figure 5.13 *Spherical aberration makes the stylus asymmetrical with respect to defocus.*

marginal focus is a *best focus,* where the spot has a minimum size. However, even at best focus, the spot is larger and less intense than the corresponding diffraction-limited (aberration-free) spot. Spherical aberration can usually be identified by the qualitative asymmetry of the spot profile near focus. On one side of best focus (toward the paraxial focus), the profile simply becomes larger and more diffuse. But in the other direction, the profile has a distinct core/halo appearance due to interference between paraxial and marginal rays. If the aberration is great enough, the profile can break up into bright, concentric bands.

One common cause of spherical aberration is the passage of a noncollimated beam through a thick, transparent plate. The effect of a beam-splitter cube in this regard is discussed in Chapter 8, Section 1. Another important example of this situation occurs when the beam is focused through a protective layer such as an overcoat, cover sheet, or transparent substrate. Since dust protection is an essential feature of optical recording media, the objective lens must be designed to compensate for the aberration that results from a protective layer of the nominal thickness. This type of correction has traditionally been applied to biological microscope objectives, which are corrected to focus through a thin glass cover slip (0.17 mm). Since most optical disks have transparent substrates of thickness 1.2 mm, a new class of lenses have been developed which are corrected for this protective-layer thickness. Any system design that calls for an unusual protective layer thickness must also address the need to provide a properly corrected objective lens.

The optical effects of a protective layer are compensated in the lens design only to the extent that the layer actually has the ideal thickness; therefore, any thickness variation is a cause for concern. Figure 5.14 illustrates a ray-tracing analysis of the aberration due to the protective layer. Suppose a transparent plate of thickness Δ and refractive index n is placed in a perfectly focused beam. Think of this plate as the uncorrected part of the protective-layer thickness, or the deviation from nominal. Paraxial rays (nearly parallel to the optical axis) are focused a distance $\Delta(1 - 1/n)$ below the original focus. The focus of the marginal rays is shifted even further down, so the best focus will be found at an intermediate point. For the case $n = 1.5$ and $NA = 0.6$, a detailed analysis shows that the best focus is shifted by 0.37Δ, compared to the paraxial focus shift of 0.33Δ (Marchant, 1983). Note that the vertical location of the layer does

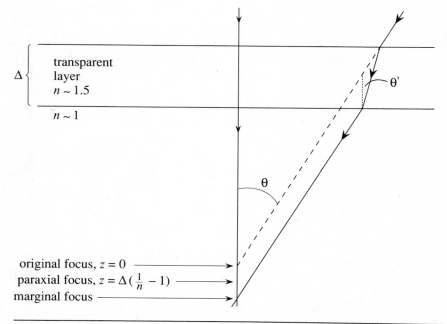

Figure 5.14 *A transparent layer shifts the focus and introduces spherical aberration.*

not affect the length of any ray or its focus intercept. The optical effect of the protective layer is independent of its location.

The first-order effect of a variation in protective-layer thickness is an apparent shift in the axial location of the recording surface. If the variations have a low spatial frequency (due to disk-to-disk variability, radial dependence, or wedge) the closed-loop focus servo will refocus the lens accordingly. However, if the thickness variation is rapid, the focus servo might be unable to compensate. Localized thickness variation may be due to material defects (slugs or striations) or the manufacturing method (lines in extruded plastic sheet or print-through on molded substrates). Figure 5.15 shows that refocusing can greatly reduce the effects of thickness variation for typical system parameters ($NA = 0.6$, $\alpha = 2$, and $n = 1.5$). The spot size plotted there is half the f.w.h.m., or the radius, r, at which $I(r) = I_0/2$. The *mark size* refers to the radius at which a fixed (threshold) irradiance is reached, $I(r) = I_{max}/2$. If the system is unable to refocus, it cannot tolerate thickness variations greater than a few microns: Since the focal shift is about $\Delta/3$, the thickness tolerance is about three times the depth of focus. On the other hand, if the system continuously positions the objective lens at the paraxial focus, the tolerance is as large as ± 30 μm. The spot quality can be improved still more if the servo can locate and maintain the best focus. Some residual degradation of the optical stylus due to spherical aberration remains. But practical aberration budgets allow for a total variability of the protective-layer thickness of approximately ± 50 μm around the nominal for $NA \sim 0.5$.

Figure 5.15 illustrates a qualitative difference between read-only drives and optical recording systems. Aberrations that increase the size of the optical stylus also decrease its irradiance. This means that an aberrated stylus forms smaller marks (at a given laser power) and is less able to resolve them, a double whammy that explains why optical recording systems have much tighter optical tolerances than read-only systems.

Several types of asymmetric aberrations can occur in optical recording systems. Coma arises when a noncollimated beam passes through a tilted plate, lens, or beam-splitter. When coma is substantial, the focused spot looks like it has a diffuse tail on one side (hence the term *coma* or "comet"). This situation occurs when the disk is tilted with respect to the optical axis. Tilt of the recording surface, per se, is not very important; coma results because the attached protective layer is also tilted. Tilted optical elements also

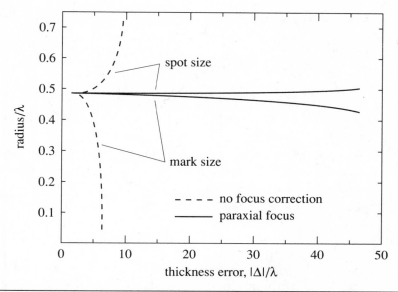

Figure 5.15 *Variation of the protective-layer thickness affects the stylus size and recorded mark size.*

cause astigmatism, a condition in which the beam forms two perpendicular line foci rather than a point focus. Astigmatism can also occur as an intrinsic defect of the laser (see Chapter 6, Section 1).

We saw that the depth of focus is proportional to NA^{-2} (Sections 5.1 and 5.3). Because of the effects of spherical aberration, the allowable variation in thickness decreases as an even steeper function of NA. In general, a high-NA system is much more sensitive to all forms of aberration. Recall that the stylus width is proportional to λ/NA and the potential data density is proportional to NA^2/λ^2. A higher NA could greatly increase the storage density, but tight tolerances on aberration limit us at present to $NA < 0.6$ in practical systems. Aberrations also increase for shorter wavelengths, but the proportionality is only $1/\lambda$. Reducing λ is a more promising route to increased packing density than increasing NA.

Strictly speaking, dust on the optics does not cause aberration, but it does degrade the quality of the optical stylus (see Figure 5.16). Suppose that particles obscure a fraction β of the objective lens. In the absence of other aberration, Eq. (5.7) allows us to estimate the central irradiance as

$$I_0 = I_{\max}(1-\beta)^2. \tag{5.44}$$

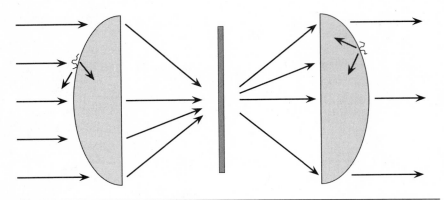

Figure 5.16 *Dust on the optics reduces the spot irradiance and further reduces the readout efficiency.*

The principal effect of a dust particle is to reduce the power in the optical stylus without changing its shape. Functionally, contamination of the optical system looks like a progressive deterioration of the media sensitivity. Moderate levels of contamination can be accommodated if excess recording power is available and the system firmware reoptimizes the recording conditions periodically. Note that the fraction of light absorbed and scattered out of the focused beam corresponds to about twice the physical cross section of the particle, $(1 - \beta)^2 \cong (1 - 2\beta)$. This result corresponds to the short-wavelength limit in scattering theory.

A tell-tale indication of dirty optics is a reduction in apparent media reflectance as measured by the optical head. When the reflected beam is focused back onto the detector, the readout signal is reduced by another factor of $(1 - \beta)^2$, for a total drop of $(1 - \beta)^4$. If the input beam power is increased to compensate, the incident irradiance on the disk increases by a net $(1 - \beta)^2$. This could be a problem, because the nominal readout power might already have been set as high as the media could tolerate in order to minimize shot noise and to maximize the raw readout signal.

This analysis of the effects of dust applies to any discrete defect on any element of the optical head, including the protective-layer surface. Such defects include scratches, pits, and inclusions as well as actual dust particles. Other kinds of contamination that cover large areas of the aperture (fingerprints, water-spots, etc.) are much more serious. They can totally ruin the system performance by distorting the overall wavefront of the focused beam instead of just obscuring part of it.

MAJOR CONCEPTS

- The optical stylus is formed by a diffraction-limited objective lens with a moderate numerical aperture. Scalar diffraction is usually an adequate approximation for calculating the characteristics of the optical stylus (Table 5.1).

- A Gaussian laser beam is optimized for optical recording when it slightly over-fills the objective lens with about 10% of the light lost outside the aperture (Figure 5.4).

- The depth of focus of the optical stylus is about $0.8\lambda/NA^2$. Eq. (5.25)

- The optimal recording power is twice the marking threshold or a bit less (Eq. 5.36 and subsequent discussion).

- Readout of high contrast marks can be understood as a convolution of the optical stylus with the reflectance pattern (Figure 5.8).

- Readout of phase features, such as preformatted pits, relies on diffraction which scatters light outside the objective lens aperture (Figure 5.11).

- Optical aberrations hurt the data signal in two ways, by reducing the recording efficiency and by reducing the readout resolution (Figure 5.15).

REFERENCES

Bouwhuis, G., J. Braat, A. Huijser, J. Pasman, G. van Rosmalen, and K. Schouhamer Immink, *Principles of Optical Disc Systems,* Adam Hilger, Ltd., Boston (1985). Chapter 2 by J. Braat includes a good formal treatment of optical disk readout theory. Chapter 3 by J. Pasman describes vector diffraction effects arising in preformatted optical disks.

Dil, J., and B. Jacobs, "Apparent size of reflecting polygonal obstacles of the order of one wavelength," *J. Opt. Soc. Am.,* **69,** 950 (1979). A description of how vector diffraction can affect optical disk readout.

Haskal, H., "Laser recording with truncated Gaussian beams," *Applied Optics,* **18**, 2143 (1979). A discussion of truncation effects on focused laser beams.

Hopkins, H., "Diffraction theory of laser read-out systems for optical video discs," *J. Opt. Soc. Am.,* **69**, 4 (1979). The basic scalar diffraction theory of optical disk readout.

Kogelnik, H., and T. Li, "Laser beams and resonators," *Proc. IEEE,* **54**, 1312 (1966).

Korpel, A., "Simplified diffraction theory of the video disk," *Applied Optics,* **17**, 2037 (1978). A qualitative diffraction model that provides simple explanations of several readout phenomena.

LaBudde, E., R. LaBudde, and R. Hazel, "Theoretical modeling and experimental characterization of Drexon recording media," *OSA Topical Meeting on Optical Data Storage,* WdD3 (1985). An explanation and example of the LaBudde contrast model.

Marchant, A., "Cover-sheet aberrations in optical recording," *SPIE Proceedings,* **421**, 43 (1983). A detailed discussion of spherical aberration from the protective layer.

Marchant, A., "Optical disk readout: a model for coherent scanning," *Applied Optics,* **21**, 2085 (1982). A methodology for computer modeling of optical disk readout.

Maydan, D., "Micromachining and image recording on thin films by laser beams," *The Bell System Technical Journal,* **50**, 1761 (1971). An in-depth analysis of thermal recording using a Gaussian optical stylus.

Noguchi, M., "Efficient use of laser power in heat-mode recording," *Applied Optics,* **21**, 2665 (1982). Optimum use of a Gaussian beam for scanned marking.

CHAPTER 6

Laser Diodes
for Optical Recording

The first true optical recording systems were assembled and demonstrated almost as soon as the laser was invented. However, the available lasers made these systems quite cumbersome. Sufficient laser power was available from relatively simple gas lasers, but their implementation was complicated. Figure 6.1 illustrates how a continuous-emission gas laser is used for optical recording. Although it emits a well collimated, circular beam, the laser cannot be modulated directly. Rapid modulation of the beam is achieved through an acousto-optic modulator (AOM). The data signal is fed to the AOM in the form of short, high-frequency bursts, which set up a temporary diffraction grating inside a crystal. During each RF burst, part of the beam is deflected through a spatial filter toward the optical head. Other types of external beam modulators such as the electro-optic modulator (EOM) are available, but the AOM generally gives the fastest possible response, a critical feature for recording at high data-rates.

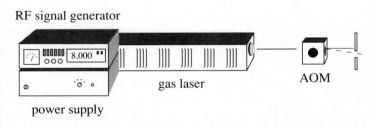

Figure 6.1 A gas laser configured for optical recording emits a well-collimated, circular beam but cannot be modulated directly.

Any gas laser powerful enough for recording is quite large (at least compared to computer peripherals). In addition, it requires a large power supply and a modulator (with an RF generator to drive the modulator). The total electrical power requirement and heat-dissipation load are quite large. One advantage to such a system is that gas lasers of very high power are available. But this advantage is mitigated by the considerable losses that occur through the external modulator, especially if it is tuned for the shortest possible rise time. Another advantage of conventional lasers is short wavelength. For example, the most powerful emission of an Argon-ion laser (Ar^+) is at 488 nm (458 nm with slightly less power), and the emission of a Helium-Cadmium laser (HeCd) is at 441 nm. These lasers are still used in optical recording for optical disk mastering because the short wavelength and high power are appropriate for photoresist exposure (see Chapter 12, Section 4).

6.1 Operating Characteristics

Even though the convenience and efficiency of conventional lasers have improved considerably over the years, no applications of optical recording technology would be commercially viable without a novel laser source, the laser diode. The laser diode offers an impressive list of advantages for optical recording:

Size. Figure 6.2 illustrates the typical configuration of a laser diode. The actual laser is only a few hundred microns in length, dwarfed by the other parts of the micro-electronics package.

Cost. By any measure, laser diodes are the least expensive lasers. In volume quantities, low-power laser diodes for CD drives cost only $10 apiece. Prices for higher power laser diodes should drop to similar levels as demand increases.

Modulation. The laser diode can be pulsed directly simply by modulating the input current. Laser diodes are also used for optical communication because they can be modulated at GHz rates, much faster than any optical recording application requires.

Efficiency. Typically, the efficiency of a laser diode (the conversion of electrical power to coherent optical power) exceeds 10%.

Even in the smallest drive, the laser diode represents a negligible contribution to a system's power demand and thermal load.

Electrical Characteristics. The laser diode operates at very low voltages (~ 2 V), so it does not require a special power supply. In the operating regime, the light output is a linear function of the injected current.

Figure 6.2 also illustrates some features of the usual laser diode package. The laser is bonded to a heat sink, which also acts as the electrical ground contact. A photo-detector is mounted a short distance behind the laser. The photocurrent from this sense diode can be used to monitor the laser output power because the rear-facet emission is proportional to the front-facet emission (in the absence of coherent optical feedback). The laser beam emerges from the laser facet through a very small active region. Any contamination of the facet (e.g., by a single sub-micron dust particle) could obliterate the beam. Therefore, the laser is packaged in a sealed container, and the beam exits through a small glass window. Electrical contact is made to the laser through three or four leads—a line for the laser drive current, a sense line from the detector, and one or two ground lines.

Figure 6.3 illustrates how a laser diode functions. The heart of the laser is a light-emitting region that is electronically similar to an LED. But in a laser diode, the emitting region is very long and narrow, and its composition is tuned to give it a much higher refractive index than those of the neighboring layers of the device. The region of optical gain is therefore a waveguide that supports light propagating only along its length, similar to a single-mode optical fiber. The ends of the laser are cleaved crystal facets which serve as mirrors at both ends of the waveguide. When the optical gain (or current density) is high enough, light trapped within the waveguide stimulates coherent emission, which emerges through the (partially reflecting) facets as laser light. The electrical contact and a patterned insulation layer concentrate the current through the gain region in order to maximize the laser efficiency.

The waveguide region that generates the laser beam is no more than a couple of microns wide along the laser junction and a fraction of a micron thick. Because the waveguide thickness is much smaller than the width, its characteristics are polarization-dependent. Less light leaks out when it is polarized with its E-field parallel to the

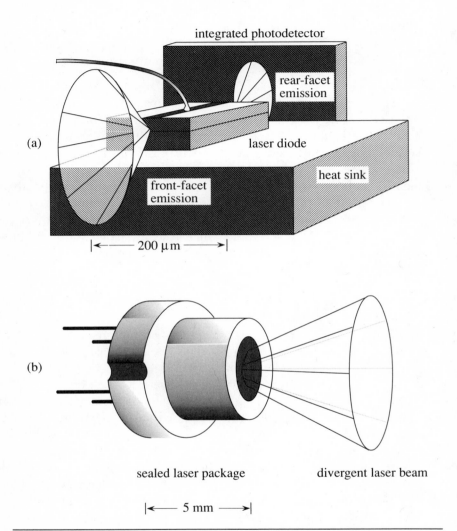

(a)

(b)

Figure 6.2 *In a laser diode assembly, the actual laser is only a few hundred microns in length.*

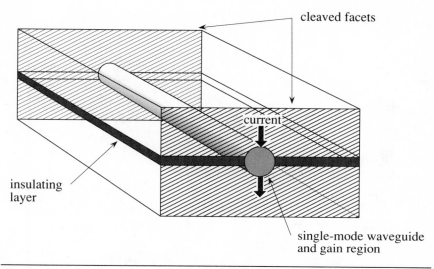

Figure 6.3 *This functional representation of a laser diode shows that the emitting region is long and narrow, and it has a higher refractive index than the neighboring material.*

junction surface (∥) than when it is perpendicularly polarized (⊥). As a result, the output of a good single-mode laser is predominantly ∥ polarized, with a polarization ratio in the range 10:1 to 200:1. The polarization ratio tends to increase with output power.

When the applied current is low, there is insufficient gain in a laser diode to induce stimulated emission. The laser behaves just like a small LED at low currents; some light is emitted, but it is not coherent. At some threshold current, coherent emission becomes possible. As shown in Figure 6.4, the optical output of the laser increases rapidly as the current is raised above the threshold. In this regime, the dependence of power on current is quite linear. Eventually, the power curve begins to saturate (usually because of thermal effects). At even higher drive current, the laser power decreases or the laser can fail catastrophically.

Although they are remarkably advantageous for optical recording, laser diodes also have several peculiarities and deficiencies:

Long Wavelength. Laser diodes are for optical recording not available with nominal wavelengths shorter than 780 nm. This places important limits on the size and irradiance of the optical stylus. The near-infrared emission is also inconvenient for laboratory investigation. Optical alignment requires the use of devices such

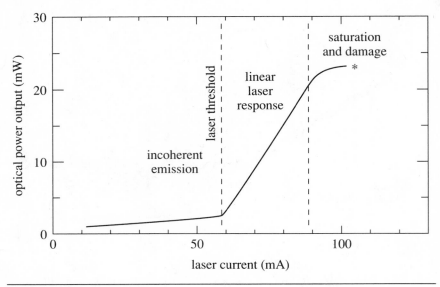

Figure 6.4 *The optical output of the laser increases rapidly as the current is raised above the threshold.*

as phosphor cards or image converters to locate and image the laser beam. And most off-the-shelf, high-performance lenses are not optimized for use in the near-infrared.

Low Power. In spite of their high efficiencies, the use of laser diodes for optical recording has been hampered by insufficient power. Development programs for high-power laser diodes have resulted in impressive demonstrations. Some lasers rated at more than 30 mW, are available, but laser diodes with output ratings higher than 20 mW are still not available in large quantities or at commodity prices.

Diverging Beam. The beam from a laser diode is not collimated; rather, it appears to diverge from a focal point slightly inside the front facet. Furthermore, the beam is very elliptical. The practical implications of this peculiarity are discussed in Section 6.2.

Astigmatism. In some laser designs, the apparent focal point of the beam is different along the ‖ and ⊥ cross sections of the beam. Astigmatism degrades the beam quality significantly if the shift is more than a few μm.

Noise. Compared to some other types of lasers, the output of a laser diode is rather noisy. The most serious noise problems are caused by fluctuations in the longitudinal mode, exaggerated by the short length of the laser cavity. Some techniques to reduce the noise are discussed in Sections 6.3 and 6.4.

Fragility. Laser diodes are among the most delicate of solid-state devices. A single current surge as short as 1 μs can destroy the laser. Therefore, special precautions must be taken in designing the laser driver circuitry. For instance, the safest way to turn off the laser is to short out its leads; simply opening the circuit can create damaging transients. Under nominal operation, the average lifetime of a laser can approach 10^5 hours. However, this lifetime is quite dependent on temperature. In a high-temperature application (say, 60 °C instead of 30 °C) the lifetime may be reduced by more than a factor of 10. The laser efficiency and damage threshold both decrease as the laser ages; if the system continuously adjusts the drive current to maintain a steady optical output, the laser operating temperature will rise over time and the rate of degradation near the end of life will be greatly accelerated.

Catastrophic failure of a laser diode (as opposed to aging) is usually due to local thermal damage. The onset of saturation and damage illustrated in Figure 6.4 can be extended if the driving current takes the form of extremely short pulses. Most laser diodes can be pulsed to powers significantly higher than the rated maximum, provided that the pulses are short and the average current and optical output (e.g., averaged over 1 μs intervals) are lower than the ratings. The pulses associated with optical recording are usually short enough ($<< 1$ μs) to make this technique useful.

6.2 Elliptical Beams

As it emerges from the facet of a laser diode, the laser beam is constrained by the waveguide to dimensions comparable to the wavelength. In Chapter 5 we found that diffraction causes such a beam to diverge rapidly; consider in particular Eq. (5.24). In fact, the beam from a laser diode is not at all collimated like a conventional laser beam; rather, it diverges at angles exceeding 30°, as shown in Figure 6.5. The beam is collimated by a collector lens focused precisely on the laser facet.

Ideally, the laser waveguide will support only the fundamental lateral mode. As a consequence, the laser beam should have a nearly Gaussian intensity profile. Any obvious deviations from the Gaussian profile, such as secondary maxima in the ∥ profile, are evidence of undesirable multi-mode emission.

Since the thickness of the emitting region is much less than its width, diffraction widens the beam more strongly in the direction perpendicular to the interface. Figure 6.5 shows that the beam diverges two to three times more strongly in the ⊥ direction than in the ∥ direction. In other words, the beam emerges as a very elliptical cone, and the collector lens forms it into a very elliptical collimated beam. In addition, the beam is strongly polarized in the ∥ direction, or along the short axis of the beam.

One laser manufacturer (Ortel) offers laser diodes with a nearly circular beam profile. Their concept holds considerable promise for simplifying laser diode applications, provided that manufacturability can be achieved. Meanwhile, we must concern ourselves with practi-

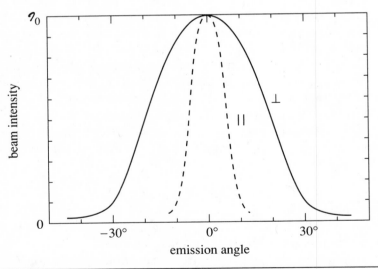

Figure 6.5 *The emission profile of a typical single-mode laser diode shows that the beam diverges more strongly in the ⊥ direction than in the ∥ direction.*

cal techniques for using ellliptical laser beams in optical heads. In Chapter 5, Section 2, we described a laser beam entering the objective lens by a circular Gaussian intensity distribution (Eq. 5.12). For a laser diode beam, the slightly more general bivariate Gaussian distribution is more appropriate:

$$\mathscr{I}(u, v) = \mathscr{I}_0 \exp(-\alpha(u^2 + v^2/\beta^2)/NA^2). \qquad (6.1)$$

In this equation, the aperture coordinates u and v correspond, respectively, to the $\parallel$ and $\perp$ directions at the laser. The beam ellipticity is described by β, the ratio of the $\perp$ f.w.h.m. of the beam divided by its $\parallel$ f.w.h.m. For typical laser diodes, β is between two and three. In writing Eq. (6.1), we assume that the laser beam, as apertured by the collector lens, fills the objective lens. The focal lengths and numerical apertures of the objective and collector lenses should ideally be matched so that the beam from the collector lens exactly fits through the objective lens.

A circular Gaussian beam optimally fills the objective lens when $\alpha \cong 2.5$, but this condition is not necessarily optimal for an elliptical beam. In Eq. (6.1), α describes the apodization in the u direction. The corresponding factor for the v direction is much smaller: α/β^2. When the objective lens is over-filled in both directions ($\alpha << 1$ and $\alpha/\beta^2 << 1$), the focused spot again has a circular, Airy profile (and very low power, because so much light is lost outside the aperture). When the objective lens is under-filled in both directions ($\alpha >> 1$ and $\alpha/\beta^2 >> 1$), the focused spot is just the Fourier transform of the beam; it is large and elliptical, with its major axis perpendicular to that of the beam, $\sigma_y/\sigma_x = \beta^{-1}$. (The media coordinates x and y correspond to u and v.) The detailed irradiance profile in the under-filled limit may be determined just as in Eq. (5.18):

$$I(x,y) = 4\pi\beta\mathscr{P}NA^2\exp[-4\pi^2NA^2(x^2 + \beta^2y^2)/(\alpha\lambda^2)]/(\alpha\lambda^2). \qquad (6.2)$$

As with the circular beam, an under-filled lens results in a low spot irradiance because the spot is too large, and an over-filled lens results in low irradiance because little of the original beam is actually focused through the lens.

When an intermediate degree of apodization is present in either direction, the focused spot shape will be somewhat less elliptical than the beam. A detailed numerical calculation of the focused spot profile for the intermediate case has been performed (Marchant, 1984).

The results for spot shape are summarized in Figure 6.6 and the corresponding irradiance values are plotted in Figure 6.7. A good approximation to these results can be obtained by modeling the focused spot with a bivariate Gaussian profile, using Eqs. (5.20) or (5.21) for σ_x and σ_y (substituting α/β^2 in place of α to calculate σ_y), and integrating Eq. (5.19) over the aperture, to find the total focused power.

In Figure 6.7, we see that the maximum spot irradiance is achieved when α/β is in the range 2–2.5. For a laser diode beam with $\beta = 3$, the optimal apodization is $\alpha \cong 7$; in this case, the beam intensity at the edge of the aperture has dropped to a negligible fraction (0.1%) of the central value along the $\parallel$ axis but only to 46% along the $\perp$ axis. It is also clear from Figure 6.7 that an elliptical beam is focused much less efficiently than a circular beam; for $\beta = 3$, the maximum irradiance is less than 70% of that achievable from a circular beam with the same total power. On the other hand, Figure 6.6 shows that the qualitative shape of the focused spot is not severely affected by beam ellipticity. With optimal apodization, the spot focused from a beam with 3:1 ellipticity has an ellipticity of only 1.6:1. The ellipticity of a laser diode beam is a drawback not so much because it affects the shape of the optical stylus, but because it reduces its irradiance.

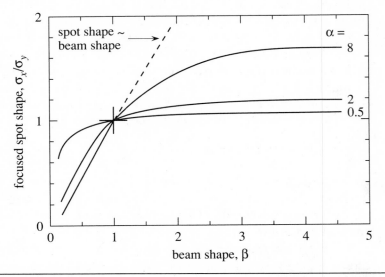

Figure 6.6 *The shape of a spot formed by focusing an elliptical beam is graphed here.*

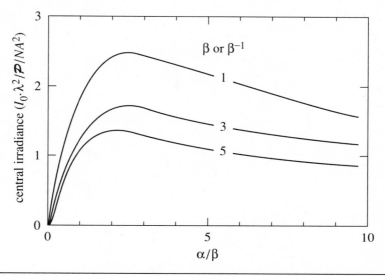

Figure 6.7 *The central irradiance of a spot formed by focusing an elliptical beam is graphed here.*

If the performance of an elliptical laser beam is unsatisfactory, additional optical elements can be added after the collector lens to circularize it. Beam circularization usually takes the form of *anamorphic beam expansion,* in which the beam is stretched in one dimension (along the ‖ axis). Figure 6.8a illustrates an anamorphic telescope composed of two cylinder lenses. In the inverting design, two positive lenses are used, and beam expansion is equal to the ratio of their focal lengths. Alternatively, the beam expander can be a Galilean telescope—a negative cylinder lens followed by a positive cylinder lens. The anamorphic telescope has several practical problems. High-quality (corrected) cylinder lenses are not readily available, so low-power lenses must be used to avoid aberrating the beam. This increases the length of the optical path and the size of the head. Both lenses also present alignment problems. One special advantage of the anamorphic telescope is that it can be adjusted to correct laser beam astigmatism.

A simpler method of anamorphic beam expansion using prisms instead of lenses was invented by Sir Brewster in the last century. In Figure 6.8b, the elliptical collimated beam passes through two identical prisms and emerges parallel to its initial path. The beam enters

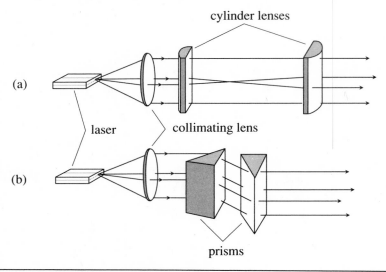

Figure 6.8 *Anamorphic beam expanders: a) a cylindrical telescope; b) a prism beam expander.*

each prism at an acute angle and is expanded by refraction in the plane of incidence. Since all the optical surfaces are planar, the beam remains perfectly collimated at every point. The two-prism beam expander is achromatic, with the optical path essentially independent of wavelength. High-quality prisms are more manufacturable than cylinder lenses. Misalignment of the prisms is not very serious because it just changes the beam size and, to a lesser degree, its direction. One drawback of the prism beam expander is that thick prisms can create a great deal of aberration (spherical and coma) if the incident beam is not very well collimated. If the laser has much intrinsic astigmatism, the collector lens cannot truly collimate it; an anamorphic telescope should be used with such lasers.

The detailed operation of a prism beam expander is explained in Figure 6.9. When a p-polarized beam is incident at Brewster's angle, it is completely refracted into the prism, with no reflective losses. Brewster's angle is $\tan^{-1}n$, where n is the refractive index of the glass. The terms p-polarization and s-polarization refer to alignment of the E-field parallel and perpendicular to the plane of incidence, respectively. A laser diode beam oriented as in Figure 6.8b is p-polarized at the prism faces. If, in addition, the apex angle of the prism is equal to $\cot^{-1}n$, the refracted beam will exit the prism normal to

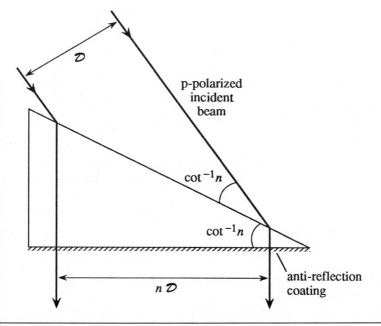

$$D$$

p-polarized
incident
beam

$\cot^{-1}n$

$\cot^{-1}n$

$n\,D$

anti-reflection
coating

Figure 6.9 *Beam expansion through a prism is detailed here.*

the second face expanded by a factor of exactly *n*. Some reflection losses will occur at the exit surface unless it has an antireflection coating.

One prism used in this fashion can expand the laser beam by a factor of only 1.5 to 1.8, depending on the refractive index of the glass material. The arrangement of two prisms illustrated in Figure 6.8b expands the beam by a factor of 2–3, perfectly circularizing a laser diode beam. It is possible to achieve more beam expansion from one prism by increasing the incidence angle; at grazing incidence, the refracted beam is expanded by an arbitrarily large factor. But large reflective losses, alignment problems, and increased sensitivity to de-collimation are caused by incidence angles much larger than Brewster's angle. The practical limit for beam expansion from one prism is about 2.5. Keep in mind that the beam might not need to be perfectly circularized. For example, if a 3:1 beam is expanded to a ratio of 1.7:1 through a single high-index prism, the irradiance of the focused spot will be nearly 90% of maximum and the profile will be nearly circular, 1.3:1. Further circularization might not be worth the trouble and cost of an additional optical element. As pointed out in Chapter 8, Section 2, the complete advantages of beam circular-ization can be obtained only at the expense of increasing the numer-ical aperture of the collector lens.

6.3 Laser Noise and Feedback Effects

In order to understand the sources of noise from laser diodes, we need to understand the spectral characteristics of laser diodes. The length of the waveguiding laser cavity determines certain preferred wavelengths that correspond to standing waves inside the laser. If d is the length of the cavity and n is its refractive index, the preferred wavelengths are

$$\lambda_N = 2nd/N. \tag{6.3}$$

At these wavelengths, the light internally reflected within the cavity combines constructively, greatly increasing the rate of stimulated emission. As illustrated in Figure 6.10, the diode provides optical gain over a range that includes several preferred wavelengths. Near

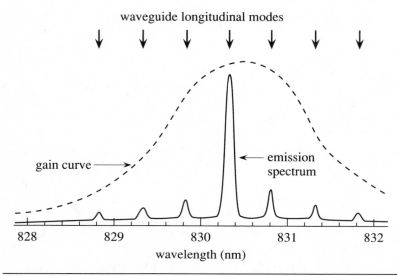

Figure 6.10 *The emission spectrum of a single-mode laser diode shows that the diode provides optical gain over a spectral range that includes several longitudinal modes.*

threshold (and in some low-power lasers) several of these *longitudi-nal modes* might coexist. But at higher powers, the wavelength with the most gain usually dominates. The laser is then said to have a *single longitudinal mode*. This characteristic is quite distinct from the single transverse-mode condition that describes the lateral confinement of the light within the waveguide.

The separation between adjacent preferred wavelengths is

$$\Delta\lambda = 2nd[1/N - 1/(N+1)] \cong \lambda^2/(2nd). \qquad (6.4)$$

For $\lambda = 800$ nm, $n = 3$, and $d = 0.25$ mm, the separation is about 4 Å. Under single-mode operation, the width of the emission line is $\delta\lambda << 1$ Å. The coherence length of a laser beam is roughly $\lambda^2/\delta\lambda$. In a single-mode laser diode, the coherence length is typically about 10 cm. In a multimode laser diode, the envelope of the (irregular) emission spectrum is just the gain curve; its width is typically $\delta\lambda \sim 30$ Å, containing 5–10 longitudinal modes. Consequently, the coherence length of a multimode laser is shorter than 1 mm.

Temperature changes affect the laser spectrum in several ways. The gain curve shifts to longer wavelength as the junction temperature increases. This causes the emission of a multi-mode laser to shift toward longer wavelengths at high temperatures, as shown in Figure 6.11. The wavelength depends similarly on the optical output, since high operating power ordinarily leads to increased laser temperature. Single-mode laser diodes show a more complicated dependence of wavelength on power. Any temperature increase causes the laser cavity to expand, and thus increases the wavelength associated with each allowed longitudinal mode. As the temperature or power output increases, the wavelength of the dominant mode increases, but not rapidly enough to keep up with the shift in the gain curve. Eventually, the laser switches to a lower-order longitudinal mode which has higher gain. This causes the discontinuous wavelength dependence of single-mode lasers, which is illustrated in Figure 6.11.

A slight shift in laser wavelength is not of itself a problem for optical recording, but laser output will change along with the wavelength, because the efficiency of the laser diode depends on the specific value of the gain at the wavelength of the dominant mode. Furthermore, if the laser happens to be operating near a discontinuity in the wavelength/temperature curve, it might switch rapidly and erratically between the two modes. Such mode hopping creates noise

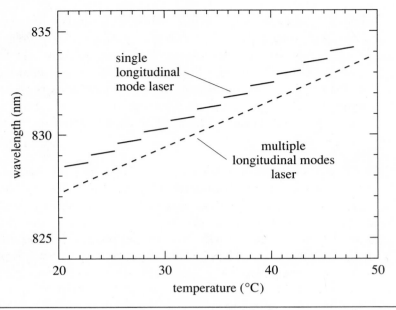

Figure 6.11 *The laser wavelength increases at high temperature.*

fluctuations in the optical output. Where laser noise is a serious concern, temperature control of the laser diode can be necessary. Rapid changes in wavelength can create tracking and/or focus errors in a system that is not achromatized.

Fluctuations in the laser output can also be caused by light that is reflected back into the laser. This external reflection increases the apparent reflectance of the front laser facet, makes the laser a bit more efficient, and therefore increases its output. In most applications of laser diodes, only a negligible fraction of the laser output is reflected back through the end of the tiny waveguide, but in an optical recording head, the optical stylus is formed by imaging the laser facet onto the (reflective) media surface. By symmetry, the head simultaneously focuses the reflected light back onto the end of the waveguide. Figure 6.12 shows how feedback can be used to identify when the optical stylus is well focused. If the laser current is held constant, the output through both the front and rear facets of the laser increases sharply when the system is perfectly focused.

Optical feedback causes an apparent increase in front-facet reflectance only if the reflected light is coherent with the light within the laser cavity. Since multimode laser diodes have such short coherence

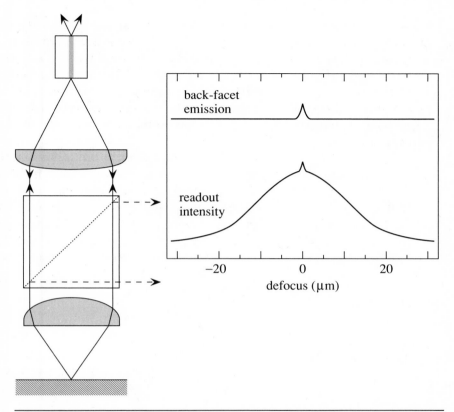

Figure 6.12 *Laser output is enhanced when the reflected beam is focused precisely back into the laser.*

lengths, they are not affected by optical feedback. Therefore none of the feedback-related problems discussed in this section apply to multiple-longitudinal-mode lasers. Even with a single-mode laser, feedback effects might not be important in a noncompact optical head, for instance in a research system laid out with an optical path much longer than 10 cm. But in the most interesting case of a high-power, single-mode laser diode in a compact optical head, the head forms an external cavity that influences the apparent reflectance of the laser. Moreover, the adverse effects of feedback are most pronounced precisely when the optical quality of the head is optimized.

The external cavity formed by the optical head has a set of preferred wavelengths in the same way that the laser cavity has preferred longitudinal modes (Eq. 6.3). The length of the external cavity shown in Figure 6.13 is defined as the optical path length from the laser diode to the media surface, $\mathscr{L} = \int dl\ n$, a line integral of the refractive index down the optical axis. If the total path, $2\mathscr{L}$, is equal to an integral number of wavelengths, the feedback adds coherently to the standing wave within the laser cavity, and the laser output is enhanced. But if $\mathscr{L}$ is changed by only $\lambda/4$, the reflected light is exactly out of phase with the internal standing wave, and the laser output drops.

The external cavity length, $\mathscr{L}$, depends directly on the media position; therefore, even the slightest change in axial position of the media surface will change the optical feedback interaction. (But note that $\mathscr{L}$ is independent of the location of the objective lens.) Figure 6.14 shows how the output of a single-mode laser can fluctuate due to a moderate amount of axial runout. As the feedback oscillates between constructive and destructive interference, the laser output

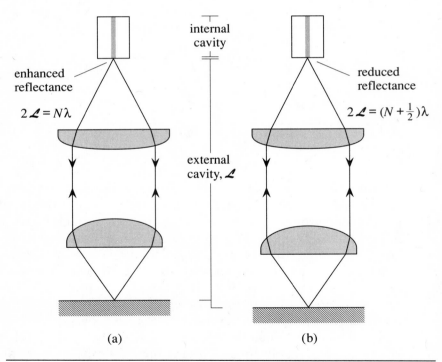

internal cavity

enhanced reflectance

$2\mathscr{L} = N\lambda$

reduced reflectance

$2\mathscr{L} = (N + \tfrac{1}{2})\lambda$

external cavity, $\mathscr{L}$

(a) (b)

Figure 6.13 *Feedback can (a) increase or (b) decrease the apparent facet reflectance.*

fluctuates. For a peak-to-peak runout of Δz, the power will undergo
N fluctuation cycles, where

$$N \cong 4\Delta z / \lambda. \qquad (6.5)$$

At the upper and lower runout limits, $\mathscr{L}$ becomes momentarily constant, and the power fluctuations hesitate. Between the turn-around
points, the laser power fluctuates rapidly. If N is of order 100, the
output oscillates at frequencies around 1 kHz. This frequency is too
low to interfere directly with the data signal, but it lies in the control-
frequency range at which the various servo systems operate. Even if
the fluctuation amplitude due to feedback is low, it can confuse the
tracking and focus sensors or excite resonances in the servos (see
Chapter 7, Section 3). Some problems due to control-frequency fluctuations from laser diodes are discussed by Arimoto and Ojima
(1984). Besides the more obvious output-power fluctuations, feedback from the disk surface can also induce changes in the wavelength
and/or transverse mode structure of the laser beam.

Optical feedback causes high-frequency noise in addition to relatively steady output oscillations. In much the same way that thermal
changes lead to longitudinal mode switching, coherent feedback can
cause the laser to fluctuate (rapidly and erratically) between different
modes. This random behavior creates very high levels of noise at all
frequencies. In the presence of optical feedback, laser diode noise

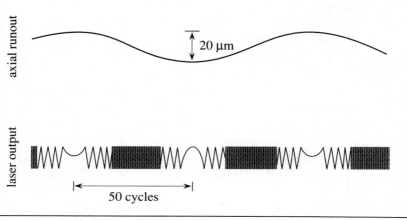

Figure 6.14 *Feedback causes the output of a single-mode laser to
fluctuate due to axial runout.*

levels as high as -75 dB are sometimes seen. This measurement is conventionally defined as the ratio of noise power in a 30 kHz bandwidth divided by the laser power. If P_{30} is the 30 kHz noise power (generally white, or independent of frequency) and P_0 is the DC laser power, the decibel rating is given by $20 \log_{10}(P_{30}/P_0)$. For a laser noise level of -75 dB, the relative power fluctuations in a 10 MHz readout channel would be approximately $P_{30}(10 \text{ MHz}/30 \text{ kHz})/P_0$ $= 10^{-3.75} \cdot 10^7/3 \cdot 10^4 = 6\%$, a totally unacceptable value even if there are no other sources of noise.

The quantitative effects of optical feedback vary greatly from laser to laser, depending on the coherence length, facet reflectance, and many other factors. But these effects can usually be neglected if the power reflected back to the laser is much less than 1%. Techniques for reducing the feedback are discussed in the next section.

It is possible to reduce the symptoms of laser diode feedback without eliminating the feedback itself. One obvious approach is to monitor the laser output and adjust the drive current to hold that output constant. The rear-facet sense diode is a convenient device for monitoring the output, but it might not be accurate, because the light level in the external cavity need not be proportional to the rear-facet output. A more direct measurement can be provided by a forward sense diode positioned to sample a part of the beam deflected by the beam splitter, as shown in Figure 6.15. If the sense diode is too large, its internal capacitance causes it to respond rather slowly to laser fluctuations. To achieve high-frequency noise reduction, the sense diode must be small. A simple field lens can be used to focus the deflected beam onto it. Note that the sense diode must be located on the opposite side of the beam splitter from the readout optics. The light reflected to the readout and servo detectors is modulated by many factors that are independent of the laser output.

Control-frequency fluctuations can easily be eliminated by a laser output servo-loop, but high-frequency-noise reduction is difficult. In principle the laser itself can be controlled at very high frequencies; however, the bandwidth of any feedback system is probably inadequate. In order to substantially reduce the laser noise over a 10 MHz channel, the total servo bandwidth must be much greater (perhaps 100 MHz). Yamada and Nakaya (1985) were able to achieve significant noise reduction, but only below 1 MHz.

RF laser modulation is another interesting method for reducing laser diode noise. During readout, the laser is driven by a very-high-

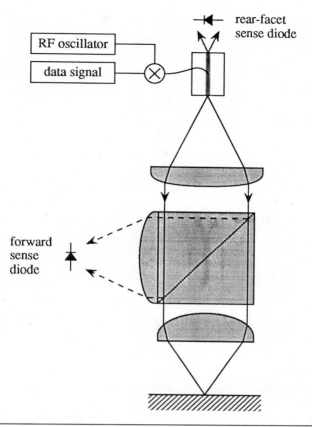

Figure 6.15 *Two methods for reducing laser noise are shown here.*

frequency signal. The frequency is so high that it is easily filtered from the data. (Typical detectors cannot resolve such high-frequency modulation anyway.) The original concept behind RF modulation was that coherent feedback could not occur if each pulse were shorter than its reflection time ($2\mathscr{L}/c$). This would have required RF modulation frequencies higher than 1 GHz, but experiments have shown that a modulation frequency as low as 100 MHz greatly reduces the effects of optical feedback. Apparently, the laser requires a fairly long time to establish true steady-state, single-mode operation. RF modulation is not as good a control method during recording, because it increases the required peak laser output for a given average power. However, the relative noise level is greatest at low readout power levels. It might be feasible to control the noise during readout and live with it during recording.

Some laser diodes have less noise than others. Within a class of lasers, this represents merely an annoying statistical variation. But some laser designs are inherently less noisy. The distributed feedback (DFB) lasers designed for fiber-optic communication have patterned waveguides that constrain the laser to operate in only one mode (Iwamoto, 1987); this technique might eventually be applied to shorter-wavelength, higher-power lasers for optical recording. Lasers with multiple longitudinal modes (several simultaneous wavelengths) cannot jump from one discrete mode to another, and the coherence length might be too short for feedback to cause constructive or destructive interference. Lasers with highly reflective facets show reduced sensitivity to feedback simply because less returned light penetrates back into the laser. These design techniques have the unpleasant effect of reducing the potential power output. In order to boost laser power, some manufacturers are designing lasers in which the back facet is highly reflective but the front facet has a low reflectance (Klume, Ito, and Kano, 1987). Such a design strategy might be a step in the wrong direction as far as feedback is concerned.

6.4   Reducing Optical Feedback

Laser feedback is a particularly serious problem for optical recording, because the optical system that images the laser onto the recording surface also images its reflection right back onto the laser. It is possible to divide the objective lens aperture into an incident-beam region, and a reflected-beam region as illustrated in Figure 6.16, eliminating any chance of feedback (from a smooth media surface). This approach reduces the effective *NA* of the system and therefore is appropriate only for low-performance head designs—for instance, optical card readers. In a very low-cost system, the laser beam probably would not be circularized. A highly elliptical beam can be fitted through a half-aperture with only a slight reduction in the available *NA* (much less than a factor of two).

The most elegant technique for eliminating reflections into the laser is the optical isolator, a device illustrated in Figure 6.17. An ideal polarizing beam-splitter cube, or PBSC, transmits 100% of p-polar-

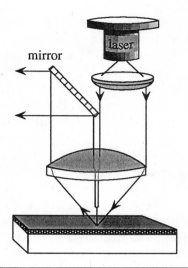

Figure 6.16 *The half-aperture solution to laser feedback divides the objective lens aperture into an incident-beam region and a reflected-beam region.*

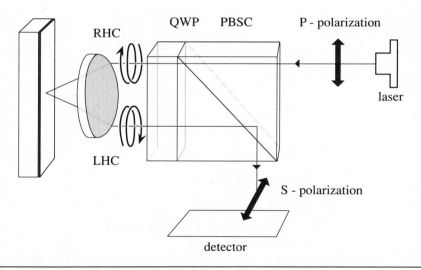

Figure 6.17 *The optical isolator is the most elegant technique for eliminating reflections into the laser.*

ized light (polarized in the plane of incidence) and reflects 100% of s-polarized light (polarized perpendicular to the plane of incidence). A quarter-wave plate, or QWP, induces a relative phase shift of $\lambda/4$ for orthogonal polarizations. The linearly polarized laser beam first passes through the PBSC; then the QWP, which is aligned at 45° to the incident polarization, converts the beam to circular polarization. After reflection, the beam is still circularly polarized, but with the opposite handedness. The QWP converts the reflected beam to the linear s-polarization state, so that it is entirely reflected by the PBSC.

We can understand the operation of an optical isolator by applying the Jones matrix approach (Jones, 1941) for analyzing polarization-dependent optics. The Jones calculus is taught in many texts, but a brief description here will prove useful because of its applicability to many aspects of optical-head design. The polarization state of the beam is represented by a two-component vector,

$$\begin{vmatrix} E_x \\ E_y \end{vmatrix}$$

which describes the field amplitude in terms of orthogonal (linear) polarization states. Each optical element in the head is represented by a 2×2 matrix of complex quantities, which operates on the field vector by matrix multiplication to show how the element alters the light amplitude and polarization. Some examples of Jones matrices are:

$$\text{a)} \quad \begin{vmatrix} 1 & 0 \\ 0 & 0 \end{vmatrix} \qquad \text{b)} \quad \begin{vmatrix} e^{i\pi/2} & 0 \\ 0 & 1 \end{vmatrix}$$

$$\text{c)} \quad \begin{vmatrix} \cos\theta & -\sin\theta \\ \sin\theta & \cos\theta \end{vmatrix} \qquad \text{d)} \quad \begin{vmatrix} \sqrt{R} & 0 \\ 0 & \sqrt{R} \end{vmatrix}$$

where (a) represents a perfect linear polarizer aligned in the x direction; (b) represents a QWP with its slow axis aligned in the x direction, (c) represents a counterclockwise rotation of the polarization or a clockwise coordinate transformation; and (d) is a normal-incidence reflection (reflectance $= R$) that just reduces the overall amplitude. The functioning of an optical isolator can be described by

$$\begin{vmatrix} 1 & 0 \\ 0 & 0 \end{vmatrix} \begin{vmatrix} \cos{(-45°)} & -\sin{(-45°)} \\ \sin{(-45°)} & \cos{(-45°)} \end{vmatrix} \begin{vmatrix} e^{i\pi/2} & 0 \\ 0 & 1 \end{vmatrix} \sqrt{R} \begin{vmatrix} e^{i\pi/2} & 0 \\ 0 & 1 \end{vmatrix} \quad (6.6)$$

$$\times \begin{vmatrix} \cos 45° & -\sin 45° \\ \sin 45° & \cos 45° \end{vmatrix} \begin{vmatrix} 1 & 0 \\ 0 & 0 \end{vmatrix} \begin{vmatrix} E_x \\ E_y \end{vmatrix} = 0$$

From right to left, the matrices that operate on the field vector represent transmission through the PBSC (aligned with the predominant *x* polarization of the incident beam); a coordinate rotation corresponding to the 45° alignment of the QWP; quarter-wave retardation; reflection from the recording layer; a second pass through the QWP; a reverse rotation back to coordinates of the PBSC; and transmission back through the PBSC. We see that no light is reflected back to the laser. If we replace the left-most matrix in Eq. (6.6) with the Jones matrix for reflection by the PBSC,

$$\begin{vmatrix} 0 & 0 \\ 0 & 1 \end{vmatrix},$$

we find that the light deflected to the detectors is

$$\sqrt{R} \begin{vmatrix} 0 \\ E_x \end{vmatrix}.$$

The detectors receive all the light that initially passes through the polarizer and is reflected from the media surface.

In addition to preventing optical feedback into the laser, the optical isolator also increases the head efficiency. Consider an optical recording head using an ordinary (dielectric, nonabsorbing) beam splitter that transmits a fraction f of the incident beam and reflects a fraction $(1 - f)$. The beam splitter reduces the intensity of the optical stylus by a factor f and reduces the signal (intensity at the detector) by $f(1 - f)$. The readout intensity is maximized by a 50/50 beam splitter ($f = 0.5$), but this maximum is only 25% of the laser power. A head using an optical isolator can deliver four times as much light to the detectors.

The optical isolator described above is not useful for magneto-optic heads because Kerr-effect readout requires a linearly polarized optical stylus. Also, a perfect PBSC would remove all polarization information from the reflected beam, including the M-O signal. However, an alternative device called a Faraday isolator could be used in M-O heads. Figure 6.18 shows how this device works. The heart of a Faraday isolator is a Faraday rotator, a magneto-optic element with a magnetic field oriented along the optical axis, which rotates the polarization of a transmitted beam. In a Faraday isolator, the path length or magnetic field within the Faraday rotator are adjusted to provide a polarization rotation of precisely 45°. The rotator is set between two ordinary polarizers, which are aligned at 45° to each other. Light passing in the forward direction has its polarization rotated so that it passes through the second polarizer without any loss, but a returning beam is rotated in the reverse sense; therefore, its polarization ends up perpendicular to the first polarizer, so no light returns to the source. See Fischer (1987) for a detailed description of the design and limitations of a Faraday isolator.

The operation of a Faraday isolator can also be understood with the Jones matrix formalism:

$$\begin{vmatrix} 1 & 0 \\ 0 & 0 \end{vmatrix} \begin{vmatrix} \cos 45° & -\sin 45° \\ \sin 45° & \cos 45° \end{vmatrix} \begin{vmatrix} \cos(-45°) & -\sin(-45°) \\ \sin(-45°) & \cos(-45°) \end{vmatrix} \begin{vmatrix} 1 & 0 \\ 0 & 0 \end{vmatrix} \begin{vmatrix} E_x \\ E_y \end{vmatrix} = \begin{vmatrix} E_x \\ 0 \end{vmatrix} ;$$

$$(6.7)$$

$$\begin{vmatrix} 1 & 0 \\ 0 & 0 \end{vmatrix} \begin{vmatrix} \cos 45° & -\sin 45° \\ \sin 45° & \cos 45° \end{vmatrix} \begin{vmatrix} \cos 45° & -\sin 45° \\ \sin 45° & \cos 45° \end{vmatrix} \begin{vmatrix} 1 & 0 \\ 0 & 0 \end{vmatrix} \begin{vmatrix} E_x \\ E_y \end{vmatrix} = 0.$$

$$(6.8)$$

Eq. (6.7) describes the forward transmission of a beam: from right to left, the matrices represent transmission through a horizontally oriented polarizer, clockwise rotation by the Faraday rotator, a coordinate change corresponding to the 45° orientation of the second polarizer, and transmission through that polarizer. The x-component

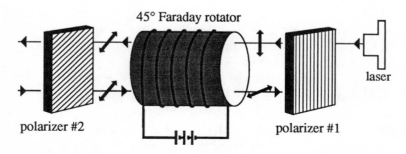

45° Faraday rotator

laser

polarizer #2   polarizer #1

Figure 6.18 A Faraday isolator transmits light in only one direction.

of the incident beam is entirely transmitted. Eq. (6.8) corresponds to a beam transmitted in the opposite direction. In this direction, no light at all passes through the last polarizer. Note that the principal difference between the two beam directions is a reversal of the sense of polarization rotation in the Faraday rotator. This occurs because the relative alignment of the magnetic field within the Faraday rotator depends upon the laser-beam direction. Finkelstein and Call (1988) have shown that the polarizers in Figure 6.18 are not absolutely necessary for noise reduction, as long as the laser is highly polarized. If the Faraday rotator returns the reflected beam with an orthogonal polarization, little interference will occur within the laser.

A Faraday isolator does not enhance the system efficiency in the same way as the ordinary optical isolator. M-O heads require a separate beam splitter. In order not to cancel out the Kerr rotation, this must not be an ordinary PBSC (see Chapter 8, Section 4). Some reduction in the recording efficiency and a further reduction in the achievable readout signal inevitably result.

Faraday isolators are not yet practical devices outside the laboratory. But they are an active topic of research and development. It might be possible to make a Faraday rotator from a highly magneto-optic material that also possesses permanent, vertical magnetization. Hibaya, Ishikawa, Morishige, Nakashima, and Ohta (1986) have demonstrated a Bi-substituted garnet material that has such properties. A 300 μm thick film of this material would provide the necessary 45° of rotation at a wavelength of 1.2 μm. However, an isolator that operates in the near-infrared will require further materials development; presently available materials are too absorptive at shorter wavelengths.

6.5 Future Prospects

Throughout the book, we have generally assumed that the optical stylus both writes and reads. However, one laser diode cannot easily be optimized for both readout and recording. Readout requires low noise; for this, a multimode laser would be effective. Recording requires high power levels; such lasers tend to be intrinsically noisy and sensitive to optical feedback. Furthermore, a single laser used

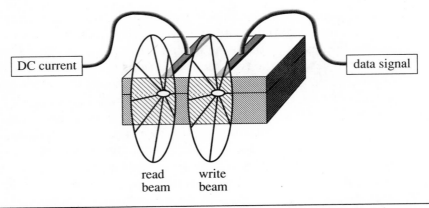

DC current

data signal

read beam   write beam

Figure 6.19 *This dual-source laser diode has one laser optimized for readout and one for recording.*

for both reading and writing must operate near both the top and bottom ends of the output vs. current curve (Figure 6.4). An attractive alternative is to integrate two lasers in one device, one optimized for readout and one for recording, as illustrated in Figure 6.19. This type of laser design also opens up the practical possibility of simultaneous writing and reading. The advantages of DRAW (direct read after write) for system reliability are discussed in Chapter 11, Section 4. A multiple-source laser diode can also be used for multichannel recording at an extremely high net data rate (see Chapter 8, Section 5). Earman (1983) has described a prototype two-channel recorder that operated at 40 Mbit/s using a dual-source laser diode.

Engineers at Sanyo have developed a three-source laser diode for use with erasable phase-change media using the direct over-write recording method described in Chapter 4, Section 4 (Yamaguchi, 1987). One source is optimized for readout with low noise at low power; another source is optimized for recording at high power; and the third source has a very wide active region, which forms a long erasure spot.

In addition to a host of design and fabrication difficulties, multiple-source laser diodes suffer from electrical and optical cross-talk. For a read/write laser pair, a considerable separation (say 100 μm) is required between the sources to keep cross-talk from the recording channel from modulating the readout laser. If simultaneous reading and writing are not required, the separation can be somewhat smaller, perhaps 50 μm.

Laser diodes with short wavelengths are also highly desirable. The size of the optical stylus is proportional to λ. All other things remaining equal, the data capacity of an optical recording system would be greatly increased at a shorter wavelength, because the areal storage density is proportional to λ^{-2} (1/stylus width/stylus length). Furthermore, a small stylus with higher irradiance could record at a higher data rate (again ∞ λ^{-2}). Alternatively, a short-wavelength laser would permit us to achieve the same data densities and performance as current systems using simpler optics (lower *NA*). A smaller *NA* would loosen the tolerances for defocus and other types of aberration.

The present lower wavelength limit for commercial laser diodes is about 700 nm. All of the available lasers are gallium arsenide devices, using different AlGaAs compositions for the various layers. Lasers with wavelengths approaching 600 nm might be feasible using a different class of materials, for example, InP. Wavelengths shorter than 600 nm might be very difficult to achieve; one possibility is to couple a high-power, long-wavelength laser diode to a frequency-doubling crystal.

Laser diodes of higher power will also be useful in the future, primarily to facilitate higher recording rates. Eventually, the 40–50 mW lasers that are available today as specialty items should reach commercialization (at commodity prices). Lasers of even higher power can be made (for example, phased laser arrays operating above 1 W), but such high laser powers will not be truly useful until corresponding breakthroughs in drive mechanics, detectors, and channel electronics occur.

━━━━━ MAJOR CONCEPTS

- Laser diodes are the most practical lasers for optical recording because of their small size, efficiency, low cost, and direct modulation capability.

- Available laser high-power diodes operate in the near-infrared, with wavelengths near 800 nm. Shorter-wavelength laser diodes are the subject of active R&D.

- The beam from a diode laser diverges strongly in an elliptical pattern. In higher performance systems, a collector lens and an anamorphic beam expander produce a collimated, nearly circular beam.

- Most laser diodes are capable of emitting in many longitudinal modes with slightly different wavelengths. A single-mode laser can undergo mode-hopping due to thermal changes or optical feedback, with a consequent increase in noise (Eq. 6.3 and Figure 6.10).

- Laser noise can be reduced by very-high-frequency modulation superimposed on the output of the laser driver circuit.

- An optical isolator using a quarter-wave plate and a polarizing beam splitter is used in many optical heads to eliminate optical feedback (Figure 6.17).

- A Faraday isolator can be used to eliminate optical feedback in an M-O head (Figure 6.18).

REFERENCES

Arimoto, A., and M. Ojima, "Diode laser noise at control frequencies in optical videodisc players," *Applied Optics,* **23,** 2913 (1984). Problems due to low-frequency laser fluctuation caused by optical feedback.

Earman, A., "A high performance optical disc drive unit for use in non-benevolent environments," *SPIE Proceedings,* **421,** 53 (1983). A rugged, write-once drive that performed two-channel recording using a dual-source laser diode.

Ettenberg, M., "Developments to watch in diode lasers," *Laser Focus,* 86, (May, 1985). A review of present laser diode designs and predicted improvements.

Finkelstein, B., and D. Call, "Laser feedback noise in magneto-optical recording," *SPIE Proceedings,* **899,** 69 (1988). A survey of techniques for reducing laser noise in M-O heads.

Fischer, G., "The Faraday isolator," *J. Opt. Commun.,* **8,** 18 (1987). The design and operation of Faraday isolators.

Hibaya, T., T. Ishikawa, Y. Morishige, J. Nakashima, and Y. Ohta, "Growth and magneto-optic properties of liquid phase epitaxial Bi-substituted garnet films for optical isolator," *NEC Research & Development,* **80,** 1 (1986).

Jones, R., "A new calculus for the treatment of optical systems," *J. Opt. Soc. Am.,* **31,** 488, 493, and 500 (1941). Three papers, which constitute the original presentation of the Jones matrix methodology for modeling polarization.

Iwamoto, K., "Long wavelength DFB lasers: efficient, fast, reliable," *JEE*, 35 (August,1987).

Kume, M., K. Ito, and G. Kano, "Semiconductor lasers for WORM, erasable and rewritable memory disks," *JEE*, 44 (August, 1987). Laser output can be enhanced by increasing the back-facet reflectance.

Marchant, A., "Focusing elliptical laser beams," *Applied Optics*, **23**, 670 (1984). A theoretical analysis of focused spots from elliptical beams.

Sharp Corporation, *Laser Diode User's Manual* (1985). An excellent review of the operational principles and engineering properties of Sharp's laser diodes designed for optical recording systems.

Yamada, M., and N. Nakaya, "Reduction of the intensity noise of AlGaAs injection laser by means of electric negative feedback," *Transactions of the IECE of Japan*, **E68**, 337 (1985). A closed-loop servo controlled the current to the laser to keep the optical output constant.

Yamaguchi, T., "Monolithic 3-beam semiconductor laser: now a practical reality," *JEE*, **24**, no. 248, 54 (1987). Description of a three-source laser diode optimized for simultaneous reading, erasing, and writing, especially on phase-change media.

Yamamoto, S., "Current trends in semiconductor lasers for optical heads," *International Symposium on Optical Memory 1987, Technical Digest,* 167 (1987). A survey of advanced developments in laser diodes for optical recording.

CHAPTER 7

Focus and Tracking Servos

We saw in Chapter 5 that the optical stylus has very small dimensions in the axial direction (normal to the media surface) as well as in the in-track and cross-track directions. In order to assure a uniformly high signal, free of cross-talk, the optical head must have means to keep the stylus centered on the data track with an accuracy much finer than the track width dimension. In relative terms, all types of recording systems share this requirement. However, because of the extremely small track pitch, the tracking tolerance for optical recording systems is much smaller than for any other: typically ± 0.1 μm. The depth of focus of the optical stylus is also very small: typically ± 0.5 μm. (The precise value of the focus tolerance depends rather strongly on the particular optical design.) No part of an optical head has to "fly" next to the media surface like a magnetic Winchester head, but the height of the objective lens must be maintained with just as much accuracy and precision. The submicron tracking and focus tolerances for the optical stylus are maintained by active servo-systems, composed of optical position sensors coupled through complex feedback circuits to high-bandwidth actuators.

The same optical beam that is used to read and write can be used to accurately sense the position of the optical stylus. Sections 7.1 and 7.2 describe optical techniques for sensing errors in the focus and tracking positions, respectively. The high-bandwidth electro-mechanical servos used to eliminate focus and tracking errors are quite similar; they are briefly described in Section 7.3. The final section, Section 7.4, describes some particular problems associated with position sensing during rapid seek operations.

7.1 Focus Sensors

For the sake of discussion, we can assume that the beam focused to form the optical stylus is initially collimated. (As the example in Chapter 8, Section 1 illustrates, it is possible and sometimes desirable to start with a diverging beam; the focus-sensing concepts described in this section, though modified, are still applicable.) If the objective lens focuses the beam perfectly onto the media surface, it must also recollimate the reflected beam. The most practical methods for sensing focus errors are actually ways of detecting slight deviations from collimation of the reflected beam.

The most obvious way to sense beam divergence (or convergence) would be to measure the size of the return beam at some distance from the objective lens. If the reflective media surface is slightly out of focus by a distance δ toward the objective lens, then the beam forms a focus at a distance $f - 2\delta$ from the lens, and the reflected beam re-emerges behind the lens from an apparent focus a distance $f^2/(2\delta)$ below it, where f is the focal length of the lens. If the media surface is out of focus in the opposite direction, the return beam forms an actual secondary focus at the same distance. At an observation point a distance l behind the objective lens, the fractional change in beam diameter due to the defocus is $2\delta l/f^2$. In order to observe a focus error of 0.5 μm as a 10% change in the beam size (for a typical objective lens with $f = 5$ mm), we would have to stand back 2.5 m from the lens. This might be feasible with a bench-top optical layout, but not with a compact recording head.

A more compact focus sensor can be made with the aid of a field lens that creates a secondary focus when the objective lens is perfectly focused. Figure 7.1 illustrates the optical layout and functioning of focus sensors based on the principle of the Foucault knife edge. In the classical Foucault test, a knife edge is positioned precisely on the nominal focal point; however, it is more practical to block off half of the field lens aperture, as in Figure 7.1a, and position a two-element photodetector (or split-detector) at the nominal focus. The illumination of the detector halves is equal when the beam is perfectly focused, but any defocus will shift the beam entirely onto one or the other of the detector halves (ignoring diffraction effects), as illustrated in Figure 7.1b.

The classical Foucault test requires precise alignment of the knife

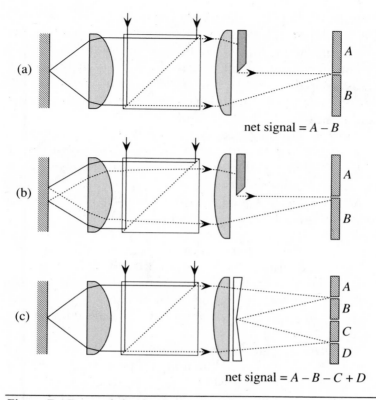

Figure 7.1 *Foucault knife-edge and half-aperture focus sensors are illustrated here.*

edge on the focus point. The half-aperture technique described here allows the knife edge to be coarsely positioned at the aperture; however, it requires the split-detector to be precisely positioned. Figure 7.1c illustrates a design that eases the tolerance on the detector position across the beam. A bi-prism acts as a dual knife edge, focusing the light from each half of the aperture onto separate split-detectors (usually on the same detector array). A lateral shift of the detector array creates false error signals at each split detector, but these are cancelled in the net error signal if the misalignment is not too large. The bi-prism technique is also more efficient because it uses all the reflected light.

Another type of focus sensor that measures the state of collimation of the reflected beam is the astigmatic sensor, illustrated in Figure

7.2. This design employs a very different type of field lens. The astigmatic lens has two different focal lengths along orthogonal axes. It does not focus the beam to a single point but rather to two perpendicular line foci. At a point intermediate between these foci, the beam has a circular profile, the *circle of least confusion*. A four-element photodetector (quad-detector) is aligned at 45° to the lens axes and positioned between the line foci where the beam is circular (for perfect focus of the objective lens). Any shift in focus causes the positions of the line foci to shift together up or down the optical axis; the beam shape on the detector is distorted into an ellipse which illuminates one pair of detectors (AD or BC) much more than the other. As indicated in Figure 7.2, the ellipticity of the spot can be quantified as the difference between $(A + D)$ and $(B + C)$. In a knife-edge focus sensor, detector misalignment perpendicular to the edge leads to a signal offset. But in an astigmatic focus sensor, such lateral misalignment does not create an offset (to first order) because the sensor primarily reacts to the shape of the spot, not its position. The astigmatic sensor can be made even more tolerant of lateral misalignment by multiplying the outputs of opposing quadrants rather than adding them; e.g., FE $\propto AD - BC$.

The output of a position sensor viewed as a function of displacement is called its *s*-curve. At the nominal position, the error signal should be zero. The signal should be roughly proportional to the position over some range of positive and negative displacements. A

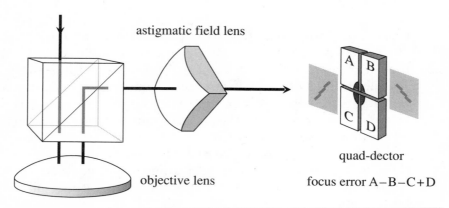

astigmatic field lens

objective lens

quad-dector

focus error A−B−C+D

Figure 7.2 *An astigmatic focus sensor converts defocus into a change in spot shape.*

steep slope over this linear range is desirable because it increases the inherent accuracy of the sensor signal. The linear region need not be wider than the range of position errors encountered while the servo-loop is closed and operating (e.g., ±0.5 μm for focus sensors and ±0.1 μm for tracking sensors). The slope should also be rather repeatable from drive to drive. The qualitative behavior of the s-curve outside the linear region is important. The error signal should have the opposite sign for positive and negative displacements over a wide range (larger than the typical open-loop runout) so that the nominal location can be acquired reliably. If the s-curve reverses sign for large displacements, the servo system could misinterpret the location and accelerate the actuator into the disk or spindle (or crash-stops).

Figure 7.3 illustrates s-curves from half-aperture and astigmatic focus sensors. The half-aperture sensor has a relatively steep linear region near the ideal focus position. Away from the linear region, the error signals remain large over a very wide range. This s-curve usually does not have any misleading sign reversal. One possible drawback is the appearance of a small inflection point exactly at focus, which occurs if the "dead-zone" dividing the split-detector is too wide. Such an inflection point would degrade both the sensitivity and reproducibility of the servo system.

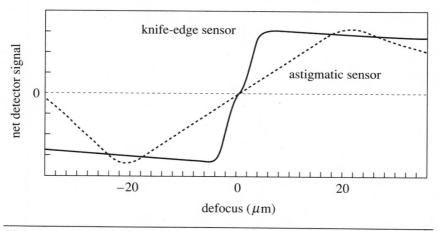

Figure 7.3 *These focus sensor s-curves show that the knife-edge sensor has a steeper response near focus than the astigmatic sensor.*

The *s*-curve of the astigmatic sensor is always quite predictable. The linear region is typically much larger (and much less steep) than for a knife-edge sensor. It is not unusual for the astigmatic sensor *s*-curve to show sign reversals for large displacements, which must be avoided by fixed stops or by a special acquisition algorithm.

The basic optics of astigmatic and knife-edge focus sensors can be understood with a simple model. Consider an objective lens and a field lens, with focal lengths f_1 and f_2, respectively, arranged to focus a collimated beam onto the media surface, to collect the reflected light, and to refocus it in the vicinity of the focus sensor. The medium is in perfect focus when it is positioned a distance f_1 from the objective lens and the secondary focus is formed at a distance exactly f_2 beyond the field lens, as illustrated in Figure 7.4a. If the surface is shifted away from focus by a small distance δ, the focal distance for light reflected back into the objective lens becomes $f - 2\delta$, so the objective lens cannot quite recollimate the beam. The secondary focus is shifted in the same direction as the media surface by a much larger distance, Δ. We can calculate Δ using the basic lens formula.

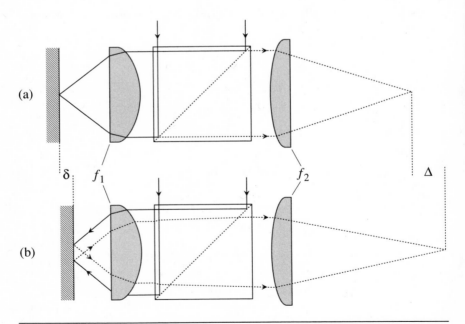

Figure 7.4 *The effect of disk defocus on the secondary focus is shown here.*

To first order in δ, Δ is independent of the distance between the two lenses:

$$\Delta \cong 2\delta f_2{}^2 / f_1{}^2. \qquad (7.1)$$

Eq. (7.1) shows us that for any focus sensor that includes a field lens, the field lens and detector must be aligned in the axial direction with a tolerance much finer than $2\delta f_2{}^2 / f_1{}^2$, where δ is interpreted as the depth of focus of the optical stylus. For example, suppose $f_1 = 5$ mm, $f_2 = 25$ mm, and $\delta = 1 \mu$m; then the axial tolerance should be tighter than 0.05 mm. In a very compact head, f_2 might be even smaller and the tolerance would be even tighter. A slight, fixed detector misalignment can be corrected by an electronic offset, which moves the nominal point on the s-curve away from zero; however, any positional shift due to vibration, thermal expansion, or other changes in alignment cannot be compensated.

Eq. (7.1) can also be applied to estimate the s-curve for the astigmatic focus sensor. Denote the two focal lengths of the astigmatic field lens by $f_2 \pm \Delta$. Then the two peaks of the s-curve, which correspond to orthogonal line foci at the detector, are reached when the disk surface is out of focus by $\pm \; 0.5\Delta f_1{}^2 / f_2{}^2$. As an example, if $\Delta = 1$ mm and $f_2 / f_1 = 5$, then the width of the s-curve is about 40 μm.

The s-curve of a knife-edge sensor cannot be explained entirely by geometrical optics. If the field lens formed a point focus, the s-curve would have a small, flat region exactly at best focus where the secondary focus was entirely lost in the narrow dead-zone dividing the halves of the split-detector. Over this flat region, the sensor would have no sensitivity at all. However, the spot size at the secondary focus is limited by the same diffraction effects that limit the optical stylus. The effective NA of the field lens is related to the NA of the objective lens by

$$NA_2 \cong 0.5NA_1 f_1 / f_2 \qquad (7.2)$$

where 1 and 2 denote the objective lens and field lens, respectively. The factor of 0.5 arises because the detector is illuminated by only half of the field lens aperture. Combining Eqs. (5.22) and (7.2), we find that the smallest possible spot width in the direction perpendicular to the detector dead-zone is

$$s_2 \cong s_1 \, 2 f_2 / f_1, \qquad (7.3)$$

where s_1 is the width of the stylus. The dead-zone must be much narrower than 10 μm (for $s_1 \cong 1\mu$m and $f_2/f_1 = 5$) in order to prevent the appearance of a flat region at the center of the s-curve. If the defocus is sufficient to shift the secondary focus away from the detector by more than

$$\Delta \sim s_2/NA_2 \cong 4s_1f_2^2/f_1^2/NA_1, \qquad (7.4)$$

then diffraction effects are minimal and only one of the detector halves is illuminated. This value of Δ corresponds to the depth of focus of the field lens. Combining Eqs. (7.1) and (7.4), we find that the focus range over which the s-curve switches between its limiting values is $\pm 2s_1/NA_1$, which is comparable to the depth of focus of the optical stylus. If the field lens is not diffraction-limited, the focus range can be increased and the sensitivity to the dead-zone reduced (but with a reduced, unpredictable s-curve slope).

7.2   Tracking Sensors

The most important method of tracking on an optical disk uses tracking grooves formed into the recording surface. In the capacitive videodisc system, a groove serves as a physical guide for the stylus, just as with an audio LP record. But grooves on an optical disk act indirectly, generating an optical tracking error signal. The tracking groove cannot directly constrain the optical stylus, but neither will it wear out.

The nature of the tracking error signal can be understood in terms of the diffraction of light from a regular, one-dimensional reflection grating. Figure 7.5 illustrates a collimated beam incident on a grating at an angle θ (from normal incidence). The beam is reflected into a zero-order reflected beam at θ and a number of diffracted beams at θ_n, where

$$\sin(\theta_n) = \sin(\theta) + n\lambda/p \qquad (7.5)$$

and p is the grating period. Higher-order diffracted beams correspond to all values of n (± 1, ± 2, etc.) for which θ_n is real. As an application of Eq. (7.5), suppose that a collimated laser beam, $\lambda =$ 800 nm, is incident at 20° on a grooved optical disk of period 1.6 μm. Besides the reflected beam (0th order), we would find the 1st

diffraction orders

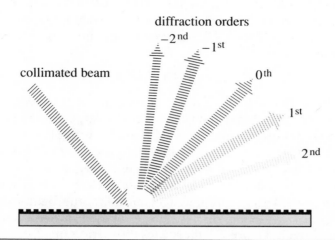

Figure 7.5 *Diffraction of a collimated beam by a grating is shown here.*

order at $\theta_1 = 57°$, the -1st order at $\theta_{-1} = -9°$, and the -2nd order at $\theta_{-2} = -41°$ (behind the incident beam). Higher diffraction orders ($+2$, -3, etc.) cannot appear.

The field amplitude in the nth order is proportional to the nth Fourier component of the grating reflectance pattern:

$$a_n = 1/p \int_0^p dx \; r(x) \exp(-i2\pi nx/p), \qquad (7.6)$$

where r is the grating reflection coefficient and x is the coordinate perpendicular to the grooves. In general, r is a complex function that includes both the relative phase of light reflected at different points and the relative reflectance. The reflectance pattern can be computed from r by ignoring any phase variations: $R(x) = |r(x)|^2$. Likewise, the intensity in each diffraction order is $I_n = |a_n|^2$.

As an important example, consider the case of a two-level grating in which each cycle consists of a strip or groove of width w and complex reflection coefficient r on a solid background (reflection coefficient r_0). The Fourier components are:

$$\begin{aligned} a_0 &= r_0 + (r - r_0)w/p, \\ a_n &= e^{-in\psi}(r - r_0)\sin(\pi nw/p)/(\pi n). \end{aligned} \qquad (7.7)$$

The phase ψ, which is superfluous at this stage of the discussion, is a linear coordinate for the alignment of the grating to the optical axis: $\psi = 0$ when a groove is centered at $x = 0$, and $\psi = \pi$ when it is centered at $x = p/2$. It can be shown that the sum of the reflected and diffracted beam intensities (normalized to the incident intensity) is

$$\Sigma I_n = |r_0|^2 (1 - w/p) + |r|^2 w/p, \tag{7.8}$$

which means that the total reflected and diffracted light just equals the average reflectance in the limit of a large grating pitch where all diffraction orders emerge at real angles. From Eq. (7.7) we also see that grooves with a 50% duty-cycle ($w = p/2$) produce no even diffraction orders: $a_n = 0$ for $n = \pm 2, \pm 4$, etc.

Up to this point in the discussion of tracking grooves, we have been considering collimated beams. But the light incident on the tracks of an optical disk is tightly focused; it defines no single incidence angle. Figure 7.6 illustrates diffraction of a focused beam from a one-dimensional grating. The focused beam can be viewed as a collection of plane waves converging around the optical axis. Each plane wave is diffracted by the grating into a discrete set of reflected plane waves, with diffraction angles and relative amplitudes given by Eqs. (7.5) and (7.6). The diffracted waves of each order form a divergent cone. If the incident beam is not focused too tightly, the cones will be discrete. However, if the effective *NA* is larger than 0.5 λ/p, then the orders are crowded together and overlap.

Now consider a laser beam focused on a typical, grooved optical

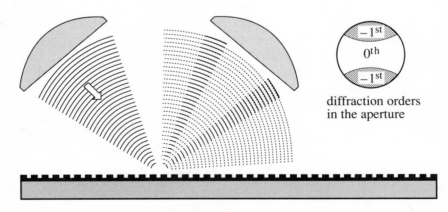

diffraction orders
in the aperture

Figure 7.6 *A focused beam is diffracted into multiple orders by a grating, though the orders may overlap.*

disk: wavelength $\lambda = 0.8\ \mu$m, $NA = 0.5$, and track pitch $p = 1.6$ μm. The 0th order reflected beam returns neatly through the lens. The center of the 1st order beam (diffracted from the optical axis) returns at the exact edge of the aperture, and the -1st order beam is similarly diffracted through the opposite side. The 1st and -1st order beams interfere coherently with the 0th order, but they do not interfere with each other because there is no region of overlap. Likewise, any higher orders have no effect because they do not illuminate the aperture at all.

From Eq. (7.7), we see that the intensities of the 1st and -1st orders are equal. In general, if the tracking groove is symmetrical, opposite diffraction orders are identical except for the phase term, $e^{-im\psi}$. When the the beam is centered directly on a groove or midway between two grooves ($\psi = 0$ or π), the 1st and -1st orders are exactly identical and they interfere equally with the 0th order. But when the beam is somewhat off-center, the orders interfere differently. Constructive interference increases the illumination through one side of the aperture, while destructive interference darkens the opposite side. This relative aperture illumination is the basis of the push-pull tracking sensor illustrated in Figure 7.7. A split detector, divided parallel to the grooves, produces a difference signal which indicates which side of the aperture is receiving more light. The precise signal

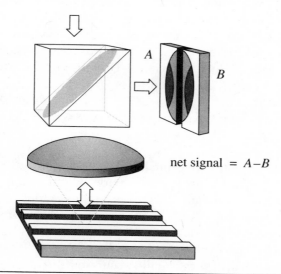

net signal = $A - B$

Figure 7.7 A push-pull sensor for tracking grooves is shown here.

amplitude depends on how the aperture is filled, but it is proportional to

$$I_{\text{push-pull}} \propto |a_0 + a_1|^2 - |a_0 + a_{-1}|^2. \tag{7.9}$$

As a function of track location, the push-pull signal is

$$I_{\text{push-pull}} \propto \sin \psi \, \text{Im} \, (a_0 \, a^*) \tag{7.10}$$

for a symmetric groove pattern, where a is defined by $a_{\pm 1} = a \cdot e^{\pm i\psi}$. In the special case of Eq. (7.7), $a = (r - r_0) \sin (\pi w/p)/\pi$. It is evident from Eq. (7.10) that the push-pull error signal is a strictly sinusoidal function of track position. This is always true, as long as only $0/\pm 1$ order overlaps occur in the aperture. If the pitch is so small that the first orders fall entirely outside the aperture, then there is no push-pull tracking signal at all.

The *s*-curve from a push-pull tracking sensor is actually a sine wave with a period equal to the track pitch. Although the region of linear response is narrow (less than $\pm p/4$), the sensitivity to tracking error is quite large because the slope of the curve is so large at track center.

The surface of a typical grooved disk can be modeled by tracks of width w, pitch p, and depth d. Since the thin-film structure is identical in the grooves and intervening land areas, the reflectance, R, is constant everywhere and the reflection coefficient is r on the lands and $re^{i\theta}$ in the grooves, where $r = \sqrt{R}$ and $\phi = 4\pi nd/\lambda$. Here, n denotes the incident index of refraction; $n = 1$ for air-incidence and $n \cong 1.5$ when the surface is viewed through a thick transparent layer. (Recall from Chapter 5, Section 1 that the scalar estimate might not yield an accurate phase depth for grooves that are narrow and/or deep). From Eqs. (7.7) and (7.10), we can calculate the groove-dependent part of the push-pull tracking signal:

$$\text{Im}(a_0 \, a^*) = -R \sin \phi \sin(\pi w/\text{p})/\pi. \tag{7.11}$$

The maximum possible push-pull tracking signal occurs when the grooves and lands are equally wide and the optical depth of the grooves is $\pi/2$. For air incidence and $\lambda = 800$ nm, the optimum tracking groove is 100 nm; for $n = 1.5$, the optimum depth is 67 nm. Note that practical tracking grooves are very shallow, many times wider than they are deep. Therefore, the model of a groove with a square profile is usually accurate (for tracking purposes) even if the slope joining land and groove is gradual.

The groove profile we have designed ($\phi = \pi/2$, $w/p = 0.5$) creates diffraction orders with coefficients $a_0 = r(i+1)/2$ and $a_1 = r(i-1)/\pi$. The 0th order contains 50% of the reflected light ($I_0 = R/2$, ignoring interference), the $\pm 1^{st}$ orders each contain about 20% of the light, the $\pm 2^{nd}$ orders vanish by symmetry, and higher orders total about 10%. In a typical system, about half of the $\pm 1^{st}$ orders re-enter the aperture to interfere with the 0th order. The total fraction of the reflected light available to the readout and servo detectors is nearly 70%. Thus push-pull tracking exacts a modest cost in reduced readout intensity.

Flat-bottomed grooves do not produce the largest possible tracking signal. The most visible groove profile can be derived by maximizing $\text{Im}(a_0 \, a^*)$, subject to the constraint of constant reflectance, $r(x) = \sqrt{R} \, e^{i\phi}$. This ideal phase profile is

$$\phi = \tan^{-1}\{1.53 \cos(2\pi x/p)\}. \qquad (7.12)$$

The corresponding low-order Fourier coefficients are $a_0 = \sqrt{R} \, 0.72$ and $a = \sqrt{R} \, 0.47 \, i$. This rounded profile scatters slightly less light outside the aperture than the best flat groove (25% instead of 30%), and its tracking error signal is 7% larger. Since this improvement is only marginal, it makes sense to stick with a two-level groove pattern, which can be fabricated using conventional photoresist techniques. (The mastering process is described in Chapter 12, Section 4.)

Although the basic concept of push-pull tracking is easy to understand, the optical situation is complicated when focus and tracking sensors are combined. For instance, when push-pull tracking is combined with astigmatic focus sensing, the spot shape at the detector is far from circular. Mansuripur (1987) illustrates the kind of detailed numerical modeling that is necessary to design and analyze a comprehensive servo system.

A push-pull tracking error signal can be obtained without continuous grooves. For example, the tracks of pits on a CD yield the same kind of cross-track diffraction, even though the track pattern is discontinuous. In some CD players, the push-pull signal is used for tracking. One difficulty here is that an asymmetrical placement of data marks might create a false error signal. Another problem in applying push-pull tracking to read-only disks is the choice of groove depth. Recall from Chapter 5, Section 4 that a phase depth of about π optimizes the full-aperture signal level from the pits on read-only disks. But from Eq. (7.11), we see that grooves of this depth yield no push-pull tracking signal at all. Clearly, the optimum design depth must be a compromise between the requirements for a strong tracking signal and high data contrast.

The push-pull tracking error signal is sensitive and convenient, but it is only an indirect indication of the stylus location, because it relies on the far-field intensity pattern of the reflected beam. Defects or dirt, which are out of focus with respect to the optical stylus, can obscure the light in one area of the reflected beam, creating a false push-pull signal. Substrate tilt, head misalignment, or movement of the objective lens can also create false error signals. A method of compensating for push-pull offsets is discussed in Chapter 10, Section 2. Another drawback of push-pull tracking is that the processes used to master and manufacture grooved substrates can increase the surface roughness or defect level, leading to lower signal quality and higher error rates than on comparable ungrooved substrates.

It is possible to avoid the difficulties of push-pull tracking and to decouple the focus and tracking systems by eliminating the continuous grooves. Several alternative tracking techniques have been developed which give a direct indication of the stylus tracking position without the need for a continuous groove. Figure 7.8a shows the layout of a three-spot, or outrigger, tracking sensor. Before entering the objective lens, the laser beam passes through a weak phase grating with a large period. The 1st and -1st diffraction orders of the beam enter the objective lens slightly off-axis and form low-power, secondary spots on either side of the main spot. The grating is aligned so that these spots are displaced by a fraction of the track pitch in the cross-track direction relative to the optical stylus, as shown in Figure 7.8b. The light reflected from the three spots is collected by the objective lens and relayed to three separate detectors. The light returned from the central stylus is used to sense the focus error and the data signal. The signals from the outrigger spots are fed into separate detection circuits, which essentially measure the strength of the high-frequency (data) signal from each spot. Any difference between the outrigger signals indicates that the track center lies closer to the outrigger with the greatest output. For example, in Figure 7.8b the stylus is slightly off track, such that the -1st outrigger is more nearly centered on the data track than the 1st order outrigger. By adjusting the beam position to balance the signal output of the two outrigger detectors, the servo system is sure to maximize the

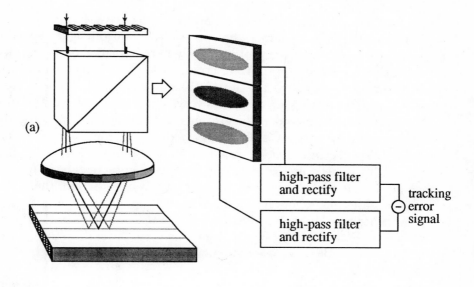

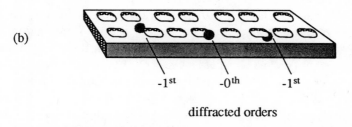

Figure 7.8 *An outrigger tracking sensor uses a diffraction grating in the incident path to create additional, low-intensity focused spots.*

signal from the stylus itself. This is precisely the functional definition of *optimum tracking*.

The optical design of an outrigger tracking sensor is not difficult to understand. As before, denote the focal lengths of the objective and field lenses by f_1 and f_2, respectively. On the media surface, the outrigger spots are separated a distance $f_1 \lambda/p$ from the central stylus (see Eq. 7.5). Refocused at the detectors, the orders are separated by a distance $f_2 \lambda/p$. For a grating pitch $p = 0.2$ mm, $\lambda = 800$ nm, and $f_1 = 5$ mm, the separation on the media is 20 μm. The separation at the detectors is much larger. Since the spots are well separated on the disk, the images relayed onto the detectors are also separate and distinct. The proper radial position of the outrigger spots is achieved by aligning the grating nearly perpendicular to the tracks; in this example, an appropriate cross-track separation of ± 0.4 μm is achieved by a grating tilt of 0.4/20 rad $\sim 1°$.

The outrigger tracking scheme is very rugged and reliable. It is also inexpensive to implement; the grating is not a precision part, and the additional detectors are easily integrated into the necessary detector array. However, the scheme requires the constant presence of a data signal. It has been implemented by Philips in a practical head for CD readout, but it is not useful in recording systems where the stylus must follow blank, unrecorded tracks.

Another technique that directly senses the optimum tracking position is *wobble tracking*. Figure 7.9a illustrates the earliest implementation of this idea. A low-frequency bias signal (10 to 100 kHz) applied to the tracking actuator causes the stylus to wobble slightly back and forth across the track. A phase-locked loop determines whether the readout signal is greater at one excursion of the stylus, indicating that the average position is not optimal. This method suffers from the same defect as outrigger tracking: It will not work in the absence of data. It also causes a slightly reduced data signal (because the stylus is slightly off-track on average) and increased cross-talk (because the stylus wanders closer to the neighboring tracks). The track pitch must be increased by an amount equal to the wobble amplitude.

The deficiencies of wobble and outrigger tracking are overcome in the *sampled tracking* method, illustrated in Figure 7.9b, which was

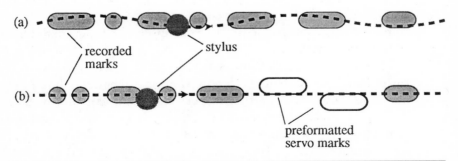

Figure 7.9 *Wobble tracking (a) directly senses the optimum tracking position. Sampled tracking (b) overcomes many limitations of wobble and outrigger tracking.*

first proposed by Hazel and La Budde (1982). In this method, which is analogous to the tracking scheme employed in high-end magnetic Winchester drives, many small servo fields are provided on each track of the disk. They can be molded onto the substrate or servo-written after the disk is manufactured. In essence, the servo fields guarantee that some "data" marks are always present. Each servo field includes a pair of marks, which are disposed inside and outside the nominal track radius, with radial displacements of $\pm p/4$. The offset positions of these marks serve the same function as a periodic wobble in the stylus location, but without requiring the stylus to deviate from the center of the track.

Sampled tracking is very simple to implement, because it requires no additional drive components other than digital circuitry for sampling at each servo field and synthesizing a continuous error signal. In a sense, the difficult job is performed at the mastering station or servo-writer where the servo fields are created. The principal disadvantage is that a high-performance sampled tracking servo requires several thousand servo fields on each track (see Section 7.4), increasing the overhead requirement for small disks. Furthermore, the synthesized error signal is much more sensitive to media defects than the continuous push-pull signal.

Tracking sensors are effective only when the optical stylus is precisely focused on the recording surface. It is necessary to acquire focus prior to locking onto tracks and to monitor the state of focus while interpreting the output of the tracking sensor. This is why the focus sensor should have a large range. It is possible to build a simple far-field focus sensor, based on the same principles as push-pull tracking (Braat and Bouwhuis, 1978), which requires neither a field lens nor careful alignment. However, this kind of sensor has a very narrow range and is accurate only when the optical stylus is on-track. A far-field focus sensor would be practical only in systems with a small *NA* (very large depth of focus) or a correspondingly small axial runout.

7.3 The Servo Loop

Positioning systems are necessary to recover data from any storage medium. When the data density is low enough, a simple *open-loop* mechanism is sufficient. For example, low-end magnetic systems, such as ordinary flexible disk drives and low-capacity Winchester drives use stepper motors to reposition the head from track to track. The controller decides how far the head should be moved and sends a corresponding signal to the motor. Since no sensor is used to verify the actual position, the performance of an open-loop servo is directly affected by any unpredictable actuator motion, media runout, thermal expansion, vibration, and a host of other factors. If the data tracks are wide enough, the net position error could be tolerable; but in optical recording systems, these open-loop errors are overwhelming, because the tracks formed by the optical stylus are so very narrow, while the various positional uncertainties are just as large as for any removable medium.

In optical drives, accurate focusing and tracking are achieved by *closed-loop* servos, which compensate for the unpredictable positioning errors. The focus servo diagrammed in Figure 7.10 illustrates the basic concept of a closed-loop position servo. An optical sensor samples the light reflected from the media surface and generates a signal proportional to the focus error (within the linear range of the *s*-curve). The error signal is amplified to a level that can drive a focus

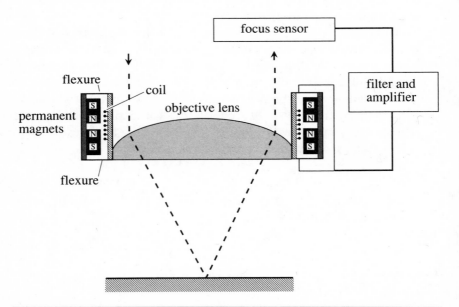

Figure 7.10 *A single-axis, closed-loop focus servo corrects unpredictable positioning errors.*

motor that holds the objective lens. The motor moves the lens in the direction that reduces the error signal, thereby improving the focus.

The single-axis focus motor in Figure 7.10 illustrates several design criteria applicable to many types of focus and tracking servos. This particular motor is a form of solenoid, in which current through the coil reacts against the radial magnetic field from an opposed pair of cylindrical permanent magnets. The efficiency of the motor and its ability to accelerate the lens rapidly are enhanced by minimizing the mass of the moving part; this is why the arrangement of a stationary magnet and a moving coil is preferred. Current can be supplied to the coil through the thin metal flexures on which the lens is supported; no extra wires are required. The flexures are constrained springs that prevent all but vertical motion. They must be stiff enough to prevent lateral motion and tilt (which cause tracking errors and astigmatism), but flexible in one direction to allow easy axial motion of the objective lens. If the lens position that corresponds to best focus does not correspond precisely with the neutral point of the flexures, a continuous current is required to keep the lens in focus. Since the servo system sends current to the motor only while a focus error is being detected, there will always be some residual error. The function of a servo system is to minimize the residual position error (below a tolerable value), not to eliminate it entirely.

A more formal description of a closed-loop servo system provides insight into its limitations. According to the flow chart of Figure 7.11, the sensor produces a signal that is proportional to the residual positional error, $\epsilon = \xi - \zeta$, where ξ is the axial position of the media surface (or the radial location of the track) and ζ is the location of

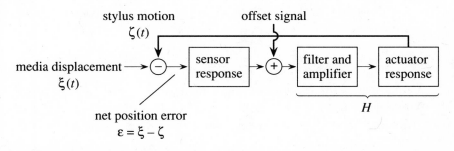

Figure 7.11 *This block diagram of a closed-loop servo system shows how the sensor produces a signal proportional to the residual positional error.*

the stylus. The filter and amplifier circuits, together with the focus motor, translate this signal into motion of the actuator, reducing (it is hoped) the residual error.

If the ideal stylus location does not coincide exactly with the zero-crossing of the sensor's s-curve, we can correct the offset by adding a bias to the sensor output. As long as it is much smaller than the peak value of the s-curve, the bias simply shifts the zero-crossing by a distance β = offset bias/sensor sensitivity. The action of the servo system can be summarized by one equation:

$$\zeta = \mathscr{H}(\xi - \zeta + \beta), \tag{7.13}$$

where $\mathscr{H}$ is an operator incorporating the combined response of the circuitry and the actuator.

The closed-loop servo (at least the analog design described here) is a linear system. Therefore Eq. (7.13) can be applied independently at any frequency, ω:

$$\xi - \epsilon = \mathscr{H}(\omega)[\epsilon + \beta\delta(\omega - 0)], \tag{7.14}$$

where ξ and ϵ are the Fourier components of the total runout and residual error, and $\mathscr{H}(\omega)$ is a complex-valued function describing the system's response to a periodic error signal at any frequency ω. Since the bias signal is constant with time, it enters Eq. (7.14) as a Dirac delta function, meaning that it contributes only when $\omega = 0$.

The overall system response function, or system gain, is the product of the sensor sensitivity, the circuit response, and the actuator response: $\mathscr{H} = \mathscr{H}_a \mathscr{H}_b \mathscr{H}_c$, where $\mathscr{H}_a$ is the ratio of actuator position to applied current, $\mathscr{H}_b$ is the sensor sensitivity (signal per μm of position error), and $\mathscr{H}_c$ is the ratio of the current sent to the motor to the sensor signal. The dynamical characteristics of a spring-loaded actuator are illustrated in Figure 7.12. The equation of motion for such an actuator is

$$m d^2\zeta/dt^2 = gI - k\zeta \tag{7.15}$$

where m is the moving mass of the actuator, g is the ratio of electromagnetic force on the coil to the electrical current, I is the applied current, and k is the spring constant. In terms of Fourier components, Eq. (7.15) reads

$$-m\omega^2 \zeta = gI - k\zeta, \tag{7.16}$$

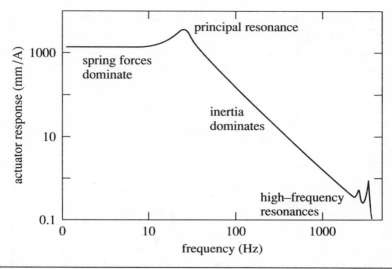

Figure 7.12 *Representative frequency response of a spring-supported actuator is illustrated here.*

or

$$\mathcal{H}_a = \zeta/I = g/(k - m\omega^2). \tag{7.17}$$

At low frequencies, the actuator response is constant ($\mathcal{H}_a \cong g/k$) because the spring force provides the dominant opposition to the motor. At high frequencies, $\mathcal{H}_a$ decreases as ω^{-2} because inertia dominates. At an intermediate frequency ($\omega = (k/m)^{1/2}$) the principal spring resonance creates a sharp peak in $\mathcal{H}$a. (The resonant peak illustrated in Figure 7.12 is dampened.) The principal resonance of an actuator is both predictable and desirable. However, parasitic resonances inevitably turn up at frequencies above 1 kHz. Because they are usually quite unpredictable, high-frequency resonances limit the overall performance of the servo. In an actuator designed without flexures or springs, the ω^{-2} behavior extends down to $\omega = 0$, and there is no principal resonance. However, such an actuator still possesses parasitic resonances.

Curves of actuator response vs. frequency are called Bode plots. The partial Bode plot of Figure 7.12 displays only the amplitude of $\mathcal{H}_a$, but the phase of $\mathcal{H}_a$ is also important. From Eq. (7.17) we see that $\mathcal{H}_a$ is positive at low frequencies (phase = 0°) and negative at high frequencies (phase $= 180°$). Where resonances occur, the phase changes rapidly.

In general, good servo performance is achieved when the servo gain, $|\mathcal{H}|$, is as large as possible. Solving Eq. (7.14) for ϵ, we obtain

$$\epsilon \cong -\beta, \qquad \text{for } \omega = 0 \qquad\qquad (7.18)$$
$$\epsilon = \xi / (1 + \mathcal{H}), \text{ otherwise.}$$

The static solution assumes that $|\mathcal{H}(0)| >> 1$ (an assumption that is always justified).

The quantity $1/|1 + \mathcal{H}|$ is called the *reduction factor;* it tells how much the servo can reduce the runout (at any given frequency). At first glance, it might seem possible to reduce the runout to an arbitrarily small value by boosting the gain of the servo (multiplying $\mathcal{H}_a$ $\mathcal{H}_b$ by a very large $\mathcal{H}_c$). The problem is that there always exists some frequency for which $|\mathcal{H}| = 1$, and if the phase of $\mathcal{H}$ at that point is near $180°$, the reduction factor will be very large at that frequency and the servo will be violently unstable. So the overall gain must be small enough to keep $|\mathcal{H}| << 1$ in the range of the high-frequency resonances.

We must choose $\mathcal{H}_c$ so that the $|\mathcal{H}| = 1$ cross-over occurs in the well controlled region between the principal resonance and the high-frequency resonances. But we noted above that the phase of $\mathcal{H}$a in this region is precisely $180°$. The solution to this dilemma is to have the servo circuit ($\mathcal{H}$c) provide a phase shift around the critical region. Unfortunately, this depresses the slope of the $\mathcal{H}(\omega)$ from ω^{-2} to ω^{-1} and reduces the low-frequency gain of the servo.

The system transfer function and net reduction factors for an optimized, closed-loop servo are illustrated in Figure 7.13. This graph uses the traditional Bode plot unit, decibels; 20 dB corresponds to a ratio of 10 in the reduction factor or transfer function. In the illustrated system, the gain has been adjusted so that it crosses 0 dB just below the first high-frequency resonance (1 kHz vs. 3 kHz); a phase filter around 1 kHz ensures that $\mathcal{H} \neq -1$; and a low-pass filter has been added to further depress the influence of high-frequency resonances.

We have seen that it is dangerous to increase $|\mathcal{H}|$ if that means amplifying the influence of resonances. However, it is sometimes possible to increase $|\mathcal{H}|$ without increasing the required bandwidth. One such trick is to position the principle resonance at the rotation frequency of the disk, usually between 15 and 40 Hz. By far the

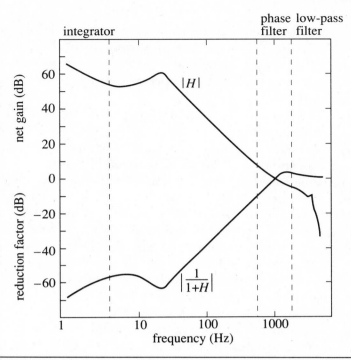

Figure 7.13 *Net reduction factor of a servo system is shown here.*

largest runouts (axial and radial) occur at this frequency because they are due to disk decenter, disk tilt, etc. The peak of the principal resonance can add several decibels to the reduction factor at the rotation frequency. Another useful technique is to add an integrator that boosts the gain at very low frequencies. This is important because it corrects for static offsets, which might result from disk-thickness variations, tracking near the limits of the actuator, or the force of gravity acting on the head. (A drive is usually required to be operable in both horizontal and vertical orientations.)

Several digital control techniques are available which can enhance the servo performance. The low-frequency gain can be enhanced by digitally calculating the periodic part of the error signal (due to decenter, tilt, etc.), amplifying it, and feeding it back to the servo as a time-varying bias. Defects on a disk can create false focus or tracking error signals. But if the defects can be identified independently (e.g., through peculiar sensor signals) the servo loop can be altered to avoid an inappropriate actuator response. For example, some CD drives freeze the actuator currents whenever the signal drops too low. Other CD drives interject a "correct" current memorized during previous rotation periods. Note that none of these techniques can improve the servo's response to nonperiodic disturbances from shock and vibration.

Figure 7.13 shows a maximum servo gain of about 60 dB at low frequencies. This value is characteristic of most focus and tracking servos. The maximum gain can be used to tolerance the mechanical precision and stability of the drive and media. For a gain of 60 dB, if the tracking tolerance is ± 0.1 μm, the disk decenter must be less than 0.1 mm (0.1 μm $\cdot$ $10^{60/20}$). A realistic budget might reduce this tolerance to ± 50 μm. Similarly, if the depth of focus is ± 1 μm, the runout due to disk tilt must be less than ± 0.5 mm. Since the gain is much reduced at higher frequencies, any high-frequency components of runout (such as focus variations due to high-frequency thickness variations) must be controlled much more tightly.

The position sensors must have a frequency response well in excess of 1 kHz in order to support a high servo gain at lower frequencies. This statement has an important implication for the sampled tracking servo: Samples must be taken at a rate of about 10 kHz (more than twice the cutoff frequency); and therefore, the number of servo fields on each track must be on the order of 1000. In practice, many more than the theoretical minimum number of fields are needed in order to accommodate occasional misampling due to media defects. The sampled tracking proposal for the 130-mm write-once disk (discussed in Chapter 10, Section 2) provides 1376 servo fields per track. The bandwidth required to minimize dynamic runout increases linearly with increased rpm, but it does not depend on disk radius, except to the extent that smaller disks usually present less runout. Therefore, all tracks require about the same number of servo fields, independent of radius. The relative overhead for the sampled servo tracking method is larger on small optical disks.

7.4 Random-access Techniques

Radial access means much more than the ability to move the head rapidly across the recording zone. The purpose of such motion is to locate a particular file on a particular track, so it is important to bring the stylus to rest precisely at the desired address. Even a miss by just one or two tracks could add significant delays to the total access time.

If the tracking tolerances were loose enough for an open-loop tracking actuator, it would not be difficult to locate a desired track. Unfortunately, the absolute radial uncertainty of tracks on an optical disk caused by non-concentricity of the tracks (radial runout), mounting errors, differential thermal expansion, and disk-to-disk variations typically totals more than 50 μm: ± 30 tracks at a pitch of 1.6 μm. However, it is possible to monitor track crossings during the seek operation. This knowledge can then be used for real-time feedback to the actuator, resulting in a precise seek operation.

In Section 7.2 we saw how a groove pattern on the disk can generate a continuous tracking-error signal. Figure 7.14 illustrates what this error signal might look like during a 10-track seek. By counting the positive-going zero-crossings of the error signal, the servo system can actually count each track crossing. Note that reversing the radial motion also reverses the error signal; then the track crossings would correspond to negative-going zeros of the error signal. This information can be used to control the final settling of the actuator, ensuring that the destination track is identified immediately and accurately.

Although this access procedure sounds straightforward, radial runout and vibration make it more complicated. Track decenter relative

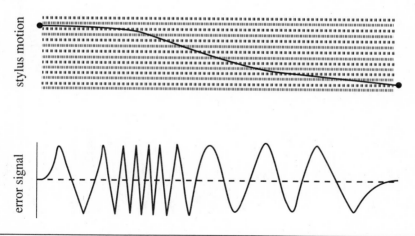

Figure 7.14 *A tracking error signal might look like this during a 10-track seek.*

to the rotation axis can easily be measured by inspecting the tracking-error signal while the head is held fixed. Figure 7.15 illustrates what this signal looks like for a slight decenter of ±2.75 tracks. The error signal is periodic, with two distinct groups of error pulses per rotation. Each track within the runout range creates one cycle of the tracking-error signal as it passes outside the stylus radius and again as it passes inside; so the decenter is equal to the number of cycles divided by 4. At the two turn-around points, the track/stylus velocity vanishes momentarily and the signal flattens out. These turn-around points appear to divide the error signal into distinct groups of pulses per revolution.

Runout complicates track access because it makes the relative velocity between the stylus and the track ambiguous. This ambiguity in turn can make it impossible to decide which zero-crossings correspond to track centers, and whether the tracks are moving inward or outward relative to the stylus. The corresponding track count can be inaccurate. Consider a track with a decenter of N tracks. Its radial position can be expressed as

$$R(t) = Np \cos(\omega t), \qquad (7.19)$$

where ω is the disk rotation frequency and p is the track pitch. One

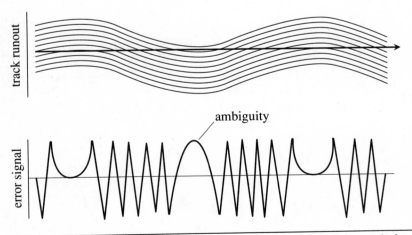

Figure 7.15 *Open-loop tracking error signals look like this for a slight disk decenter of ±2.75 tracks.*

apparent period of the (open-loop) tracking-error signal at a turn-around point corresponds to τ_{max} where

$$R(\tau_{max}/2) = (N - \tfrac{1}{2})p \qquad (7.20)$$

$$\tau_{max} \approx 2/\omega\sqrt{N}. \qquad (7.21)$$

That is, during the interval τ_{max}, the stylus moves a distance of half the track pitch and back again. In order to prevent the possibility that the relative stylus/track velocity might switch sign, the servo system must maintain an apparent velocity greater than

$$v_{min} >> p/\tau_{max}. \qquad (7.22)$$

Once the destination track has been located, the head should be decelerated relative to the tracks very quickly in an open-loop procedure; the apparent velocity must drop to zero within $\tau_{max}/2$ so that the servo will lock onto the correct track. To achieve this, the actuator must supply a large acceleration,

$$a >> 2v^2_{min}/p. \qquad (7.23)$$
$$> Np\,\omega^2.$$

Note that the required acceleration depends only on the absolute runout, independent of the track pitch. For a typical runout tolerance of ± 50 μm and a rotation rate of 30 rps, the acceleration/deceleration requirement for reliably landing on the destination track is about 1 g.

A formatted track usually does not contain a completely continuous tracking groove. There can be blanks provided for balancing the tracking sensor (see Chapter 10, Section 2); preformatted headers can contain irregular blank intervals; and disk defects could interrupt the groove. These circumstances could cause the servo system to lose count of the track during a seek if the interruption length is comparable to or larger than the interval the stylus spends crossing each track. Defects and interruptions must be much shorter than $\omega Rp/v$, where v is the maximum seek velocity of the head. For $\omega R = 10$ m/s, $p = 1.6$ μm, and $v = 0.8$ m/s, this critical size is about 20 μm. In order to make long seek operations reliable, the servo system must have a means of recognizing missed tracks. This could take the form of a PLL or a clock (loosely) synchronized to the track crossings. Even so, most of the track crossings must be detectable.

The sample tracking method is not suitable for very-high-performance systems because of this drawback. Since the servo fields mark only a fraction of each track, most of the track crossings are undetectable. In the $5\frac{1}{4}$" sampled tracking proposal, the gaps between servo fields are 16 bytes long, roughly 150 μm. Chapter 10, Section 2 describes how coarse track-counting information can be recovered from the servo fields during an access stroke; in principle, this method permits the system to monitor the location during seeks to within a few tracks, but it is still not possible to locate a target track with perfect accuracy.

MAJOR CONCEPTS

- The focus-error signal is usually produced by refocusing the reflected beam and measuring the position of the secondary focus using a half-aperture or astigmatic sensor (Figure 7.4).

- A push-pull tracking sensor uses a split photodiode to detect diffraction of the laser beam by the tracking grooves on the disk. The push-pull signal is maximized by a track pitch of $\sim\lambda/NA$, a groove depth of $\sim\lambda/(8n)$, and a groove width equal to half the pitch (Eq. 7.11).

- The three-beam outrigger tracking sensor provides a more direct and rugged tracking signal for read-only systems. The sampled servo provides a similarly rugged tracking signal for write-once and erasable systems (Figures 7.8 and 7.9).

- Most tracking and focus servos provide a low-frequency gain of 50 to 60 dB. They require a bandwidth of at least several kHz.

REFERENCES

Bouwhuis, G., J. Braat, A. Huijser, J. Pasman, G. van Rosmalen, and K. Schouhamer Immink, *Principles of Optical Disc Systems,* Adam Hilger, Ltd., Boston (1985). Chapter 4 by G. von Rosmalen is a clear presentation of mechanical and electro-mechanical considerations in the design of several early optical recording systems.

Braat, J., and G. Bouwhuis, "Position sensing in video disk read-out," *Applied Optics,* 17, 2013 (1978). A discussion of focus and tracking sensors based on scalar optics.

Earman, A., "Optical focus servo for optical disk mass data storage system application," *SPIE Proceedings*, **329**, 89 (1982). An illustrative, detailed design for a closed-loop focus servo system.

Fukui, Y., M. Miura, and M. Suzuki, "A new servo method with eccentricity correction circuit," *SPIE Proceedings*, **695**, 147 (1986). Use of a memory circuit for open-loop correction of disk decenter.

Hazel, R., and E. LaBudde, "Preformatting method for random recording and playback of an optical memory disk," *SPSE 35th Annual Conference Proceedings*, B7 (1982). The first description of a sampled servo technique for optical disk tracking.

Mansuripur, M., "Analysis of astigmatic focusing and push-pull tracking error signals in magnetooptical disk systems," *Applied Optics*, **26**, 3981 (1987). A numerical model of the optics of a combined astigmatic focus and push-pull tracking system.

CHAPTER 8

Optical Head Designs

8.1 The Basic Read-only Head

In a read-only optical recording system, the optical stylus is required only to read data, not to record marks. This permits relatively simple head designs. Figure 8.1 illustrates the optical components of a read-only head. The laser has the general characteristics of a laser diode, as discussed in Chapter 6. It is a low-power (5–10 mW) laser with multiple longitudinal mode emission; consequently, the noise level and sensitivity to optical feedback are low. A low *NA* collector lens is placed at a large distance from the laser, on the other side of a beam-splitter. Since the beam diverges rapidly, the collector lens is

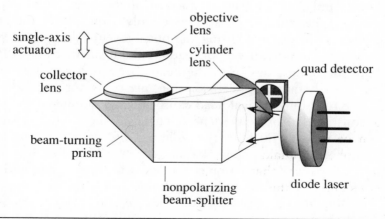

Figure 8.1 *This optical layout shows the optical components of a read-only head.*

illuminated by only the central core of the beam. Overfilling makes the illumination of the objective lens nearly uniform. The optical stylus is both small and circular. The efficiency of this incident path is quite low, but only a small fraction of the total laser power (1–2 mW) is needed for readout of (highly reflective) read-only media.

Between the laser source and the collector lens is a beam splitter and possibly a beam-turning element like a prism. The only purpose of a beam-turning element is to flatten the head profile for use in a compact drive. (See the miniature CD player in Figure 2.2.) The collector lens must be designed to correct for the thick glass elements (beam-splitter and prism). Otherwise the collimated beam will include a lot of spherical aberration. After the collector lens, the beam is well collimated, so it can be focused through a standard, infinite conjugate objective lens. The reflected beam is recollimated by the objective lens and passes back through the collector lens, which now acts as a field lens. Part of the reflected light is focused back at the laser; the rest is deflected by the beam-splitter and focused in the vicinity of a photodetector, which senses the high-frequency data signal as well as the tracking- and focus-error signals. The beam-splitter should not be a polarizing beam-splitter because the incident and reflected beams have essentially the same polarization. Instead, the beam-splitter should transmit 50% of the incident beam and reflect 50%. This maximizes the efficiency of light from the laser to the detector. Ignoring losses at the optical surfaces, the detected power is only $0.25\, f\, P\, R,$ where P is the laser power, R is the media reflectance, and f is the (small) fraction of the laser beam that passes through the collector lens. This is only a quarter of the efficiency that could be obtained using an optical isolator design, but plenty of excess power is available for readout and it can be traded off to simplify the optical design of the head. Because low-power lasers are particularly quiet, optical isolation, per se, is not required.

The read-only optical head can be further simplified by the use of a nonstandard objective lens. Figure 8.2 shows how a single lens can be used to fill both the collector and objective lens functions (Sunohara, Tanaka, Nagaoka, and Ueda, 1987). Recall from Chapter 5, Section 1 that an objective lens can be designed with a finite conjugate; in this simplified read-only head, the conjugate is very short, equal to the distance from the laser diode to the objective lens. Axial motion by the lens as it follows the dynamic runout of the

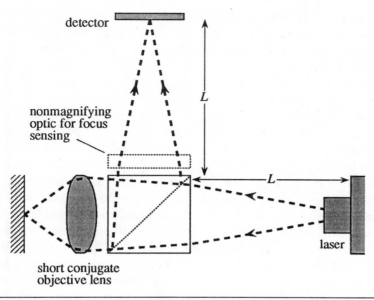

detector

nonmagnifying
optic for focus
sensing

L

L

laser

short conjugate
objective lens

Figure 8.2 *One lens can serve as both collector and objective lens.*

medium results in a change in the actual conjugate distance. This variation is tolerable only if the nominal conjugate distance (laser to lens) is much longer than the objective-lens focal length (lens to disk) or if a high quality, diffraction-limited spot is not required. When the disk is perfectly in focus, the reflection of the laser facet is imaged at a point just as far from the lens as the laser. In other words, the laser and detector array must be at the same distance from the beam-splitter. A short-conjugate objective lens must be designed to correct spherical aberration arising from the other optical components. The corresponding servo sensor must also be designed with wide tolerance for spherical aberration. The conjugate changes associated with disk runout aberrate the incident beam somewhat, but the reflected beam receives twice as much aberration.

The head in Figure 8.1 includes a cylinder lens, which generates an astigmatic focus-error signal in the quad detector. A push-pull tracking-error signal can also be derived from the quad detector. Since both types of position error are sensed optically, a large tracking error can create the (false) appearance of a slight focus error, and vice versa. The system is required always to remain near focus except at start-up or after a major drive disturbance; but full-scale tracking errors are encountered whenever the stylus is moved to a new track. Therefore, false focus-error signals during track seeks are the most serious type of servo cross-talk. Cross-talk can result from beam misalignment or optical aberrations such as astigmatism or coma, but in an otherwise optically perfect system, cross-talk may also arise from the sensor design. Figure 8.3a shows how cross-talk is created by the combination of astigmatic focus sensing and push-pull tracking when the cylinder lens is aligned parallel or perpendicular to the track direction. An off-center track diffracts the beam predominantly into one quadrant of the detector, resulting in a false defocus signal in addition to the tracking signal. The bright overlap region between the 0th and 1st or −1st orders is centered in one quadrant (c.f., the discussion in Chapter 7, Section 2). In the preferred sensor design, Figure 8.3b, the lens axis is oriented at 45° to the tracks. When the beam is diffracted by a decentered track, the bright interference pattern is divided between two detector quadrants; therefore, no cross-talk results. As illustrated, the deflection is parallel to the tracks— even though from the discussion in Chapter 7, Section 3 we would expect the beam to be deflected perpendicular to the grooves. The deflection of the circle of least confusion is twisted because the beam

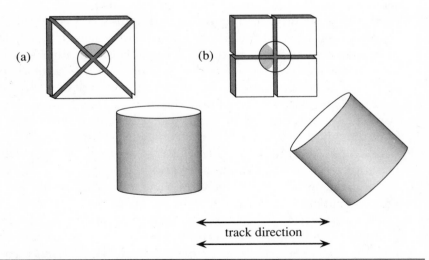

Figure 8.3 *Combining an astigmatic focus sensor with push-pull tracking can cause cross-talk.*

is only half focused at the detector by the astigmatic optics. In Chapter 10, Section 2 we will discuss beam deflection due to the tracking motion of a two-axis actuator and how it creates a spurious offset in the tracking error signal. This beam deflection also creates a focus offset in the configuration of Figure 8.3a, but not in the preferred configuration of Figure 8.3b.

The simplest read-only heads employ single-axis objective lens actuators, which maintain focus. In these systems, tracking motion is provided by fine motion of the same mechanism that moves the head for coarse radial access. To support the needs of both fine tracking and radial access, the tracking actuator must operate very smoothly and must provide high acceleration. These requirements are not insurmountable for lower-performance read-only systems like CD drives. However, many drive designs use two-axis lens actuators to minimize the performance requirements on the coarse actuator (see, for instance, Figure 8.8).

8.2   Special Lenses

Conventional objective lenses are heavy, complicated, and expensive. Figure 8.4a illustrates an objective lens design that includes several glass elements. Conventional grinding and polishing techniques produce relatively heavy glass lenses with spherical figures on each surface. Multiple refracting surfaces (several component lenses) are required in order to minimize spherical aberration under the con-

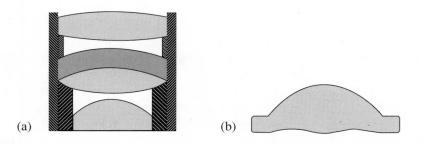

(a)   (b)

Figure 8.4 *A conventional objective lens assembly (a) is complicated, heavy, and expensive compared to a molded, aspheric lens (b).*

straint of spherical lens surfaces. The lens elements will not work together properly unless they are carefully mounted and accurately aligned. Each lens element must be antireflection coated; otherwise the multiple reflection losses within the assembly are severe. Many designs incorporate doublets: paired lenses made of different types of glass with different refractive indices. If, in addition, the lens must handle a wide wavelength range or a large field of view, the conventionally designed lens will be particularly complicated, heavy, and expensive.

The collector lens is simpler than the objective lens, in the sense that it has a lower *NA*. The choice of *NA* for the collector is a trade-off between lens cost (including head-assembly tolerances) and efficient use of the laser power. The read-only head described in Section 1 represents the extreme choice of low *NA* to minimize the part count and to maximize the assembly tolerances at the expense of optical efficiency. However, in write-once and erasable systems, the need to preserve efficiency results in different prescriptions for the collector lens *NA*. If no beam circularization is provided, the optimum apodization of the beam is $\alpha \sim 1$ along the $\perp$ profile of the beam (see Chapter 6, Section 2). From Figure 6.5, we see that the marginal ray, $\mathscr{I}_{\perp} \sim \mathscr{I}_0 / e$, emerges from the laser at about 20° for a typical laser. Therefore, the collector lens must have a numerical aperture of $NA_{coll} \sim 0.35$. On the other hand, if the beam is perfectly circularized, the optimum apodization is $\alpha \sim 2.5$ (see Chapter 5, Section 2) and the marginal ray emerges at about 30°. In terms of efficiency, the full advantage from beam circularization can be obtained only with a very fast collector lens, $NA_{coll} \sim 0.5$. However, such a high numerical aperture is not usually chosen.

If arbitrary surface profiles are possible (and if the requirements for wavelength range and field-of-view are minimal), a simple lens with a high numerical aperture and a perfect figure can be designed. An ideal aspheric singlet lens is small, lightweight ($<< 1$ g), and easy to align. In the past, aspheric lenses were extremely costly to manufacture because special equipment was required to grind and polish each surface. Molded plastic aspheres were cheap, but they suffered from poor surface replication, irregular shrinkage, and stress-induced birefringence. However, it is now possible to mold high-quality aspheric lenses of virtually any design. Several companies (including Eastman Kodak Company) have demonstrated mass-produced, diffraction-limited aspheric lenses molded from both glass and plastic. Optical testing (even though it is highly automated) is the most expensive manufacturing step. In addition to performance advantages, molded aspheric lenses have convenience advantages. Reference features, like the ridge shown in Figure 8.4b, simplify handling, alignment, and assembly. Features also identify the direction of intrinsic stress orientation (which should be aligned parallel or perpendicular to the incident polarization).

Molded plastic aspheres perform well as objective lenses in optical recording systems. This is precisely where they are most desirable, because of moving-mass limitations. Molded plastic lenses are much less suitable as collector lenses and field lenses, even though the requirements for NA and/or surface-quality can be less stringent in these applications. The reason for this disparity is that most plastics have a large expansion coefficient compared to that of glass, $\sim 5 \cdot 10^{-5} \, K^{-1}$ versus $\sim 5 \cdot 10^{-6} \, K^{-1}$. If the temperature of the optical head changes, the fractional change in the focal length of a lens will be comparable to the thermal expansion coefficient times the temperature change. The focal length of a plastic collector lens with $f_{coll} = 10$ mm can increase by as much as 10 μm if it is heated by just 20°C, while the focus of a comparable glass lens would shift by less than 1 μm. An objective lens can accommodate a relatively large change in focal length, because the focus servo repositions it continuously to maintain optimum focus. But f_{coll} must remain precisely equal to the distance from the collector lens to the laser facet, or else the beam will be decollimated. Recall that the focus sensor is accurate only if the input beam is collimated (Chapter 7, Section 1). Therefore, the focus of the collector lens must be fixed precisely on the laser facet. Similarly, a focus offset is created if the focal length of the field lens is not equal to the distance to the detectors. The only practical solution to these tolerance requirements in a high-performance head is to use glass collector and field lenses. Fortunately, it is possible to mold high-quality glass aspheres for these applications. Another alternative for the collector lens is to fabricate it from a glass rod with an axial refractive index gradient. The design freedom provided by the index gradient allows a simple plano-convex lens design with very good optical quality (McLaughlin, Toyama, and Kitano, 1986).

The same material constraints that apply to the collector and field lenses also apply to other special lenses in the head, such as lenses used for astigmatic focus sensing (Chapter 7, Section 1). As illustrated in Figure 8.5, a single toric lens (with substantially different focal lengths along two axes) could replace the field lens/cylinder lens pair. Molding is the only way to make a toric lens at a reasonable cost.

8.3 Heads for Write-once Systems

Compared to read-only heads, optical heads for write-once drives require more parts and higher-quality components. Figure 8.5 illustrates the layout of a typical write-once head. Because laser power is usually at a premium, write-once heads are optimized for optical efficiency. The collector lens has a relatively high numerical aperture, so that it can collimate most of the laser light. After collimation, the beam is circularized; the head in Figure 8.5 uses two Littrow prisms. The polarizing beam-splitter transmits virtually the entire beam because it is p-polarized. A subsequent beam-turning element is used merely to reduce the head profile; a right-angle prism is useful for this purpose because it reflects fully 100% of the beam (by total internal reflectance). These design features ensure that the maximum amount of light is available for recording. Readout efficiency and optical feedback suppression are provided by the quarter-wave plate used in conjunction with the PBSC as an optical isolator (Chapter 6, Section 4). The efficiency and manufacturability of the head are improved by combining optical elements wherever possible. Thus the PBSC, QWP, field lens, and two of the prisms are cemented together

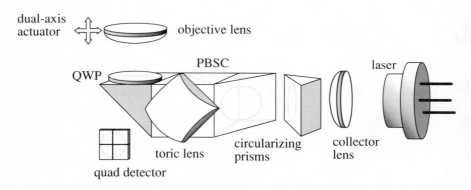

Figure 8.5 *In this representative write-once optical head, a single toric lens replaces the field lens/cylinder lens combination.*

to eliminate reflection losses. The integrated toric lens eliminates the losses (and costs) associated with a separate cylinder lens.

The optical isolator operates by controlling the polarization of the light at the reflective surface of the medium. Any polarization-dependent optical effects between the beam-splitter and the medium tend to degrade the performance of the optical isolator. Birefringence (in which the optical thickness of a transparent material depends on the direction of polarization) is the best-known source of such trouble. (Substrate birefringence is discussed in more detail in Chapter 12, Section 5.) But a typical head has several other sources of polarization trouble. Examples include polarization-dependent reflection in beam-turning elements, inaccuracy in the QWP phase shift or alignment, and polarization-dependent transmittance through the objective lens. Using the Jones matrix formalism from Chapter 6, Eq. (8.1) describes the field amplitude in the reflected beam when polarization dependent element is present between the QWP and the medium:

$$
\begin{vmatrix} 0 & 0 \\ 0 & 1 \end{vmatrix} \begin{vmatrix} \cos 45° & -\sin 45° \\ \sin 45° & \cos 45° \end{vmatrix} \begin{vmatrix} 1 & 0 \\ 0 & i \end{vmatrix} \begin{vmatrix} \cos \beta & -\sin \beta \\ \sin \beta & \cos \beta \end{vmatrix} \begin{vmatrix} r_1 & 0 \\ 0 & r_2 \end{vmatrix} \begin{vmatrix} \cos \beta & \sin \beta \\ -\sin \beta & \cos \beta \end{vmatrix}
$$

$$
\times \begin{vmatrix} 1 & 0 \\ 0 & i \end{vmatrix} \begin{vmatrix} \cos 45° & \sin 45° \\ -\sin 45° & \cos 45° \end{vmatrix} \begin{vmatrix} 1 & 0 \\ 0 & 0 \end{vmatrix} \begin{vmatrix} E_x \\ E_y \end{vmatrix} = E_x/2 \cdot \begin{vmatrix} 0 \\ r_1 + r_2 \end{vmatrix}. \qquad (8.1)
$$

This equation is identical in form to Eq. (6.6) except for the presence of a generalized polarization effect. The major axis of the polarization effect is aligned at an arbitrary angle β relative to the QWP, which itself is oriented at 45° to the PBSC. The polarization effect is represented by an apparent difference between the medium's complex reflectance (or double-pass transmittance) for the two orthogonal polarizations. For example, if the effect is a relative phase shift (or retardation) of δ radians (for double-pass transmission through a birefringent element or reflection off a mirror) the appropriate reflection coefficients are $r_1 = \sqrt{R} \, e^{i\delta/2}$ and $r_2 = \sqrt{R} \, e^{-i\delta/2}$, where R is the media reflectance. Alternatively, if the effect acts like a polarization-dependent transmittance, T_1 and T_2 with no retardation, the appropriate coefficients are $r_1 = T_1 \sqrt{R}$ and $r_2 = T_2 \sqrt{R}$.

By squaring Eq. (8.1), we find that the beam intensity deflected to the detectors is

$$
I_{\text{det}} = I_x |r_1 + r_2|^2/4. \qquad (8.2)
$$

The light returning to the laser can be modeled by switching the first matrix in Eq. (8.1). The resultant feedback intensity is

$$I_{feedback} = I_x|r_1 - r_2|^2/4. \qquad (8.3)$$

If the polarization effect is purely a phase difference with a double-pass retardation of δ radians, the detected light intensity is

$$I_{det} = I_xR[1 - sin^2(\delta/2)]. \qquad (8.4)$$

The readout signal is proportional to I_{det}; therefore, the signal is reduced by any retardation, but only as a second-order effect. Ignoring all the reflection losses, the light that is not sent to the detectors returns to the laser. Therefore, the approximate feedback into the laser is a fraction—$Rsin^2(\delta/2)$—of the emitted power. Notice that the signal reduction and feedback amplitudes are independent of the retardation orientation. This is because the incident light is circularly polarized, with no preferred orientation.

Figure 8.5 includes a beam-turning prism used to shorten the profile of the head. Almost any type of optical element used to deflect light produces some retardation. Figure 8.6 illustrates three types of beam-turning elements. The total-internal-reflection prism (Figure 8.6a) has the virtue of reflecting all the light of whatever polarization (except for losses at the entrance and exit surfaces if they are uncoated). However, a relatively large phase shift is created between the p- and s-polarizations. For 45° incidence at a glass/air interface ($n_0 = 1.5$, $n_f = 1$), the Fresnel equations (Eq. 3.1) yield a phase shift of 37°, or a huge double-pass retardation of 74°. The cube (Figure 8.6b) represents a half-silvered beam splitter with a 12.5 nm silver film ($n_{Ag} = 0.15 + 5.0i$) between the glass prisms. A detailed Fresnel calculation shows that the reflectances are $R_p = 30\%$ and $R_s = 60\%$ at $\lambda = 800$ nm, with a relative phase shift of 23°. This sort of beam-splitter is too inefficient for a write-once head, but a variant can be useful in M-O heads, as discussed in Section 4. The front-surface mirror (Figure 8.6c) has an opaque aluminum film modeled with $n_{Ag} = 3.0 + 8.0i$ at $\lambda = 800$ nm. At 45° incidence, Eqs. (3.1) predict reflectances $R_p = 80\%$ and $R_s = 90\%$, with a relative phase shift of only 9° (a double-pass retardation of 18°). The front-surface mirror causes the least retardation of any simple beam-turning element. However, thick oxide layers or protective coatings increase the retardation dramatically.

Entering a retardation of 18° into Eq. (8.4), we see that the rela-

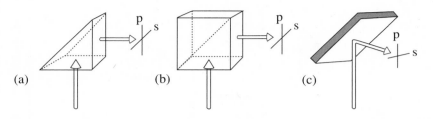

Figure 8.6 *Retardation is caused by some beam-turning elements.*

tive drop in signal amplitude due to retardation from a first-surface mirror might be only 3%. This is a very slight signal loss, but the corresponding laser feedback could still be detrimental. The best solution to the problem of retardation from beam-turning elements is to place them before the QWP (further from the medium), where they see light of only one polarization (p or s). An expensive alternative, which cancels all polarization effects, is to turn each corner dog-leg fashion, using two identical elements.

The action of an optical isolator can be spoiled by amplitude polarization as well as by phase retardation. For instance, suppose that the light is obliquely incident on a plane glass surface. From Eq. (3.1) we can calculate that r_p is significantly less than r_s, and therefore that the transmission efficiency is higher for the p-polarization. Yet there is no relative phase shift between these polarization states (at least in the absence of thin-film coatings). The transmission coefficients can be described simply as real numbers; i.e., $t_{1,2} = \sqrt{T}(1 \pm \Delta/2)$, where T is the average transmittance and Δ is the relative transmission difference (single-pass) for the p- and s-polarizations. The detector intensity is $I_x \, R \, T^2/4$, and the feedback intensity is $I_x \, R \, T^2 \Delta^2/4$. Just as with retardation, amplitude polarization creates second-order signal modulation and feedback effects that are independent of orientation.

A major example of unintentional beam polarization occurs in the objective lens. At the margins of the lens, the light rays are obliquely incident through several surfaces. These marginal rays become somewhat polarized in the radial direction with respect to the optical axis (which corresponds at each point to the p-polarization). This effect can be seen by placing the objective lens between crossed polarizers, as shown in Figure 8.7. The illumination through the lens is not

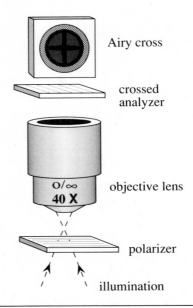

Airy cross

crossed analyzer

objective lens

polarizer

illumination

Figure 8.7 *The effect of partial polarization in the margins of an objective lens can be seen by placing the objective lens between crossed polarizers.*

perfectly nulled out. Rather, an Airy cross appears, in which the light is extinguished only on the optical axis and along the polarization directions of the polarizer and analyzer. The amount of leakage light in this demonstration is indicative of the amount of laser feedback the lens would allow through an otherwise-perfect optical isolator. Since objective lenses with high *NA* are necessary in high-performance systems, a slight amount of feedback is unavoidable.

Polarization effects at the margins of the aperture can also be caused by the recording medium itself. For instance when the medium has a complex layer structure, tuned for minimum reflectance (Chapter 13, Section 2), the reflectance at large incidence angles can be quite different for p- and s-polarizations.

The impact of polarization effects is exacerbated when two polarization-dependent elements are present. If the first such element has a pure phase retardation, the general situation can be modeled by replacing the matrix representing the QWP in Eq. (8.1) by

$$\begin{vmatrix} 1 & 0 \\ 0 & ie^{i\epsilon/2} \end{vmatrix}$$

where ϵ is the double-pass retardation through the first element. This matrix looks formally like the description of an imperfect QWP. The first retarding element would not be expected to be aligned with an axis of the QWP; but if the QWP is perfect, the incident light is circularly polarized, so that alignment of the subsequent set of elements is irrelevant. (This simplification can be derived rigorously by inserting additional rotation matrices and following through with the algebra in Eq. 8.1.) The angle β should be understood as the angle between the major axes of the two polarization-altering elements. The matrix representation for the E-field at the detector in this case is

$$E_x / 2 \quad \begin{vmatrix} 0 \\ r_1 \ ]\cos^2\beta \ + \ \sin^2\beta \ (e^{i\epsilon})] \ + r_2 \ [\sin^2\beta \ + \ \cos^2\beta \ (e^{i\epsilon})] \end{vmatrix} . \qquad (8.5)$$

Now suppose that the second polarization alteration is also a retardation (δ, double-pass). To second order in ϵ and δ, the detector intensity is

$$I_{\text{det}} = I_x R[1 \ - \ (\delta^2 \ + \ \epsilon^2)/4 \ - \ \delta\epsilon \ \cos(2\beta)/2]. \qquad (8.6)$$

In this case, the readout level and feedback amplitude are no longer independent of the orientation of the polarizing elements. For instance, if δ is created by substrate birefringence with a uniform direction of orientation, then β corresponds to the substrate rotation relative to the aperture. The signal amplitude will fluctuate sinusoidally at twice the rotation frequency. The orientation dependence arises because the two sources of retardation can either enhance or cancel each other, depending on their relative orientation. A single polarization-altering element can be tolerable in the optical head if some optical feedback and a slight reduction in signal are acceptable, but a second such element greatly compounds the problem, especially if the orientation of its major axis is ill-defined or time-varying.

System performance, and especially faster radial access, is more important for write-once drives than for read-only drives. Write-once heads usually include two-axis objective lens actuators, which increase the servo bandwidth, and hence increase the supportable disk-rotation rate and the speed of track jumps. These motors move the lens independently in both the axial direction (for focusing) and the radial direction (for tracking). Suppose that the range of useful motion is ± 0.1 mm in either direction. This is enough to maintain focus anywhere on a (decent) disk and to follow the radial runout of any track near the optical axis. However, radial access using only this motor is limited to about 100 tracks. The radial motion of a two-axis actuator is intended to support the needs of the closed-loop tracking servo and perhaps to permit rapid jumps to neighboring tracks, but a second, larger actuator (which usually moves the entire head) is required for general seek motions.

One concept for a two-axis actuator is illustrated in Figure 8.8. A four-wire suspension restricts the lens actuator motion onto a (nearly flat) two-dimensional surface. Two sets of coils on the lens housing react with the magnetic field from fixed, permanent magnets to provide the focus and tracking forces. This illustration is only one example of a practical two-axis actuator. A fascinating variety of actuators using sleeve bearings, pivots, spiral flexures, air bearings, and so on, have been designed and implemented in optical recording heads.

Several optical problems can occur when fine tracking motion is accomplished by moving the objective lens. Frequently, the tracking motion is accompanied by some degree of tilt. Since the simple, lightweight objective lens has a very limited field of view, the tilt can cause coma and astigmatism in the optical stylus. Another difficulty is that the axis of the objective lens (which points to the optical stylus) is not coincident with the center of the incident beam when the actuator is off-center. Therefore, the reflected beam is displaced relative to the incident beam, even though it is not tilted. The displacement can create false tracking-error signals (Chapter 10, Section 2).

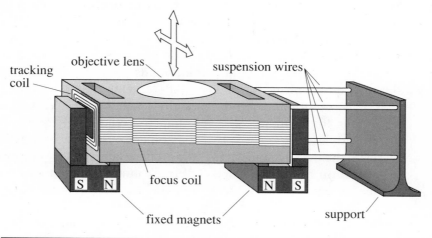

Figure 8.8 *An example of a dual-axis actuator for focus and tracking motion is shown here.*

8.4   Concepts for Magneto-optic Heads

A minimal magneto-optic head is shown in Figure 8.9. The optical layout, the actuators, and the tracking and focus sensors are similar or identical to those of other optical heads. This particular design is stripped down in several respects. The laser beam is only partially circularized by a single prism. This represents a trade-off between simplicity and laser efficiency. No feedback isolation is provided, so most of the reflected light returns to the laser. Only a single readout channel is illustrated; one detector array generates the tracking-error signal, the focus-error signal, and the data signal (a sum of all four quadrants). A variety of additional features could be added to enhance the head's performance. For instance, a high-performance head might include features such as high-frequency laser modulation or some other noise-reduction technique, additional elements to circularize the beam, a Faraday element to eliminate feedback, separate servo and data detectors, and so on.

It is easy to see that the M-O head in Figure 8.9 has no optical isolator, because there is no QWP. Furthermore, the beam-splitter is not a standard PBSC but a modified design that is detuned with respect to its efficiency in transmitting the p-polarization. Other types of beam-splitters, such as the half-silvered cube described in Section 8.3, can also be used but with lower operating efficiency. As de-

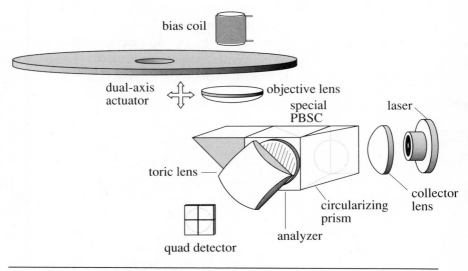

Figure 8.9 *A simple M-O head is shown here.*

scribed in Chapter 4, Section 1, data readout through the magneto-optic Kerr effect relies on a linearly polarized optical stylus and detectors that sense a very slight rotation in the polarization of the reflected beam. A perfect PBSC would form a well-polarized stylus, but it would also perfectly polarize the reflected beam in the perpendicular direction, erasing any information about the sense of rotation (and virtually eliminating the readout beam's intensity as well, when the rotation is slight). Instead, a modified PBSC is used, one with $R_s \cong 100\%$ and $R_p = 10$–30%. These beam-splitter characteristics can be engineered by slight modifications to the usual multilayer coating structure. The modified PBSC still forms a well-polarized stylus (though with reduced efficiency), but the beam reflected toward the detectors includes both p- and s-polarization components. The small s component, created by the Kerr rotation, is completely reflected, along with only a fraction of the incident p-component. The net effect is to increase the apparent angle of polarization rotation (in the absence of large retardation from the beam splitter and other components).

An inexpensive film polarizer can be used as the analyzer in the head configuration of Figure 8.9. Most types of Polaroid sheet polarizer do not have good extinction at near-infrared wavelengths; those that do have good extinction tend to be slightly absorbing. For this reason, and because of aberrations that the plastic backing can cause, film polarizers should not be used to polarize the optical stylus, but they can be used as analyzers in the readout path.

The basic M-O readout optics can be modeled easily using the Jones calculus. Suppose the magneto-optic recording surface has complex reflection coefficients r_{cw} and r_{ccw} for clockwise and counterclockwise circularly polarized light. The Jones matrix for reflection from this surface is

$$\underline{r} \begin{vmatrix} 1 & \mp k e^{i\kappa} \\ \pm k e^{i\kappa} & 1 \end{vmatrix} \tag{8.7}$$

where $\underline{r}$, k, and κ are defined by Eq. (4.2) The alternate signs correspond to the two possible states of magnetization, up or down. For the time being, assume that $\kappa = 0$ or that all sources of ellipticity are compensated by a phase shift designed into the beam splitter. (We will consider the problem of polarization ellipticity later.) The polarized beam reflects off the media surface, reflects from the special beam-splitter, and passes through an analyzer oriented at θ_a (relative to the s-polarization direction). The field amplitude of the light incident on the detector is

$$
\begin{vmatrix} 0 & 0 \\ 0 & 1 \end{vmatrix}
\begin{vmatrix} \cos\theta_a & -\sin\theta_a \\ \sin\theta_a & \cos\theta_a \end{vmatrix}
\begin{vmatrix} (1-f)^{1/2} & 0 \\ 0 & 1 \end{vmatrix}
\begin{vmatrix} \underline{r} \\ \end{vmatrix}
\begin{vmatrix} 1 & \mp ke^{i\kappa} \\ \pm ke^{i\kappa} & 1 \end{vmatrix}
\begin{vmatrix} \sqrt{f} & 0 \\ 0 & 0 \end{vmatrix}
\begin{vmatrix} E_x \\ E_y \end{vmatrix}
$$

$$
= \sqrt{f}\, E_x \underline{r} \begin{vmatrix} 0 \\ (1-f)^{1/2}\sin\theta_a \pm ke^{i\kappa}\cos\theta_a \end{vmatrix}. \tag{8.8}
$$

From right to left, the matrices in Eq. (8.8) correspond to: the incident laser beam, predominantly polarized in the x direction so that $E_y << E_x$; transmission through a special beam-splitter that transmits a fraction f of p-polarized light, reflects $(1 - f)$ of the p-polarization, and reflects 100% of any s-polarized light; reflection from the magneto-optic medium; deflection by the beam splitter; a rotation corresponding to the orientation of the analyzer; and transmission through the analyzer. The case $\theta_a = 0$ would correspond to an analyzer aligned in the y direction (an orientation that completely extinguishes the incident polarization in the absence of any Kerr rotation). The detector photocurrent is proportional to the beam intensity

$$
I_{det} \propto f\,P\,R[(1-f)\sin^2\theta_a + k^2\cos^2\theta_a \pm (1-f)^{1/2}k\cos\kappa\sin 2\theta_a] \tag{8.9}
$$

where P is the laser output power through the collimator and $R = |\underline{r}|^2$ is the reflectance of the medium. As the laser beam scans over a recorded pattern with large domains, the photocurrent is correspondingly modulated between the extreme values. Eq. (8.9) can be divided into a constant, background photocurrent, and a variable signal component that depends on the illuminated magnetization pattern:

$$
<I> \propto Rf\,[(1-f)\sin^2\theta_a + k^2\cos^2\theta_a] \tag{8.10}
$$

and

$$
I_{signal} \propto \pm Rf(1-f)^{1/2}\,k\cos\kappa\sin(2\theta_a). \tag{8.11}
$$

In the following discussions, the background photocurrent is referred to as the *DC component*. Several characteristics of Kerr readout are revealed by Eq. (8.11). The signal is proportional to the product of media reflectance and the rotation angle, $R\,\theta_k$. (Recall that $\theta_k \cong k\cos\kappa$.) Several optical enhancement techniques have been proposed to boost the Kerr rotation angle. Many of these techniques, such as those described in Chapter 13, Section 2, decrease R just as much as they increase θ_k; consequently, the net signal increase is small or nonexistent. However, the rotation angle and signal level can be maximized independently of R by eliminating or compensating the ellipticity term ($\kappa = 0$). Any optical element between the recording surface and the analyzer, especially beam-turning elements and the beam splitter, can introduce a phase shift between the incident and orthogonal polarizations. Such phase shifts add directly to the value of κ, which is intrinsic to the medium. Thus any of the retardation sources mentioned in Section 8.3 can directly degrade the readout performance of an M-O system. On the other hand, system phase shift could be designed in to compensate for the media phase shift. Since the beam-splitter already includes a precision thin-film stack, this could easily be modified to provide virtually any desired compensatory phase shift.

Figure 8.10 illustrates how the signal level depends on the analyzer angle. In Figure 8.10a, the analyzer is oriented at a very small angle, nearly perpendicular to the incident polarization. From Eq. (8.10), we see that the DC component of the photocurrent is minimized when $|\theta_a|$ is less than the Kerr rotation angle, but the signal is also reduced when the analyzer is nearly crossed. The *modulation index* is formally defined as

$$\mathcal{M} \equiv (I_{max} - I_{min})/(I_{max} + I_{min}). \tag{8.12}$$

From Eqs. (8.10) and (8.11), the value of the modulation index is

$$\mathcal{M} = (1 - f)^{1/2} \, k \cos \kappa \, \sin(2\theta_a)/[(1 - f) \sin^2\theta_a + k^2 \cos^2\theta_a]. \tag{8.13}$$

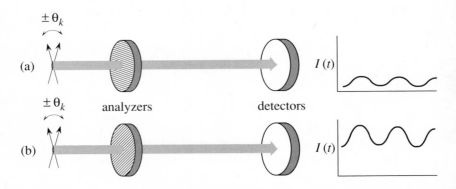

Figure 8.10 *The analyzer orientation affects the signal amplitude and depth of modulation.*

The maximum modulation of $\mathcal{M} \cong \cos \kappa$ is achieved when the analyzer angle is a bit larger than θ_k:

$$\theta_a \cong \pm k(1 - f)^{-1/2}. \tag{8.14}$$

Although high contrast is possible with a small analyzer setting, the corresponding signal level is very small in absolute terms. We can see directly from Eq. (8.11) that the signal level is maximized by an analyzer setting of $\theta_a = 45°$. This alignment, illustrated in Figure 8.10b, results in the largest possible signal, but the contrast is low because fully half of the light deflected through the beam splitter reaches the detector.

Differentiating Eq. (8.11) with respect to f, we find that the signal level is maximized with respect to the beam-splitter when its characteristics yield $f = 2/3$, i.e., when the beam-splitter transmits 67% and reflects 33% of the light in the incident p-polarization state. This would be a valid optimization if the system were laser-power limited. However, for the purpose of readout, the available power is not limited by the laser's rating but by the damage threshold of the medium. For a given incident power (fixed $f P$), the signal level is maximized in the limit $f \to 0$. Of course, a head using this kind of beam-splitter would be exceedingly inefficient for recording. In practice, f is chosen as small as possible consistent with other requirements for recording efficiency.

Other optimization criteria for M-O readout systems can be derived from considerations of the signal-to-noise ratio (SNR). In the simplest case, the dominant noise is unrelated to the readout beam. For instance, thermal noise, electronic cross-talk, or EMI (electromagnetic interference) can dominate. Then the SNR is maximized at $\theta_a = 45°$, where the signal is greatest.

Other types of noise are proportional to the light received at the detector. Examples include laser noise (fluctuations in P), substrate defects, and irregularity in the magnetic domains, which create unwanted readout modulation. If such noise sources dominate, the SNR is proportional to $I_{signal} / <I>$, which is the modulation index defined in Eq. (8.12). In the limit of small k, we have already seen that $\mathcal{M}$ is maximized when the analyzer angle is comparable to θ_k.

The third major type of noise is shot noise. The propagation of light is most easily understood as a wave phenomenon, but light is detected in the form of discrete photons. The average rate at which photons are absorbed in the detector is proportional to the beam's intensity, but the instantaneous rate fluctuates randomly, due to quantum processes. Further, within the detector and amplifier, each absorbed photon gives rise to a number of photoelectrons. The various quantum processes conspire to create stochastic fluctuations in the photocurrent, which are termed *shot noise*. The typical amplitude of the fluctuations (averaged over a fixed time interval) is proportional to the square root of the readout beam intensity, $<I>^{1/2}$. Generally, shot noise is more serious when the readout intensity is low or when a high-gain detector, such as an avalanche photodiode, is used. If shot noise is dominant, the SNR is proportional to $I_{signal}/<I>^{1/2}$. This ratio is maximized when the analyzer angle is

$$\theta_a = \sin^{-1}\{[(1-f)^{1/2}\, k - k^2]^{1/2}/[1 - f - k^2]^{1/2}\}. \qquad (8.15)$$

To first order in k, the optimized analyzer angle in regards to shot noise is approximately equal to the square root of the Kerr rotation angle

$$\theta_a \cong [k(1-f)^{-1/2}]^{1/2} \qquad (8.16)$$

and the maximum value of the SNR scales as

$$I_{signal}/<I>^{1/2}|_{max} \sim 2\,\theta_k\,(P\,R_{\parallel}\,f)^{1/2} \qquad (8.17)$$

if shot noise dominates. The antireflection techniques described in Chapter 13, Section 2 usually increase θ_k while reducing reflectance, and the product $R\,\theta_k$ is roughly constant. This trade-off does not increase the signal amplitude, but it does increase the ratio of signal to shot noise, as shown in Eq. (8.17).

A large value of f serves to increase the apparent Kerr rotation for purposes of optimizing the analyzer angle (Eqs. 8.14 and 8.16). However, the maximum signal contrast and SNR (c.f., Eqs. 8.13 and 8.17) are essentially independent of f because the product Pf is directly limited by the media sensitivity—too much read power delivered to the surface could inadvertently alter the existing data.

The dependence of SNR on the analyzer angle is graphically summarized in Figure 8.11. Line (a) is the absolute signal level normalized to the maximum value (from Eq. 8.11). This corresponds to the SNR for electronic noise. Line (b) is the modulation index, which corresponds to the SNR when media or laser noise dominate. Line (c) corresponds to $I_{signal}/<I>^{1/2}$, the shot-noise-limited SNR, from Eq. (8.17). Typical system values are assumed in Figure 8.11 for the Kerr rotation ($\theta_k = 0.01$ rad $= 0.5°$) and beam-splitter effi-

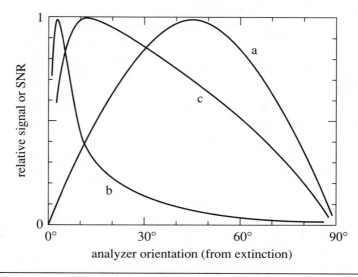

Figure 8.11 *Dependence of the M-O readout signal on the analyzer orientation is graphed here, where (a) is signal amplitude, (b) is signal versus laser noise or media noise, and (c) is signal versus shot noise.*

ciency ($f = 75\%$). Curves (a) and (c) have relatively broad maxima; any analyzer angle from 25° to 45° provides both a good signal amplitude and a moderately low shot noise. The depth of modulation, on the other hand, has a relatively sharp maximum. If the depth of modulation must be maximized, the techniques that increase the apparent value of θ_k (a beam splitter with high f or an antireflection media design) increase the optimum angle and make the analyzer angle less critical.

When a single analyzer and detector are used for M-O readout, less than half of the total light from the beam splitter reaches the detector. The rejected light could be used to enhance the signal if it were collected by a second detector. Figure 8.12 shows a PBSC used to divide the light between two photodetectors in a *differential detection* readout system. For one detector, the PBSC acts as an analyzer set at $\theta_a = 45°$; for the other, it acts at $\theta_a = -45°$. From Eqs. (8.10) and (8.11), we see that the two detectors pick up signals of opposite polarity superimposed on identical DC components. Associated circuitry differences the two photocurrents, forming a signal twice as large as the signal from a single-detection system. The differential detection signal also has no DC component. Of course, the DC com-

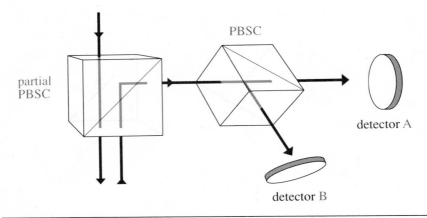

Figure 8.12 *Differential detection for M-O readout is shown here.*

ponents exist within each channel and they contribute independently to the shot noise, but other types of noise that are independent of polarization are eliminated from the net signal by the differencing operation. Such *common-mode* noise sources, which include fluctuations in laser power and reflectance variations on the recording surface, are usually the dominant causes of noise in M-O systems. By minimizing them, differential detection usually can increase the SNR by 5 to 10 dB.

Differential detection always increases the signal amplitude, but its ability to eliminate common-mode noise depends on whether the two detectors are equally illuminated. Obvious factors that can create an imbalance include analyzer (or beam-splitter) misalignment and unequal gain in the detectors. Substrate birefringence and other sources of retardation also contribute to this problem. In connection with write-once heads in Section 8.3, we discussed various sources of polarization alteration within an optical head. In an M-O head, most of the retarding or polarizing elements are aligned in the incident or orthogonal polarization directions, so they simply serve to alter the beam ellipticity, κ, without rotating the average polarization direction. But those polarization effects that depend on the angle of incidence (polarization in the objective lens, oblique reflectance from the medium, and especially substrate birefringence) have a range of orientations around the aperture. They create situations in which the light from one part of the aperture preferentially illuminates one of the detectors. Even if the total light reaching each detector is the same, any noise source that is not uniform across the aperture cannot be fully rejected by differential detection in the presence of retardation. See Marchant (1986) for a more detailed description of this problem.

The PBSC in Figure 8.12 is rather clumsy to handle, because it requires two separate detector assemblies. In addition, a thick beam-splitter might not perform well in the convergent beam from the field lens. A more compact differential detection system can be designed using a polarizing beam-splitter made from birefringent crystals. Rochon, Sènarmont, and Wollaston beam-splitters are made by bonding together two prisms with orthogonal fast axes. (They differ only in the orientations of the fast axes relative to the optical axis.) A beam of light passing through one of these beam-splitters is refracted in a polarization-dependent way, and two beams with orthogonal polarization emerge at slightly different angles. Figure 8.13 illustrates how a Wollaston beam-splitter can be used in a differential readout system. Placed after the field lens, it deflects the orthogonal polarizations onto separate (but otherwise identical) detectors. Since a Wollaston prism is still thick (compared to a film polarizer), the design of the field lens (a toric lens in Figure 8.13) should be modified to correct the resultant spherical aberration. The Wollaston prism is preferred over the Rochon and Sènarmont designs because it refracts both beams equally, permitting a higher-quality optical design.

Probably the most obvious difference between a write-once head and an M-O head is that the M-O head is actually two heads in one. In addition to the optical assembly, some type of magnetic head is required to provide a reversible magnetic bias field for erasure and recording. The bias head must satisfy several requirements: It must

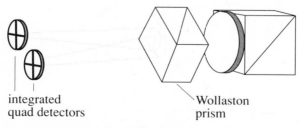

integrated
quad detectors

Wollaston
prism

Figure 8.13 *The Wollaston prism can be used for differential detection.*

operate with a large spacing, comparable to or exceeding the air gap beneath the objective lens; it must provide enough field to overcome demagnetization (say, >300 G); and it must switch rapidly between the erasure field and the (opposite) recording field. A switching time longer than a few ms could create significant delays between erasure and the subsequent recording operation.

Figure 8.14 shows why the magnitude of the bias field is so important. If the recording material has a large demagnetization field, like iron-dominated FeTb films, domains can be made even without a bias field. Larger, more uniform domains can be recorded with a bias as low as 100 G. However, bias fields greater than 300 G might be required to achieve saturated performance in Tb-dominated TbFe films. The composition-dependence shown in Figure 8.14 changes when erasure is considered. Films with low demagnetization (high RE content) can be fully erased with the same amount of bias as is used for recording (but opposite orientation); again, 300 Gauss will usually do. But films with high demagnetization (low RE content) require a significantly higher bias or higher laser power for complete erasure. Note that Figure 8.14 does not tell the full story in the limit of high field. A bias field exceeding the room-temperature coercivity would erase large areas of the disk whenever it was turned on. Fortunately, a fairly wide range of bias field (say, 300–600 Gauss) is usually consistent with the various requirements for recording, erasure, and data integrity.

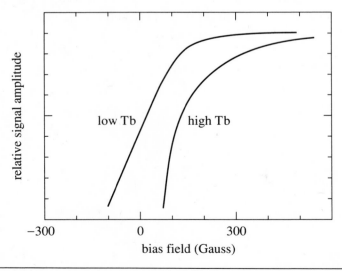

Figure 8.14 *The M-O readout signal depends on the magnetic bias field.*

Typically, the bias field is provided by a coil on the opposite side of the medium from the optical components. A small coil can be switched (erase/record/off) relatively rapidly without a large drain on the drive's power supply. Mounted on the opposite side of the medium, it should not disturb the focus and tracking motors; but a moving coil hanging on a long support arm is a mechanical challenge for the overall drive design, because it makes the head bulky, massive, and mechanically unreliable.

An alternative solution is to produce the bias field using permanent magnets. High-efficiency permanent magnets with fields of several kG are readily available. A magnet with a long pole face can supply the bias field across the entire disk, eliminating the need to move the bias coil along with the optical head during radial access. The primary challenge in using permanent magnets in this application is the need to switch the fields rapidly. Figure 8.15 shows how a small motion of the permanent magnet switches the bias-field polarity in the vicinity of the optical stylus. The elimination of the power requirement for the coil can more than compensate for the power needed to move this magnet.

8.5 Future Head Designs

In Chapter 1, Section 1 we noted the ability of conventional optical systems to transfer information at extremely high rates by simultaneously imaging a complete two-dimensional pattern. The focused beam can be thought of as a highly multiplexed data channel, with each point in the (dynamic) image representing an independent data stream. Since the imaging ability of a lens works with coherent

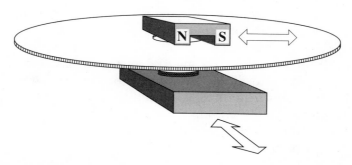

Figure 8.15 *A permanent magnet can provide the bias field.*

sources as well as with ordinary incoherent images, it is possible to transfer many data channels simultaneously through one optical head in an otherwise-conventional optical recording system.

In an impressive demonstration of this concept, RCA used a diffraction grating to divide the beam from a high-power gas laser, forming nine independent optical styli (Reno, 1983). For recording, each laser beam was independently modulated by an AOM. For readout, the reflected beams were focused onto separate elements of a detector array. Because of the many beam deflection and modulation elements, the difficulty of forming, aligning, modulating, and maintaining these beams was formidable, but the demonstrated data rate was astounding.

The simplest way to build a multichannel head is to start with a multisource laser diode. In Chapter 6, Section 5 we saw that lasers can be fabricated with a row of independent sources spaced as closely as $d = 50$ μm. The beams can be simultaneously collimated through a single collector lens and then focused onto the medium through one objective lens. However, simple optical recording lenses are designed to work only on-axis. More advanced lens designs (larger and heavier) are needed to provide a wide field of view.

Although multiple beams emerge collimated through the collector lens, they are not parallel. Relative to the optical axis, the propagation direction of the nth beam is

$$\theta_n = nd/f_{\text{coll}}, \qquad (8.18)$$

where f_{coll} is the focal length of the collector lens and $n = 0$ refers to a source on the optical axis. These angles also apply as the beams enter the objective lens (though they may be affected by a beam expander). The simplest lens designs have very little field of view; that is, they form diffraction-limited spots only from beams that are nearly parallel to the optical axis. Off-axis beams tend to be seriously aberrated, especially in terms of coma. In order to focus a laser array, the collector and objective lenses need as large a field of view as possible. A field of view extending to 1° off-axis is generally considered good for high-power microscope objectives. For $d = 50$ μm and $f_{\text{coll}} = 8$ mm, Eq. (8.18) shows that sources beyond $n = \pm 3$ would be outside this field of view. To support more than seven simultaneous readout and recording channels, we would require even larger lenses, closer spacing of the sources, or some form of two-dimensional laser array.

If the sources in a laser diode array are separated by a large distance at the laser facet, the optical styli will also be widely spaced at the recording surface. Given a source spacing of d, the spot spacing is $\Delta = d/M$, where M is the net magnification of the optical system. For a simple collector/objective lens combination, the magnification is just the ratio of the numerical apertures, $M = NA_{obj}/NA_{coll}$. Anamorphic beam expansion acting along an axis parallel to the source junction can affect the magnification in this direction. If a typical laser beam (see the parallel profile in Figure 6.5) is expanded to fill a lens with $NA_{obj} \sim 0.5$, the net magnification is about 3 × to 4 ×. Therefore, the focused spots will be separated by more than 10 μm. Since the source locations are well defined on the laser facet, the relative spot positions at the media surface are very steady, insensitive to thermal changes and mechanical changes in the head.

Figure 8.16 illustrates an implementation of multi-channel recording with a three-source laser diode array. In order to record neighboring tracks, the laser array must be slanted nearly parallel to the

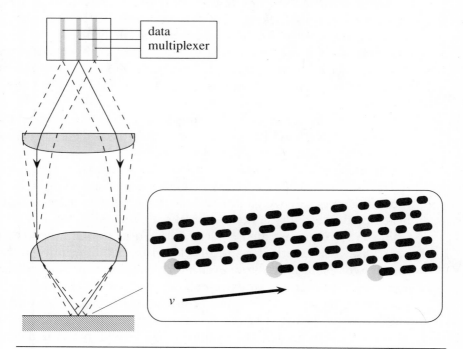

Figure 8.16 *Multichannel recording with a laser diode array is illustrated here.*

tracks, because the three optical styli are rather widely spaced. The requisite angle is

$$\theta_{\text{array}} = p/\Delta. \tag{8.19}$$

If the stylus spacing is $\Delta = 12$ μm and the track pitch is $p = 1.6$ μm, the laser alignment angle must be $\theta_{\text{array}} = 8°$. A detection system is not shown in Figure 8.16. A typical beam splitter and field lens could focus the reflected beams onto a detector array, where each detector would produce a separate data stream. The detector spacing must be comparable to the source spacing, because the field lens produces a secondary image of the laser. Recall that optical and electrical interference are the major limitations to laser-source spacing. These factors also tend to interfere with the operation of the detector array.

A multichannel head can increase the performance of a system by increasing the data rate; but in most cases, the sustained data rate is not as important to the overall performance as the access time. If the majority of file-access operations cross only a few tracks, a high-performance, fine-tracking actuator can significantly reduce the average access time. Two-axis actuators (recall Figure 8.8) provide rapid access in a zone of a hundred tracks or so. Even faster track motion (over a smaller range) can be obtained using a galvo scanner, which deflects just the beam, not the objective lens. A number of fascinating scanning concepts have been described by Towner (1986). If the requirements of a simple disk-shaped substrate and a simple objective lens are relaxed, an optical recording system with rapid, scanned access to all tracks is possible.

The alternative approach to reduce the access time is to reduce the mass of the head. Currently available heads (especially those for recording) typically weigh in at about 100 g. However, much lighter heads could be built. Nakano, Suzuki, Houma, Kinoshita, and Sasaki, (1987) demonstrated a 10 gram head using miniaturized (but otherwise conventional) optical elements. Unconventional techniques will eventually allow even more reduction in size and mass. Figure 8.17 illustrates an extremely lightweight head which utilizes integrated optics materials and techniques (Ura, Suhara, Nishihara, and Koyama, 1986). The laser diode source is coupled directly into a thin-film waveguide. The beam diverges one-dimensionally to fill a holographic lens (a complicated grating structure formed on the waveguide layer), which diffracts the beam out of the head and focuses it on the medium. The holographic lens also collects the

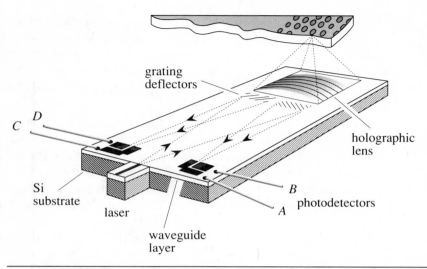

Figure 8.17 *This waveguide optical head is very lightweight.*

reflected light and couples it back into the thin-film head. The (low-efficiency) grating deflectors split a fraction of the collected light between several integrated photodetectors, which can generate focus, tracking, and data signals. Referring to Figure 8.17, note that $(A + C) - (B + D)$ corresponds to the focus error; $(A + B) - (C + D)$ corresponds to the tracking error; and $A + B + C + D$ is the data signal.

Holographic optical elements are already being designed into read-only optical heads. Pencom produces a very simple read-only head in which a special grating replaces the usual beam-splitter. Goto, Mori, Hatakoshi, and Takahashi, (1987) have described a holographic lens that could serve as an objective lens in a read-only head (but only if the laser has a narrow, tightly-controlled wavelength). Research into completely integrated heads faces many challenges. Current holographic lenses have relatively low performance—demonstrated spot sizes approach only f.w.h.m. $= 2 \ \mu$m. The lens efficiency, both for focusing and re-collecting the reflected beam, is quite low. Simplified position sensors are particularly prone to servo cross-talk, and integrated optical elements for M-O readout or other special techniques further complicate the head design and waveguide requirements. But notwithstanding the difficulties, integrated heads will be very important in the future. The low mass will permit rapid access times comparable to those of high-performance magnetic disk drives. The short profile of the head might permit the design of multiplatter optical disk drives. And (eventually) the integrated-optics head could be manufactured with much less alignment and adjustment, and therefore at lower cost, than conventional optical heads.

In a radical design reduction, Ukita, Katagiri, and Uenishi (1987) proposed eliminating the intermediate optics altogether and using the emission facet of the laser diode as the optical stylus . The "flying optical head" itself is very simple, but it greatly complicates the head/media interface. The reliability, wear, and interchange difficulties would be comparable to those of Winchester disk drives.

The moving mass of a conventional head can be reduced by a number of more conventional techniques. For example, the back end of the head (source, collimator, beam splitter, detectors) can be fixed permanently in the drive in such a way that the collimated beam passes parallel to the media surface. Then only the front end (beam deflector, objective lens, and focus actuator) must be moved for radial access. This approach was taken in a high-performance 14" drive developed by Storage Technology Corp. Barnes, Lee, and Smith (1986) have described a related technique using optical fibers: Laser beams are transmitted by flexible, single-mode fibers and focused by high-*NA* micro-lenses formed on the ends of the fibers. The fiber ends could be mounted in an aerodynamic slider, like a Winchester magnetic head, but with a much greater flying height. The slider would provide a passive focus control. Tracking would be maintained by an active tracking servo based on the sampled-servo or outrigger concepts of Chapter 7, Section 2. In another integrated head design (Kuwayama and Matsumoto, 1986), the output of the single-mode fiber is focused through a holographic lens, which preserves the basic advantage of a large working distance. To date, the performance of single-mode fibers and attached micro-lenses have been studied experimentally, but no drives using optical-fiber heads have been demonstrated.

══════ MAJOR CONCEPTS

- In a low-efficiency read-only head, a collimator lens of long focal length also serves to circularize the laser beam.

- Focus-error signals, tracking-error signals, and even the data signal can be derived from a common optical path and detector array.

- Molded, aspheric lenses are used throughout the optical head to reduce mass and cost.

- Retardation due to substrate birefringence or other optical components reduces the effectiveness of an optical isolator.

- M-O heads incorporate a modified polarizing beam-splitter that accentuates polarization rotation and signal contrast.

- Maximum signal and minimum noise in an M-O system are achieved using differential detection (Figure 8.12).

- The bias field in an M-O system can be generated by either an electromagnet or a motorized permanent magnet.

- Multiple laser beams can be focused through one objective lens for multichannel optical recording (Figure 8.16).

▬▬▬ REFERENCES

Barnes, F., K. Lee, and A. Smith, "Use of optical fiber heads for optical disks," *Applied Optics,* **25,** 4010 (1986). A proposal for an optical head based on single-mode optical fibers.

Bouwhuis, G., J. Braat, A. Huijser, J. Pasman, G. van Rosmalen, and K. Schouhamer Immink, *Principles of Optical Disc Systems,* Adam Hilger, Ltd., Boston (1985). Chapter 2 by J. Braat contains engineering information explaining the design of read-only heads.

Goto, K., K. Mori, G. Hatakoshi, and S. Takahashi, "Spherical grating objective lenses and application for the optical disc pickups," *Japanese J. Appl. Phys.,* **26** suppl. 26–4, 135 (1987). A holographic element to replace the objective lens in CD heads.

Kuwayama, T. and K. Matsumoto, "Optical head and method of detecting the focus thereof," U. S. Patent #4,626,679 (1986). Some integrated optical head designs utilizing optical fibers and holographic lenses.

Marchant, A., "Retardation effects in magneto-optic readout," *SPIE Proceedings,* **695,** 270 (1986). A description of how birefringent substrates and other polarization-sensitive optical components affect M-O readout.

McLaughlin, P., M. Toyama, and I. Kitano, "Axial gradient index singlet collimator lens for the compact disc system," *SPIE Proceedings,* **695,** 194 (1986). An application of GRIN technology to the design of a simple, high-performance collector lens.

Nakano, T., S. Suzuki, K. Houma, M. Kinoshita, and I. Sasaki, "Optical head controlled by double diffraction patterns," *Japanese J. Appl.*

Phys., **26** suppl. 26–4, 249 (1987). A minature optical head weighing only 10 grams.

Reno, C., "Optical disk recording techniques for data rates beyond 100 Mbps," *SPIE Proceedings*, **421**, 156 (1983). A description of an optical disk system built by RCA, which recorded and read nine tracks simultaneously at a net data rate of 300 Mb/s.

Sunohara, M., Y. Tanaka, Y. Nagaoka, and M. Ueda, "Single lens CD player pickup system using a bi-aspheric molded glass lens," *IEEE Transactions on Consumer Electronics*, **CD-33**, 520 (1987). A simplified optical head design, in which the objective lens also serves as the collector lens.

Towner, D., "Scanning techniques for optical data storage," *SPIE Proceedings*, **695**, 172 (1986). A number of concepts for scanning systems to position the optical stylus rapidly.

Treves, D., "Magneto-optic detection of high-density recordings," *Journal of Applied Physics*, **38**, 1192 (1967). The earliest description of differential detection for M-O readout, including optimization of the analyzer angles.

Ukita, H., Y. Katagiri, and Y. Uenishi, "Readout characteristics of micro-optical head operated in bi-stable mode," *Japanese J. Appl. Phys.*, **26** suppl. 26–4, 111 (1987). Experiments aimed at readout and recording using a flying optical head.

Ura, S., T. Suhara, H. Nishihara, and J. Koyama, "An integrated-optic disc pickup device," *Transactions of the IECE of Japan*, **J39-C**, 609 (1986). Basic design principles and test results for an integrated waveguide optical head.

PART III

FORMATS AND CODES

The ability to store information is not sufficient for a computer memory. The recording system must also have a convenient, reliable, digital data channel. The information must be encoded in header and data fields in a fashion consistent with the medium's recording and readout characteristics (much as the analog video signal is FM encoded for the videodisc). Chapter 9 defines the concept of a modulation code, compares the tradeoffs in choosing an appropriate code for an optical recording channel, and describes basic methods for judging the quality of digital signals.

Convenience depends on a physical track layout that permits data to be recovered quickly in blocks of appropriate length. Recall that an important feature of the optical videodisc is its capability to produce freeze-frame analog signals; this is possible only when each frame fills exactly one track. Chapter 10 describes the layout of digital data on optical disks and how various format features mesh with the drive characteristics to optimize the overall system performance for computer memory applications.

High-density optical recording systems are much more sensitive to tiny media defects than conventional magnetic disk systems have been in the past. Therefore the raw error rates from optical disks are unavoidably large. Chapter 11 describes the concepts of error management that are so important in such circumstances. General strategies for error management are described, in addition to the basic techniques of error correction.

CHAPTER 9

The Digital Channel

9.1 Simple Coding

The simplest way to represent binary information is to pulse the signal for each 1 and leave the signal low for each 0. Technically, this is referred to as return-to-zero (RZ) encoding, because the signal drops back to zero at the end of each bit interval. If the pulse length is equal to the bit cell, the signal remains high during any sequence of 1's. This special case is known as non-return-to-zero (NRZ). After low-pass filtering, RZ and NRZ signals look identical; the only distinction is that long-mark sequences in RZ are rendered as sequences of short, nominally identical marks.

In a similar modulation scheme, the level of the signal is switched whenever a 1 is encountered, but left in the prior high or low state for any 0. This method is called NRZI encoding. RZ, NRZ, and NRZI encoding of a data stream are illustrated in Figure 9.1. For random data, NRZ and NRZI signals have nearly identical characteristics: The minimum pulse length equals one bit cell, $\mathcal{T}$; high and low levels are equally likely; the average pulse length equals $2\,\mathcal{T}$; and the signal can remain in a high or low state for an arbitrarily long time, given some possible data patterns (all 1's or all 0's for NRZ; all 0's for NRZI).

Optical recording using NRZ or NRZI modulation is simple; the digital input gates the laser modulation, forming marks (which correspond to the high signal pulses) and spaces (which correspond to the low signal pulses). Decoding RZ or NRZ signals requires no special logic, because the (full-aperture) detector output looks like a low-pass replica of the original digital input. The decoder sets a

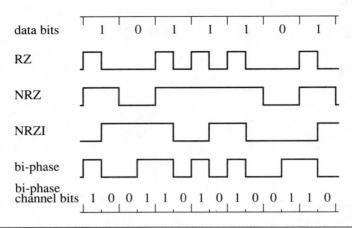

Figure 9.1 *Digital information encoded by RZ, NRZ, NRZI, and bi-phase modulation is shown here.*

threshold midway between the high and low signal levels, and whenever the signal crosses this threshold, it reports a 1 (NRZI) or a change in the bit value (NRZ).

Threshold detection does not distinguish between marks and land areas. The choices of mark and land length should take on the same values. In particular, the minimum mark and land length in an NRZ or NRZI pattern should be

$$L_{min} = v\mathcal{T},\qquad(9.1)$$

where v is the scan velocity. In subsequent formulae in this chapter, we will ignore the value of v, with the understanding that it is the conversion constant between time and distance. The in-track data density is maximized by making $\mathcal{T}$, and therefore L_{min}, as short as possible. For reasons of reliability and recording linearity, the system should not attempt to make marks shorter than the length (f.w.h.m.) of the optical stylus. From Eq. (1.1), the shortest feasible mark length is

$$L_{min} \geq 0.6 \lambda/NA.\qquad(9.2)$$

For typical system parameters ($\lambda = 0.8\ \mu$m and $NA = 0.5$), L_{min} is about 1 μm, so the in-track data density for NRZ or NRZI patterns is $\rho = 1$ bit$/L_{min}$ or 1 bit$/\mu$m.

Because of several deficiencies, NRZ and NRZI encoding are seldom used for recording. Their most serious deficiency is the lack of clock stability during readout. There is no guarantee that the decoder clock will be synchronized with the data pattern, or that the scan velocity will even be the same as when the data was recorded. Velocity variations can result from motor-speed fluctuations, disk decenter, thermal expansion of the disk, vibration, and so on. In some systems (i.e., CD or videodisc players) a third closed-loop servo system is provided to correct the scan velocity by adjusting the motor speed. Thus the position of the optical stylus is servo-controlled in three dimensions. For digital readout, it is generally acceptable to adjust the decoding clock to match the rate at which data are scanned. Some variation in the rate of the incoming readout signal is tolerable, provided that the system has a means of sensing such variation and resynchronizing the clock. Since code transitions (mark/land and land/mark) are recorded at a fixed phase of the data clock, they can be used to sense and correct a slow relative drift of the readout clock. But modulation codes like NRZ and NRZI permit arbitrarily long intervals between transitions; during such quiet passages, any velocity change can desynchronize the clock.

A related problem with simple modulation methods is the large DC content of the readout signals. *DC content* is defined as the fraction of time the signal is high during a long data sequence minus the fraction of time it is low (or vice versa). The maximum DC content of NRZ and NRZI is 100%. In a practical readout channel, the signal must be *AC-coupled* to filter out low-frequency drift, which could make the decoding threshold inaccurate. Low-frequency drift might be caused by media reflectance variations, which alter the signal baseline, or sensitivity variations, servo errors, and other problems, which reduce the signal modulation. An automatic gain control circuit (AGC) can remove low-frequency signal variation, and a high-pass filter (with a cutoff around 1 kHz) removes baseline variations, but when a passage with a large DC content is encountered, such circuits shift the signal level relative to the threshold, creating peak shift and increasing the probability of a decoding error.

Simple solutions to the problems of timing and DC content are provided by the bi-phase (or Manchester) modulation code. In this technique, the signal is high during one half of each bit cell and low during the other half, with the choice of phase determined by whether the data bit is 0 or 1. A bi-phase signal is illustrated in Figure

9.1. Since each bit cell is half high and half low, the bi-phase signal clearly has 0% DC content. The maximum mark and land length is $\mathcal{T}$, so transitions occur very frequently; therefore, a bi-phase signal provides plenty of resynchronization information. Modulation codes like bi-phase, which provide a guaranteed rate of pulses suitable to generate timing information, are called self-clocking codes.

An alternate representation of the bi-phase encoded signal is written at the bottom of Figure 9.1. The data stream is converted into a *channel-bit* stream by defining two channel bits for each data bit; a datum 1 becomes 10, and 0 becomes 01. These channel bits are converted into a signal using RZ or NRZ modulation rules and then recorded accordingly. The concept of a channel-bit representation will be useful in describing more advanced modulation codes. Note that each channel bit does not usually correspond to one independent bit of information, because the sequence of channel-bit values is constrained by the rules of the modulation code. The channel bits should be viewed only as short timing windows, T, which are fractions of the data-bit cell, $\mathcal{T}$, in which distinguishable signal changes (pulses or transitions) could occur.

A bi-phase signal is recorded as the NRZ implementation of its channel-bit representation, but the decoding method is more rugged than the threshold detection usually used for NRZ. The signal is sampled twice for each bit, at the center of each channel-bit window, and the value of the data bit is determined by whether the first sample is larger than the second or vice-versa. This method is called *differential* decoding. It avoids most of the practical problems resulting from threshold drift, DC content, signal modulation, and so on. Data channels using differential decoding can tolerate about twice as much noise as channels using ordinary threshold detection.

The obvious drawback to bi-phase modulation is the low data density. The minimum pulse length is half a bit cell, and by symmetry, the minimum mark and land lengths should correspond to this interval; Eq. (9.1) becomes

$$L_{min} = T = 0.5 \, \mathcal{T} \tag{9.3}$$

For the same value of L_{min}, a bi-phase encoded track can store only half as much information as NRZ or NRZI modulation.

An elaborate variant of the concept of bi-phase modulation has been proposed by Philips for optical recording: the so-called 4/15 code (see Steenbergen, Lou, and Verboom, 1985). Each byte is divided into 15 channel bits, and exactly four of these are assigned the value 1. Table 9.1 illustrates the 4/15 channel-bit representations for a few byte values. In practice, a look-up table like this is used to encode and decode 4/15 signals; however, $2^8 = 256$ separate table entries are not needed because the most significant and least significant nibbles are treated independently. As with bi-phase, these channel bits are recorded to the disk using the NRZ representation and recovered using differential decoding. The four channel bits with the highest signal levels are compared with the tabulated patterns to determine the data-byte value.

The 4/15 data density is 8 bits/15T, only 6% higher than bi-phase density expressed in the same terms. However, 4/15 modulation can operate with smaller values of T than bi-phase. The 4/15 code rules allow one, two, or three 1's in a row (i.e., mark lengths corresponding to T, 2T, or 3T), but the spaces are always at least 2T, compared to spaces of length T in bi-phase. Although bi-phase patterns are constrained by Eq. (9.2), it is possible to record a 4/15 pattern with T somewhat smaller than L_{min}. Consequently, 4/15 encoding can support a higher data density.

Ordinarily, the minimum mark length is set equal to the f.w.h.m. of the optical stylus, so that the marks are all well resolved. With 4/15 modulation, the constraint of Eq. (9.3), combined with Eq. (9.2), would limit the in-track data density to 0.53 bit/μm in a typical system. Under these conditions, the signal from a mark that spills over into a neighboring blank channel-bit cell is no more than 50% of the peak level. And because they are well resolved, all marks produce about the same signal. But if T were set as small as f.w.h.m./2, a much larger signal level would spill over into neighboring bit cells, because the spacing would be much smaller than the size of the optical stylus and because the recorded marks would be physically

TABLE 9.1 Channel-bit Representations of Some Byte Values in 4/15 Modulation

BYTE PATTERN (HEX)		MARK LOCATIONS
00000000	(00)	110011000000000
00000001	(01)	110001100000000
00011110	(1E)	010000011000100
00011111	(1F)	111000010000000
11111110	(FE)	000000001001110
11111111	(FF)	000000011100100

longer than vT. If the mark length were reduced along with T (by recording carefully at near-threshold power), the signal from the shortest marks would be much weaker than that from the longer marks, and again clear differentiation of the four marked channel-bit cells would be difficult. (Recall from Figure 5.10 that the signal amplitude drops sharply for marks shorter than the optical stylus.) For example, the code pattern for 1E could easily be confused with the pattern for FF (see Table 9.1). Using 4/15 modulation, the smallest value of T consistent with differential decoding is probably about 0.7 f.w.h.m./v; the maximum data density is about $\rho = 0.8$ bit/μm, perhaps 50% more than for bi-phase.

The DC content of a 4/15 signal approaches $(11 - 4)/15 = 47\%$ (though the actual value depends on the ratio of mark length to vT). However, the DC content averaged over any 1-byte interval is constant, because each interval contains exactly four mark positions. Uniformity of the DC content eliminates any problems from baseline drift.

A major advantage of bi-phase encoding is that the signal includes clock information to keep the decoder clock synchronized to the data. The same approach is possible, in principle, with 4/15 modulation, but the irregular character of the code patterns and the long spaces that sometimes separate marks (up to $9T$) make this type of synchronization more difficult. The 4/15 channel code was designed with a spectral null at $f = 2/T$ (half the channel-bit frequency). Originally, this permitted the use of a substrate with a buried clock, tracking grooves with slight, periodic width modulations. The influence of the groove modulation could be filtered from the readout channel, creating a separate clock signal without altering the actual data signal. More recently, the 4/15 modulation code has been recommended for use with sampled-servo tracking formats. The frequent servo bytes fill a dual role, generating a tracking-error signal and also providing regular timing updates to resynchronize the clock (see Chapter 10, Section 2).

9.2 RLL Codes

Historically, modulation codes like NRZ were avoided for magnetic recording because of a peculiarity in the readout characteristics of conventional magnetic heads. Because they sense domains inductively, they cannot faithfully reproduce low-frequency signals; there-fore, practical modulation codes for magnetic recording must not allow long intervals between transitions. This particular problem does not apply to optical recording systems; most systems can record arbitrarily long marks and reproduce the corresponding readout pulses without difficulty. However, the codes still have problems with DC stability and timing synchronization. Furthermore, there is great interest in finding modulation codes that can support a higher data density. Run-length-limited (RLL) codes offer improved per-formance in each of these areas.

An RLL modulation code is defined by code rules that convert the data into a (longer) sequence of channel bits (and vice versa). The channel-bit rate is usually much higher than the data rate, $T < < \mathcal{T}$. The code is classified by two basic parameters (d, k), which describe the channel-bit run lengths permitted under its code rules. The number of 0's following each channel bit 1 is at least d and at most k. A practical RLL code is further constrained to map some number of data bits onto a fixed number of channel bits so that a constant channel clock corresponds to a constant data rate. In a more complete code parameterization, (d, k, m, n), m is the number of data bits mapped onto n channel bits.

Suppose for the time being that the RLL channel bits are recorded using NRZI code rules, so that a transition (mark/land or land/mark) identifies every 1 in the channel-bit stream. The minimum mark (or land) length is

$$L_{min} = (d + 1)T. \tag{9.4}$$

In general, the code allows $(k - d + 1)$ different mark lengths spaced evenly from L_{min} to

$$L_{max} = (k + 1)T. \tag{9.5}$$

If the different lengths can be clearly distinguished, they represent an enhancement in the information content of the signal. The informa-tion contained in the distance from one transition to the next is

$$\text{information/mark} = \Sigma p_i ln(p_i), \tag{9.6}$$

where p_i $(i = d$ to $k)$ is the probability, given random data, that a particular run length will be prescribed. The probabilities satisfy a normalization constraint $\Sigma p_i = 1$. Eq. (9.6) is dimensionless; the usual definition of information is such that 1 bit $= ln(2)$. The infor-mation per mark would be maximized by making all the p_i equal.

But the information density (bits per unit length) is inversely proportional to the average mark (or land) length,

$$L_{avg} = \Sigma p_i L_i, \qquad (9.7)$$

where $L_i = L_{min} (i + 1)/(d + 1)$. The overall code efficiency, or number of bits per unit distance, is

$$\rho = \Sigma p_i \ln p_i /(\ln 2 \ \Sigma p_i \ L_i) \text{ bits.} \qquad (9.8)$$

The maximum possible bit density can be calculated using the method of Lagrange multipliers. The result is

$$\rho_{max} = -\ln_2(x^{d+1}) \text{ bits}/L_{min}, \qquad (9.9)$$

where x is defined transcendentally by

$$x^{d+1}(1 - x^{k-d+1}) = 1 - x. \qquad (9.10)$$

Some numerical solutions to Eqs. (9.9) and (9.10) are listed in Table 9.2. The table is not a list of data densities associated with actual RLL codes. Rather, the entries are the theoretical limits for in-track density for each choice of d and k. Note first of all that the data density increases with k in every case. By increasing k, we create more possibilities for the length of the interval following each transition. The code rules could ignore the longer lengths, resulting in no change in ρ; but if the code utilizes the longer lengths appropriately,

TABLE 9.2 Theoretical D-M Code Efficiencies (bit/L_{min})

k	d			
	0	1	2	3
0	0			
1	0.694	0		
2	0.879	0.811	0	
3	0.947	1.103	0.863	0
4	0.975	1.235	1.217	0.893
5		1.302	1.395	1.287
6		1.338	1.494	1.498
7		1.358	1.552	1.623
8			1.558	1.700
9				1.750
∞	1.000	1.387	1.655	1.860

more clock stability

← increased phase margin

ρ will increase at least a little for any increase in k. Increases in d, with fixed k, also increase the possible data density, but only when $d << k$. This increase occurs because the allowable interval lengths are all compressed down toward L_{min}, reducing L_{avg}. But as d approaches k, the number of length choices decreases so much that eventually no information can be transmitted; when $d = k$, only a tone with frequency $1/[T(2d + 2)]$ is allowed by the RLL restrictions.

As k becomes much larger than d, the information density approaches an asymptotic value, listed in the table on the $k = \infty$ line. In this limit, ρ increases monotonically with d; however, its functional dependence is not very steep. For large d and $k = \infty$, the density is approximately $\rho_{max} = \ln_2(d + 1)$ bits/L_{min}. The information density increases with d because the system is expected to distinguish finer and finer gradations in mark length. Therefore, the increase in data capacity is not free. When d is large, the mark-length gradations, T, are much smaller than the size of the optical stylus [f.w.h.m. $\sim L_{min} = (d + 1)T$]. They can be distinguished by looking for slight variations in pulse length; but if the pulse length is uncertain due to noise, peak shift, thresholding errors, and so on, then decoding errors can occur. Therefore, RLL codes can operate only in a channel with low noise and a high degree of signal fidelity. In Section 9.3 we will quantify the signal-to-noise ratio (SNR) needed to support a data channel using RLL modulation. We will see that the required SNR increases sharply with d. Conversely, for a channel with a given signal quality, the phase margin or system ruggedness can be increased by reducing d.

Another drawback associated with RLL codes is error propagation. Errors caused by noise or small media defects usually affect only one or two channel bits (i.e., a 1 is missed or shifted to displace a neighboring 0). But, depending on the coding rules, a single channel-bit error could cause a misinterpretation of several succeeding data bits. All useful RLL codes are designed to limit the maximum length of such error bursts, but still they increase the measured BER. The error-correction methods discussed in Chapter 11, Section 3 treat the data not as bits but as 1-byte characters, so the additional errors associated with RLL codes do not increase the difficulty of error correction unless decoding error bursts frequently cross byte boundaries.

When a modulation code is chosen to increase the in-track data density, the data rate is also increased. The maximum scan velocity during recording is proportional to the media sensitivity divided by the delivered laser power, and is little influenced by the details of laser modulation. Therefore, the data rate is simply determined as

$$\mathscr{R} = \rho v. \tag{9.11}$$

Any future system improvement that increases the in-track data density, especially advanced modulation code, will also serve to increase the data rate proportionately.

From Eqs. (9.4) and (9.5), we see that the maximum mark and land lengths are roughly proportional to k/d:

$$L_{max} = L_{min} (k + 1)/(d + 1). \tag{9.12}$$

RLL codes with $k = \infty$ cannot provide guaranteed clocking information. NRZ and NRZI are special examples of $(0, \infty)$ RLL codes, and they are not self-clocking. But any code with a reasonably small ratio of k/d will have good self-clocking capability. An optimum value for k/d cannot be defined in general, because the synchronization requirements depend on the quality of the spindle bearing, motor-speed stability, and drive-to-drive reproducibility. Furthermore, the allowable synchronization error is proportional to the channel-bit window $[T = L_{min}/(d + 1)]$; therefore, more accurate timing must be maintained for codes with large d. If we wish to maximize the data density for a particular system, we should choose d to be as large as possible while leaving sufficient phase margin and then choose the RLL code with the highest value of k consistent with the difficulty of clock synchronization.

Figure 9.2 illustrates mark patterns corresponding to some simple RLL modulation schemes. After NRZ and NRZI, probably the next simplest RLL code is *modified frequency modulation* (MFM), which is sometimes called Miller code. MFM is a $(1, 3)$ code with $T = \mathscr{T}/2$ and three allowed lengths: $2T$, $3T$, and $4T$. Each data bit is separately encoded as two channel bits ($m = 1$ and $n = 2$). The specific code rules are listed in Table 9.3. A data 1 is encoded as 10, while a 0 is encoded as 00 or 01, depending on whether it was preceded by a 1 or another 0.

The data density in MFM is 1 bit/L_{min}, exactly the same as in NRZ. The $(1, 3)$ entry in Table 9.2 indicates that 10% more density is achievable, but the simple MFM code rules reduce the efficiency somewhat. In an MFM pattern for random data, the average spacing

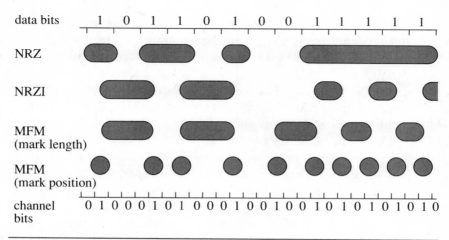

Figure 9.2 *Data can be repressented on an optical disk by various modulation codes.*

between transitions is $(8/3)T$, or $(4/3)L_{min}$. This illustrates a general characteristic of RLL codes: The average spacing is less than the average of L_{min} and L_{max}; shorter run lengths are preferred. Periodic tones can be generated from an MFM encoder: Repeating sequences of FF or 00 generate a high-frequency, $2T$ pattern; AA generates a low-frequency, $4T$ pattern; and 924 generates the intermediate fre-

TABLE 9.3 Code Rules for MFM and IBM (2,7) Modulation Codes

DATA BITS	CHANNEL-BIT REPRESENTATION
MFM	
1	01
(1)0	00
(0)0	10
IBM (2, 7)	
10	0100
11	1000
000	000100
010	100100
011	001000
0010	00100100
0011	00001000

quency, $3T$. However, these frequencies seldom show up distinctly in the signal from a random data pattern. As Figure 9.3 indicates, most of the power in a random MFM signal resides in the frequency range $f_{min} = 1/(2L_{max})$ to $f_{max} = 1/(2L_{min})$. The most notable spectral peak is at $1/(2L_{avg})$. For most RLL codes, this is the critical spectral range. Higher and lower frequencies can be filtered out without changing the waveform appreciably.

The high-frequency tail of the MFM signal is due to the squared-off shape of the processed digital waveform. It is not present in a raw RF signal with rounded peaks. However, the power at low frequency is an unavoidable result of the DC content of MFM. Consider the pattern corresponding to a repeating DB6 data pattern; it is a sequence of $4T$ marks and $2T$ spaces or vice versa, depending on the initial signal polarity. The DC content for this worst-case pattern is 33% (though a sustained shift of this magnitude would occur infrequently in a random data stream). The corresponding offset to the decoding threshold could affect the timing accuracy, but as a trade-off between channel ruggedness and capacity, most RLL codes are designed with 30% to 40% maximum DC content.

To this point, we have discussed RLL codes implemented using the NRZI implementation of the channel bits, so that each mark or space length represents the distance from one 1 to another. In Figure 9.2, this is referred to as *mark-length* encoding. The alternative is to

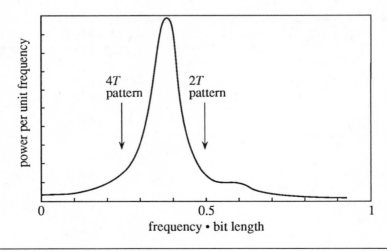

Figure 9.3 *This graph represents the power spectrum for random data encoded in an MFM channel.*

write the channel bits using RZ rules; this is called *mark-position* encoding. In this case, all the marks are identical and the spacing from one mark to another represents the distance between 1's. Twice as many marks must be recorded in mark-position encoding; consequently, it entails a significant reduction in data density. But because a mark-position pattern uses only one size of mark, decoding is relatively immune to defocus, sensitivity variations, and other system problems that would cause severe peak-shift for a mark-length pattern. Mark-position encoding has been proposed and used in many first generation optical disk systems. However, it is generally recognized that mature systems should use mark-length encoding to increase the data rate and density. See Ozaki (1986) for a discussion of trade-offs between mark-length and mark-position encoding.

The basic characteristics of NRZ and MFM modulation are described in Table 9.4, along with the parameters of three other codes that have been used in important optical recording applications. The so-called "three-phase" (3-ϕ) RLL code was developed at RCA specifically for an optical recording system (Tarzaiski, 1983). Since $d = 1$, the ratio between T and L_{min} is the same as for MFM; therefore 3-ϕ requires about the same signal quality. However, because k is much larger, 3-ϕ has a higher efficiency. The in-track data density for this code is 1.33 bits/L_{min}, only 2% less than the theoretical limit for the (1, 7) class. The 3-ϕ coding rules generate six channel bits for each four data bits (m = 2, n = 3). Of course, the large ratio of k/d permits some code sequences with a very high DC content.

One of the most important modulation codes in recent times is the (2, 7) RLL code developed by IBM. This code, which has an efficiency of 1.5 bits/L_{min}, was developed to enhance the data rate and capacity of magnetic disk drives. The code rules, included in Table 9.3, generate two channel bits for each data bit ($m = 1$, $n = 2$).

TABLE 9.4 Comparison of Selected D-M Codes

CODE	d	k	BITS/L_{min}	WINDOW WIDTH/BIT	MAXIMUM DC
NRZ	0	∞	1	1	100%
MFM	1	3	1	0.500	33
3-ø	1	7	1.333	0.667	56
IBM(2, 7)	2	7	1.500	0.500	40
EFM	2	10	1.412	0.471	0

Groups of two, three, or four data bits are encoded together, depending on the specific pattern. Just as with MFM, high- and low-frequency tones are generated through a (2, 7) encoder from some repeating data patterns: 492 produces a $3T$ pattern; 33 generates the low frequency $8T$ pattern. IBM (2, 7) is an attractive modulation code because of its high efficiency, but it requires a higher-quality signal than a $d = 0$ or $d = 1$ code, because the timing window, T, is only $L_{min}/3$.

The last code listed in Table 9.4 is *eight to fourteen modulation* (EFM), which was developed for the CD system. EFM starts with a (2, 10) code with an efficiency of 1.5 bits/L_{min}. With the use of a look-up table, a group of eight bits is converted into sixteen channel bits. However, a major design goal for EFM was the elimination of all problems with DC content. For this purpose, a linking bit is added after each group of sixteen channel bits to even out the signal and remove all DC content. Shinn (1987) has shown how this general technique can be applied to any RLL code to eliminate baseline shifts at the expense of some code efficiency. In EFM, it reduces the efficiency by 6%.

9.3 Measures of Signal Quality

When a mark-length-encoded MFM signal (for random data) is displayed on an oscilloscope and triggered at the nominal threshold, the display looks like Figure 9.4. Three lines, which correspond to the three allowed mark lengths, extend from the trigger point. Further across the screen, the lines merge into a braided pattern. Diamond-shaped spaces run through the center of the display. This pattern is called an eye diagram; the diamond-shaped spaces are the "eyes." If the channel quality is poor, the lines will be fuzzy (made up of many separate traces) and distorted. The lines corresponding to different mark lengths might merge together, indicating a high likelihood of decoding errors. The openness, or width, of the eyes is a good qualitative indication of signal quality because it tells how easily different mark lengths can be distinguished.

An oscilloscope trace from a mark-position-modulated signal is similar in character to an eye diagram. But in this case, the "eyes" are found just below the signal peaks, not centered, and the height

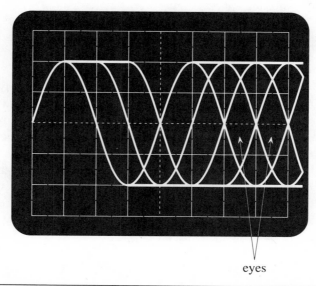

eyes

Figure 9.4 *This eye diagram for a pseudo-random MFM signal displays high signal quality.*

of the eye is more important than the width. In order for the eye diagram from a mark-position signal to be a useful indicator of channel quality, the triggering technique must be comparable to the peak-detection circuit from the particular digital decoder.

Digital decoding of an RLL-encoded signal is essentially a matter of establishing the timing of waveform transitions (or peaks, in the mark-position method). At the time of recording, the corresponding laser pulses are centered within specific channel-bit windows, each of which has width T. Ideally, transitions (or peaks) in the readout signal should trigger transitions in the decoding circuitry at the center of the corresponding channel-bit windows, but the channel is never ideal. If the decoding clock is not perfectly synchronized, the detected transitions will tend to occur early or late in the window. Even if the clock is perfect, other factors such as power fluctuations, sensitivity variations, resolution limitations, or interactions between neighboring marks can displace the transitions. Furthermore, nominally identical marks will not trigger transitions with precisely the same timing, because slight variations in mark shape and other types of system noise spread out the distribution of transition times. The general decoding situation is illustrated in Figure 9.5. The actual detected transition time is distributed (mostly) within the timing window, but occasionally, a detection might be made outside the window, resulting in a decoding error.

The distribution of detection times is commonly modeled as a Gaussian curve with variance σ^2 displaced a distance μ from the center of the channel-bit window, where σ is a measure of the overall noise and μ is a measure of the peak-shift. If the peak-shift is pattern-dependent, then different values of μ and σ apply to the different transitions in each type of pattern. In order to estimate the error rate, we need to compare μ and σ to the width of the timing window. In dimensionless terms, the distance from the center of the timing distribution to either of the neighboring decoding windows is

$$x_{\pm} = (T/2 \mp \mu)/\sigma. \qquad (9.13)$$

The decoding error probability, ϵ, is equal to the area of the distribution that falls outside the intended window. For a Gaussian noise distribution, the rate is

$$\epsilon = \epsilon_- + \epsilon_+ = \mathrm{erfc}(x_-) + \mathrm{erfc}(x_+), \qquad (9.14)$$

where $\mathrm{erfc}(x)$ is the complementary error function,

$$\mathrm{erfc}(x) = (2\pi)^{-1/2} \int_x^{\infty} e^{-y^2/2}\, dy. \qquad (9.15)$$

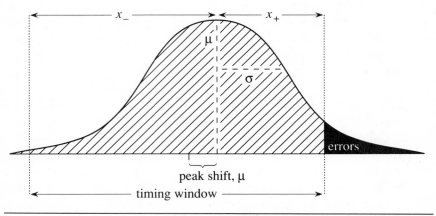

Figure 9.5 *Code pulses are distributed around a timing window.*

For essentially error-free operation ($\epsilon < 10^{-12}$), we require

$$x_{\pm} > 7. \qquad (9.16)$$

Consider an RLL-encoded signal (using mark-length modulation) with a signal amplitude E. Suppose that the noise is approximately white, with a power density of n per unit frequency. In order to minimize the effects of noise, we can low-pass-filter the combination of signal and noise at a frequency just higher than $f_{max} = 1/[2\ T\ (d + 1)]$. For a pattern corresponding to the highest code frequency, the filtered signal will be

$$\mathcal{S}(t) \sim E \sin(2\pi\ f_{max}\ t), \qquad (9.17)$$

and the signal power will be

$$S = E^2/2. \qquad (9.18)$$

The filtered noise, $\mathcal{N}(t)$, will have a total power

$$N = n\ f_{max}, \qquad (9.19)$$

and an rms amplitude $\sqrt{N}$. Sampled at random times, the noise amplitude has an essentially Gaussian distribution with zero mean and variance,

$$\sigma_n^2 = N. \qquad (9.20)$$

Decoding entails looking for zero crossings, $\mathcal{N}(t) + \mathcal{S}(t) = 0$, and deciding which clock window the zero crossing falls within. In the absence of peak-shift, the correct window is an interval $\pm T/2 = \pm L_{min}/[2\ (d + 1)]$ centered on $t = 0$. (Recall that d parameterizes the resolution level of the RLL code.) Using the same kind of analysis that led to Eq. (9.16), we find that (essentially) error-free operation can be achieved only if

$$7\ \sigma_n < \mathcal{S} \qquad (9.21)$$

in the beginning and end of the timing window. In the presence of some peak shift, the window is offset from $t = 0$ and is centered instead at

$$|t| = \text{FPS} \cdot T/2, \qquad (9.22)$$

where the fractional peak-shift is defined as $\text{FPS} = 2\mu/T$. Combining Eqs. (9.17) and (9.22) with Eq. (9.21), the requirement for reliable decoding becomes

TABLE 9.5 SNR Required to Achieve an Error Rate $< 10^{-12}$

PEAK SHIFT	$d = 0$	$d = 1$	$d = 2$
0%	14 db	17	20
20	14	19	22
40	16	21	24
60	19	24	28
80	24	30	34

$$\sigma_n < E \sin[\pi \, (1 - \text{FPS})/2/(d + 1)]/7. \qquad (9.23)$$

Dividing Eq. (9.18) by Eq. (9.20) and substituting for σ_n, we obtain the signal-to-noise requirement for an error-free channel:

$$\text{SNR} > 24.5/\sin^2[\pi \, (1 - \text{FPS})/2/(d+1)]. \qquad (9.24)$$

This result is tabulated in decibels in Table 9.5. (The decibel scale is logarithmic, with each 10 dB representing a relative power increase of a factor of 10.)

The details of any SNR analysis depend on the specific detection method, noise characteristics, and so on. For example, see Treves and Bloomberg (1986) for a detailed model of noise in a magneto-optic channel. However, the SNR rules estimated here are generally accurate. Table 9.5 indicates the price that must be paid to use a high-efficiency RLL modulation code. In order to increase d from 0 to 1 or from 1 to 2, the signal-quality requirement must be increased by 3–5 dB. Table 9.5 also demonstrates the cost associated with peak-shift. Typically, a channel must be designed to handle more than 20% FPS. Initially, the system should have much less peak-shift than this; but misalignment, media aging, and any number of external factors can cause the number to degrade. Therefore, an additional SNR margin of several dB is required.

So far, our discussion has been limited to errors caused by noise and peak-shift. In practice, most errors in optical recording channels are caused by media defects. The timing errors caused by defects cannot be usefully characterized as extensions of the noise distribution; rather, they should be treated as a separate class of event. Defect-induced errors are fairly insensitive to the overall quality of the channel, but noise-induced errors are very sensitive to the SNR if the criteria of Eqs. (9.16) or (9.24) are not exceeded. Therefore, a well-designed optical recording system *must* have a high-quality data channel, even if the anticipated raw error rate is large.

Except in theory, the SNR is not a readily measurable characteristic of a data channel; but for many purposes, the carrier-to-noise ratio (CNR) can be used instead. The CNR is measured as shown in Figure 9.6, using a spectrum analyzer. This measurement can be made only on a fixed-frequency signal sent through the data channel—for instance, by using the special data patterns that produce signals at f_{min} or f_{max} (recall the discussions of MFM and IBM (2, 7) in Section 9.2). In Figure 9.6, the signal frequency is 3 MHz, perhaps corresponding to f_{max} from a 6 Mbit/ s MFM channel or a 9 Mbit/ s (2,7) channel. The CNR is loosely defined as the difference (in dB) between the signal peak and the noise level at a nearby frequency, about 52 dB in Figure 9.6. The CNR cannot be measured from a random data pattern, because then the spectrum analyzer cannot separate the noise from the signal.

Although the CNR is not perfectly equivalent to the SNR, it can be used for quantitative comparison of signal quality, provided that common measurement parameters are used. By convention, the measurement bandwidth of the spectrum analyzer is set at 30 kHz. Ordinarily, this is much wider than the signal peak, so that the peak of the trace is the total signal power. Usually, the noise level is measured at a frequency within a few hundred kHz of the

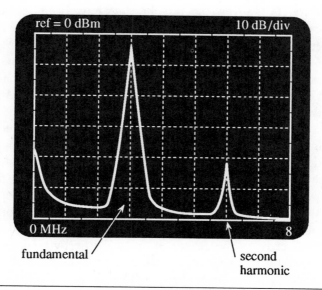

Figure 9.6 *Spectrum analyzer measurements of CNR are used in place of a rigorous determination of SNR.*

carrier signal. The noise spectrum is not necessarily white (constant with frequency). The media-noise component drops off at high frequency due to optical resolution, and the preamplifier electronics usually filter out high-frequency and/or low-frequency noise. In addition, the noise spectrum can be affected by the structure of the substrate or recording peculiarities in the medium. But if the noise is approximately white across the channel bandwidth, and if the overall frequency response of the channel is fairly flat (independent of frequency), the SNR is approximately equal to CNR times the ratio of the measurement bandwidth to the total signal bandwidth. As Figure 9.3 illustrates, the signal bandwidth does not extend much higher than the maximum carrier frequency. Recall that $f_{max} = 0.5/L_{min}$ for mark-length modulation. For mark-position modulation, achievable spatial frequency is much higher (nearly $1/L_{min}$). Suppose that a 1-Mbyte/s data channel is enoded using mark-length-encoded MFM. The ratio of measurement bandwidth to signal bandwidth is about 30 kHz/10 MHz = −25 dB. In this situation, a 45 dB CNR is roughly equivalent to 20 dB SNR, not quite enough for reliable operation. To guarantee 25 dB SNR, the CNR should exceed 50 dB.

The CNR is useful as a quick gauge of signal quality, but a more powerful analytic tool is needed to debug the channel or to characterize it in detail. Several such techniques have been developed for magnetic disk drives, and they are directly applicable to optical recording systems. Figure 9.7 illustrates a technique called *phase-margin analysis* (Geyer, 1984). A phase-margin analyzer is essentially a decoding circuit in which the width of the decoder window can be adjusted between 0 and 100% of the channel-bit cell (T). As the window width decreases, the number of errors should increase, because more and more of the timing distribution falls outside the window (see Figure 9.5). Figure 9.7 is a typical plot of error rate versus decoder window width; in order to accumulate enough statistics, each measurement usually combines many readout passes of a given track. At 0% window width, the number of errors equals the number of bits received. As the window opens up, the number of errors should drop off rapidly. Any plateau indicates that the timing distribution has been offset from the center of the window by peak-shift. When the error rate begins to drop, the slope is an indication of the noise level; a channel with low noise (small σ) has a very sharp error-rate threshold. But on an optical disk, the error rate typically does not drop to

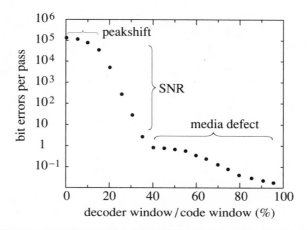

Figure 9.7 *This typical phase margin plot shows error rate versus decoder window width.*

zero. If the track passes through any media defects, the error rate flattens out at a value equal to the number of defects. Some defects can cause "soft errors," where the signal disturbances do not always create large timing errors. Soft errors are identified as secondary plateaus at the bottom of a phase margin plot. The phase margin of the channel is measured from the plot by extrapolating the curve down to a very low error rate (say, 10^{-10} below the peak), ignoring the harder defects. The residual phase margin is 100% minus the decoder window width at that extrapolated point. In Figure 9.7, the phase margin is nearly 60%—a very good value; usually 40% phase margin is considered acceptable.

Another technique for detailed characterization of a digital channel is *time-interval analysis*. A time interval analyzer measures the lengths of all pulses in the data signal and plots the overall timing distribution. As with other methods of channel characterization, a thresholding or peak-detection circuit must be supplied as part of the channel being tested.

Figure 9.8a shows a time-interval plot for a 5-Mbit/s MFM channel. The three pulse lengths permitted in MFM show up as discrete peaks centered on the ideal lengths. The base level of the distribution corresponds to errors caused by media defects. Figure 9.8b corre-

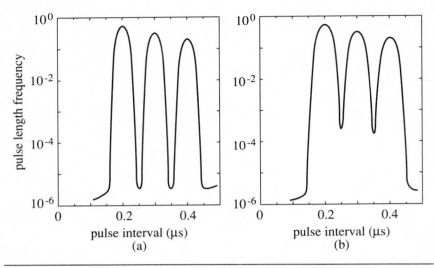

Figure 9.8 *Pulse length distributions for 5 Mbit/s MFM signals are graphed, where (a) shows adequate margin and (b) shows pulse crowding.*

sponds to a noisy data channel attempting to operate at the same rate. The excessive noise causes the peaks to run together. The bit error rate (bits in error divided by total bits transferred) for this channel would exceed 10^{-4}; any additional noise or peak shift would increase the error rate drastically.

More information about the data channel can be obtained by selecting particular thresholding polarities in the decoding circuit. Figure 9.9a compares the time interval plots for land lengths versus mark lengths. In this case, the mark lengths are shorter than the corresponding land lengths, possibly indicating insufficient recording power, low media sensitivity, or problems in the laser-driver circuit. In mark-length modulation, this type of imbalance results in substantial peak-shift.

Figure 9.9b shows a comparison of time intervals measured from the front of one mark to the front of the next, versus intervals measured from end to end. A difference between these distributions indicates that one end of the mark is more regular and predictable than the other, or that the front and back ends of the mark have different shapes. For example, thermal diffusion can cause the marks to form asymmetrically (Chapter 13, Section 3). If an asymmetry like this is

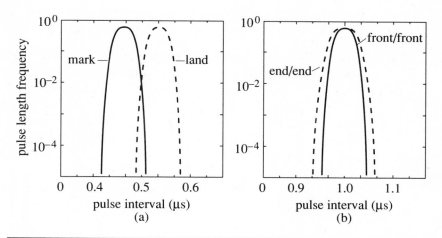

Figure 9.9 *Time interval distributions for a 1-MHz tone are graphed, where (a) shows mark intervals versus land intervals and (b) compares periods measured from the fronts and ends of the marks.*

understood, it can be functionally eliminated by precompensation, or shaping of the recording pulse (Sukeda, Ojima, Takahashi, and Maeda, 1987).

The peak-shift and noise identified by phase-margin analysis or time-interval analysis of the channel could have many causes. Sources of peak-shift include the following.

Clock Synchronization. The decoding clock should be precisely synchronized in frequency and phase with the recording clock (which is implicit in the recorded pattern).

Readout Resolution. An optical system cannot reproduce a pulse shorter than the transit time of the optical stylus (about 1 $\mu m/v$).

Cross-Talk. If the track pitch is too small, the readout system detects a residual signal from neighboring tracks. The cross-talk is also exaggerated if the marks are particularly wide. In erasable systems, another sort of cross-talk comes from incompletely erased marks. Since the cross-talk amplitude is strictly limited (not a broad Gaussian distribution), cross-talk acts more like peak-shift than like noise. Electronic cross-talk (from the servos or other components of the drive) is similar in its effect to optical cross-talk.

Recording Resolution. Usually the recorded mark is at least as large as the optical stylus. Somewhat smaller marks can be used in mark-position modulation, or with codes like bi-phase or 4/15. Extremely small marks can be made in some recording media by operating at power levels barely above threshold, but such marks are usually quite irregular in size or shape. Some recording media add their own peculiarities to the recording process; for instance, ablative media have a minimum mark size which could be comparable to or even larger than the stylus. Especially at low recording rates, thermal spreading can increase minimum mark size (Chapter 13, Section 3).

Signal Nonlinearity. Just as some kinds of media are limited as to the smallest recordable mark, other types are limited in the range of sizes possible. Bubble-forming media typically have a preferred mark length (at a given recording power and scan velocity). Marks of variable length cannot be written simply by varying the duration of the recording pulses proportionately. This situation can be improved by pre-emphasis, which adjusts the lengths of recording pulses in a nonlinear way, or post-emphasis, which filters the readout signal to reduce its nonlinear characteristics.

Inter-symbol Interference. Thermal diffusion can cause length errors that are correlated between neighboring marks on the same track. Pre- or post-heating can lengthen a mark written too close to its neighbor. This kind of peak-shift is sometimes called inter-symbol interference. The minimum mark and land length required to prevent inter-symbol interference is a systems issue involving both the drive optics and the media recording physics.

Noise can arise from the media, the recording process, or the readout channel. Some important sources of noise are:

Sensitivity Variation. For instance, the recording mechanism in Te films relies on very small surface "defects" to trigger hole opening. If such defects are not there, some intended marks simply do not form.

Irregular Mark Shape. Marks can develop irregular shapes because of instabilities in the recording process itself. Flow instabilities can effect the shape of pits in organic media. Magnetic instabilities can create irregular domains in some magneto-optic media.

Irregular Film Structure. Even if the recording process is smooth, irregularities such as texture or a polycrystalline structure can affect the mark shapes.

Debris. Ablative or pit-forming materials throw up small particles which can accumulate as a visible pattern on the recording surface. Debris is particularly a problem if readout and recording are air-incident; otherwise, the debris is partly hidden behind the recording layer.

Recording-Power Fluctuation. If the laser power fluctuates during recording, the size of the marks will be irregular. The subsequent effect on readout looks like media noise.

Readout-Power Fluctuation. The readout signal includes any noise emitted by the laser during readout. The noise-reduction techniques discussed in Chapter 6, Sections 3 and 4 are even more important during readout than during recording. Laser noise is a common-mode noise, so it can be reduced in magneto-optic readout by differential detection.

Shot Noise. This is a statistical fluctuation in the signal due to the low number of photo-electrons produced in the detector. At readout powers around 1 mW, shot noise is usually not important.

Electronic Noise. The preamplifiers and other electronic components can add considerable noise to the channel. Since low-noise circuitry is expensive, it is important to determine how much electronic noise is tolerable before the circuits are designed.

MAJOR CONCEPTS

- The minimum practical mark length is $L_{min} \sim 0.6\ \lambda/NA$. The maximum data density for NRZ encoding is $\rho = 1$ bit$/L_{min} \sim 1$ bit$/\mu$m (Eqs 9.1 and 9.2).

- Advanced modulation codes can increase the data density beyond $\rho = 1.5$ bit/L_{min} (Tables 9.2 and 9.4).

- Modulation codes are designed to facilitate decoding, limit the maximum run length, and reduce the low-frequency content of the raw signal.

- For error-free operation, the channel should have a signal-to-noise ratio exceeding 20 dB. The SNR is generally estimated in terms of the CNR, which is measurable using a spectrum analyzer.

- Phase-margin analysis and time-interval analysis directly demonstrate channel limitations and capabilities, including the effects of noise sources and signal distortion.

REFERENCES

Geyer, F., "Unified measure of optical disk performance: phase margin analysis," *Topical Meeting on Optical Data Storage, Technical Digest,* WC-C4 (1984). Characterizing an optical recording channel using phase margin analysis.

Ozaki, M., T. Furukawa, K. Tanaka, and T. Kubo, "An effective reproducing method on digital optical disk," *Video, Audio and Data Recording. 6th Int. Conf.,* 105 (1986). The tradeoffs between mark-length and mark-position modulation.

Shinn, C., "Charge constrained (1, 7) code for magneto-optic recording," *Topical Meeting on Optical Data Storage, Technical Digest Series 1987,* **10,** 115 (1987). Demonstration of a general technique for removing the DC content of RLL modulation codes.

Steenbergen, C., D. Lou, and H. Verboom, "Working document for development of a standard for a modulation code to be used with an optical media unit for digital information interchange using a 130 mm nominal diameter disk," ANSI submission, X3B11/85-135 (1985). Definition of differential decoding using the 4/15 modulation code.

Sukeda, H., M. Ojima, M. Takahashi, and T. Maeda, "High-density magneto-optic disk using highly controlled pit-edge recording," *Japanese J. Appl. Phys.,* **26** suppl. 26-4, 243 (1987). Precompensation used to correct mark asymmetries in M-O recording.

Tarzaiski, R., "Selection of 3ϕ (1, 7) code for improving packing density on optical disk recorders," *SPIE Proceedings,* **421,** 113 (1983). An

RLL modulation code optimized for moderate efficiency and large channel margin.

Treves, D., and D. Bloomberg, "Signal, noise, and codes in optical memories," *Optical Engineering,* **25,** 881 (1986). A discussion of noise sources in M-O readout and the wide-band SNR needed for error-free operation.

CHAPTER 10

Optical Disk Formats

10.1 Track Layout

Data on magnetic disks are arranged in concentric, closed tracks, each with the same number of sectors. All early magnetic disk drives used open-loop tracking schemes, requiring perfectly circular tracks with radial runouts much smaller than the track width. However, optical drives all use closed-loop tracking servos which can accommodate considerable track non-circularity. This has opened up an important format option: data tracks can be either discrete and concentric, or they can form a close, continuous spiral.

A close-pitched spiral (e.g., 1.6-μm change in radius per revolution) offers some advantages over concentric tracks. With a spiral, there is no need to fit an exact integral number of sectors onto each revolution; therefore, the sector size can be optimized independent of the disk size. Consider a $3\frac{1}{2}$" disk with concentric tracks and an inner recording radius of 25 mm. If the required sector length is 1024 user bytes with 40% additional overhead and if the maximum data density is 1 bit/μm, then each sector takes up at least 11.5 mm of track circumference. If the track were a continuous spiral, it could accommodate 13.7 sectors per cycle, but with concentric tracks, this must be rounded down to 13 sectors per track, or 5% less data density. This factor could be important for small optical disks. Disks of 12" or 14" diameter hold so many sectors per track that the roundoff error is always slight.

In some cases, a spiral layout can also speed up the transfer rate. In the past, data files were quite small, much smaller than the capacity of a track. However, newer applications are evolving toward a demand for very large files. Even considering future technical improvement, it is unlikely that the capacity of individual tracks will keep pace with the increasing file sizes. Recording and retrieval of very long files on concentric tracks require repeated jumps to neighboring tracks. These delays are avoided if the data are written in one long, continuous sequence of sectors on a spiral track. This technique could also be convenient for the high-speed data-streaming applications that have traditionally been served by magnetic tape.

With a concentric format, the transfer rate for long files is not quite as high as with a spiral format, because each revolution requires a track-jump operation. However, the delay can be minimized by skewing the sectors—adjusting the azimuthal location of sector zero on each track so that a jump from the end of one track lands just before the beginning of the next track.

Concentric tracks are convenient when frequent, multiple passes are necessary. For instance, repetitive passes are also important in some real systems such as conventional magneto-optic drives (where erasure and writing require two passes over each track) and write-once drives when the EDAC strategy depends on verification (see Chapter 11, Section 4). Disk operating systems have been designed around magnetic disk drives that all use a concentric format. Therefore, a concentric optical disk format might be needed if the system is intended to be transparently compatible with existing disk memories.

A related format choice for optical disks is whether to store the same amount of data on each track (or cycle of the spiral). Conventional disk drives operate in a constant angular velocity, or CAV, mode, keeping both the rpm and the data rate constant (see Figure 10.1a). In this case, each track holds exactly the same amount of data and the same number of sectors. Consider a disk with an outer recording radius r_{max}, a track pitch p, and a maximum in-track data density ρ. The raw capacity of the disk depends strongly on the inner recording radius, r_{min}, because each track can hold no more information than the inner track, $2\pi r_{min} \rho$. The possible number of tracks is $(r_{max} - r_{min})/p$; so the available capacity in a CAV format is

$$C = 2\pi \rho \ r_{max}^2 (x - x^2)/p, \qquad (10.1)$$

where $x = r_{min}/r_{max}$. Eq. (10.1) has a maximum at $x = \frac{1}{2}$, so the maximum capacity

$$C_{max} = \pi \rho \ r_{max}^2/(2p) \qquad (10.2)$$

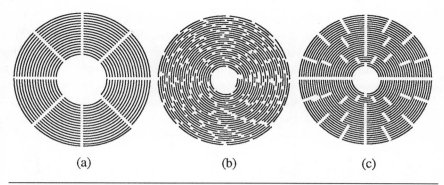

(a)   (b)   (c)

Figure 10.1 *Track layouts for an optical disk are shown here: (a) is CAV; (b) is CLV; (c) is QAV.*

is achieved when $r_{min} = r_{max}/2$. Notice that Eq. (10.1) has a very soft dependence on x near the maximum. For example, if x is increased to 0.7, the capacity is reduced by only 16% below C_{max}, but the stroke (maximum radial head motion) is reduced by 40%. This could be a desirable trade-off of capacity for access time.

The opposite approach to CAV is constant linear velocity, or CLV, recording (see Figure 10.1b). This is the approach used in CD and CDROM systems to maximize the data capacity. In CLV, the disk-rotation rate is adjusted continuously with radius to maintain a constant scanning velocity for the optical stylus. Data are written and read at a fixed rate and constant in-track density, regardless of location on the disk. The available capacity in a CLV format is

$$C = \pi \rho \ r_{max}^2 (1 - x^2)/\text{p}. \qquad (10.3)$$

In this case, the capacity is maximized when r_{min} is as small as practical, and the maximum capacity is almost twice as large as for the CAV format.

Another practical advantage of CLV is that the recording and read-out operations are independent of radius, because the scanning velocity, data rate, and data density are constant. If the disk has a homogeneous construction, its sensitivity is independent of radius, so the recording power can be held constant. The readout power can likewise be held constant. And since the spatial representation of data on the disk is everywhere identical, no changes in signal processing or precompensation are needed.

CLV offers a dramatic capacity increase but at a cost of significantly slower access time. The tracking actuator is slower because the stroke (recording-zone width) is much larger than for a CAV system with the same size disk. Adjustment of the motor speed adds an additional factor to the calculation of the total access time. Besides the delays for radial positioning and rotational latency (see Chapter 1, Section 4), the average time for radial access includes a delay while the motor speed adjusts for the new radial location. In the case of CD drives, this change in rpm averages as much as 0.5 sec. Acceleration and deceleration of larger, more massive disks can take much longer.

A more complicated disk format, which we may call QAV or quantized angular velocity, has performance characteristics intermediate between CAV and CLV formats. In QAV, the recording zone of the disk is divided into several zones and the rotation rate is held constant within each (see Figure 10.1c). The rpm within each zone is chosen, as in the CAV format, to obtain the maximum possible in-track data density at the inner edge of the zone. For a QAV disk with n zones, the maximum data capacity is

$$C = 2\pi \rho/p \sum_{j=0}^{n-1} r_j(r_{j+1} - r_j) \qquad (10.4)$$

where r_j is the inner radius of the jth zone, $r_0 = r_{\text{min}}$, and $r_n = r_{\text{max}}$. For a fixed choice of x and n, the total disk capacity is optimized at a value of

$$C = \pi \rho \; r_{\text{max}}^2/p \; \{2x(1 - x) + (1 - x)^2 (n - 1)/n\} \qquad (10.5)$$

when the zones are evenly spaced:

$$r_j = \{j(1 - x)/n + x\} \, r_{\text{max}}. \qquad (10.6)$$

The maximum possible capacity of

$$C_{\text{max}} = \pi \rho \, r_{\text{max}}^2/p \; \{n/(n + 1)\} \qquad (10.7)$$

is achieved when $x = 1/(n+1)$; but since the head usually will not fit so close to the disk's hub, the more general Eq. (10.5) should be used to estimate the available capacity. When the number of zones is large, QAV has the same performance characteristics (pro and con) as CLV. However, dividing the disk into a small number of zones can offer some useful advantages. The access time between positions within the same zone is quite short because there is no change of motor speed and a relatively small radial motion. If n is small enough so that each zone contains a substantial data capacity, then the QAV optical disk looks like a set of small-capacity, high-performance disks with rapid mount/demount times and a total capacity significantly higher than CAV can provide. QAV is attractive primarily in systems with large, high-capacity disks. Kodak has proposed a QAV format with five bands for its model 6800 14" write-once optical disk (Chapter 3, Section 4). The outer recording radius is 175 mm and the inner radius is 70 mm ($x = 0.40$). By comparing Eqs. (10.2) and (10.5), we calculate that QAV offers a 53% increase in capacity over CAV in this case.

The system performance is not the same from zone to zone in a QAV system. Besides differences in capacity, there are major differences in access time. In the Kodak Optical Disk System 6800, for instance, the rotation period is 75 ms on the outer band but only 37.5 ms on the inner band. The hierarchy of access times is further complicated by differences in seek time. The fine-tracking actuator allows access to neighboring tracks (in a window of 27 contiguous tracks) with a seek time of only 3 ms; within a zone, the average access time (including latency) is about 125 ms; but from band to band, the access time can exceed 400 ms, because of changes in the rpm. However, the access time in this type of system is unimportant when the drive is used in a juke-box application. The zones can each be considered as separate, independent volumes, and the average access time within the library is practically unaffected by the zone-to-zone access speed; a much slower demount/mount operation is usually required whenever a new volume is requested.

All the disk formats described so far implicitly assume that the data rate is constant. However, it may become practical to build a channel with a variable data rate. For this kind of system, the disk could be divided into zones with different data rates to provide a capacity enhancement comparable to that obtained by QAV, but it would retain all the access-time advantages of CAV. Ishihara, Yoshimaru, and Chikamori, (1987) have described such a format, which they call *modified constant angular velocity,* or MCAV. The most efficient use of this concept requires spiral, not concentric, tracks because there is not generally an integral number of sectors on each track. Optimization of the recording and readout channel for a variable data rate drive will be much more difficult than for either CAV or CLV. For CLV, the system performs the same at all radii; for CAV, optimization is required only at r_{min} because the data density is much lower toward the outside; but if the data rate is optimized at each radius, the system must operate at high-data-density for a wide range of scan velocities. Nevertheless, the MCAV format will be an attractive option in the future. Maxtor had planned to use this technique (under the name *zoned CAV*) in a high-performance $3\frac{1}{2}$" system.

The rotation direction has no effect on system performance. By (arbitrary) historical precedent, the disk rotation should be counter-clockwise as viewed from the optical head. In the future, the rotation direction will play a role in limiting the applicability of two-sided optical disks. At present, there are no two-headed drives capable of reading and writing to both sides of a disk at once, so two-sided disks are used as "flippies," meaning that the disk must be ejected from the drive and turned over to access the opposite side. But when a two-headed drive is developed, it will have trouble playing the current two-sided disks. In such a drive, the two disk sides rotate oppositely (as viewed by their respective heads); therefore, the two sides should have mirror-image format and data patterns.

10.2   Tracking Requirements

Continuous/Composite Format

In Chapter 7, Section 2, we noted that misalignment can cause trouble for push-pull tracking sensors. Disk tilt, lens tilt, thermal drift, and so on can cause the reflected beam to wander on the tracking detector, creating a false tracking-error signal which would appear even in the absence of tracking grooves. Figure 10.2 shows that the lateral tracking motion associated with two-axis lens actuators also creates a false tracking-error signal. These alignment offsets can be partially compensated electronically by noting the level of the push-pull signal in the absence of any groove or marks and using this level as an offset in the tracking servo circuit. Special mirror areas or servo offset patterns can be mastered into the substrate for this purpose. The tilt of the disk and the position of the objective lens can fluctuate rapidly due to axial and radial runout, so the servo signal must be readjusted frequently; one servo offset area per sector is probably adequate.

A false tracking offset sometimes is apparent only when a groove is present. The push-pull sensor operates by interfering the reflected beam with itself (or rather, with its diffracted orders). Any asymmet-

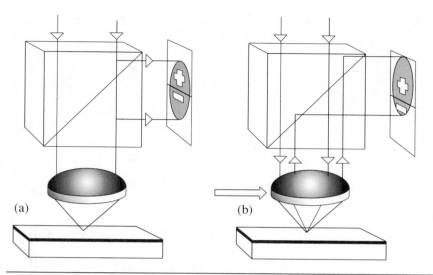

Figure 10.2 *Tracking actuators can cause imbalance at a push-pull error sensor.*

rical phase aberrations in the beam can lead to an irregular interference pattern and a false error signal where tracks are present; but in a mirror area (no diffraction) the irregular pattern would disappear. Such aberrations can result from disk tilt or intrinsic defects in the optical head. A tracking groove that is asymmetrical from side to side (like a blazed grating) also creates a false error signal that appears only in the presence of grooves. If these error sources are significant, they cannot be compensated using mirror areas. An independent means of track calibration is required.

A pair of off-center "wobble" marks can be used to generate an independent and absolute tracking signal, as discussed in Chapter 7, Section 2 (Figure 7.9b). The servo offset area can contain either a mirror area or offset marks or both (see Figure 10.3). In any case, the offset areas need not be very large; typically the length is equivalent to 1 byte ($\sim 10 \ \mu$m). But in order to use small features to generate accurate offsets, the drive must know in advance when they will appear. Therefore, the servo offset areas must be positioned following accurate synchronization features such as sector marks or address marks (described in Chapter 10, Section 3). A push-pull tracking groove interrupted by a servo offset area and a header before each sector is referred to as a continuous/composite format.

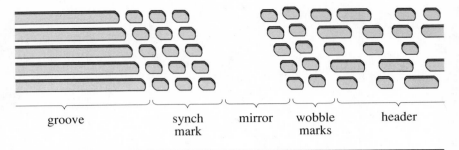

groove   synch   mirror   wobble   header
               mark   marks

Figure 10.3 *Servo offset fields for a continuous/composite format can contain either a mirror area or offset marks or both.*

Push-pull tracking reduces the data-channel performance if the surface quality of grooves is poor. On a groove pattern mastered using the photoresist process as described in Chapter 12, Section 4, the land surface replicates the smooth surface of the original photoresist coating, but the edges of the grooves correspond to incomplete exposure and development of the resist. Therefore, the edge profile is relatively rough. Roughness is particularly apparent when very narrow grooves are mastered at low laser power, as shown in Figure 10.4a. Grooves in such masters also tend to be shallow, with residual photoresist irregularly distributed within them. The figure also suggests that roughness is particularly visible when the groove is narrower than the diameter of the optical stylus; rough groove edges that pass near the center of the focused beam diffract and disturb the readout beam much more strongly than do edges that barely skirt the beam.

When the readout signal is low (e.g., from M-O media), the signal quality from an optical disk is often limited by noise caused by groove roughness. To minimize this noise, the groove should be wide, as shallow as possible, and completely developed, as illustrated in Figure 10.4b (Ohta, Murakami, Inui, Takahashi, Deguchi, and Katoh, 1987). Wide grooves (with a width greater than 0.8 μm) produce several dB less noise than narrower grooves do. The mastering process for wide grooves usually requires high power (on the mastering machine) and results in complete development within the grooves. The resulting grooves have a very flat floor (replicating the polished glass surface of the master disk), with relatively little photoresist residue. For most practical purposes, we can consider such grooves to have a square profile; the edges slope somewhat, but the

(a)

(b)

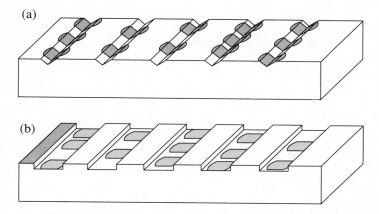

Figure 10.4 (a) Roughness is apparent when narrow grooves are mastered at low laser power. (b) Minimal noise is observed if the groove is wide, shallow, and fully developed.

groove has such a low aspect ratio (depth/width ~ 5%) that the edges cover a neglible fraction of the groove's width.

Servo offset areas, synchronization fields, and other sorts of information, which we will discuss in the next section, must be preformatted along with the grooves. If the disks are intended for on-groove recording, the format information is relatively easy to master: the power of the mastering laser is modulated to expose format patterns; the laser is held steady for featureless grooves; and format information is stored in the form of groove interruptions. However, there is considerable interest in recording on the intermediate land areas instead of on the grooves. The optics of push-pull tracking work as usual in this case, except that the polarity of the tracking s-curve is reversed. In essence, the land areas look like grooves with a reversed phase shift. In Chapter 7, Section 2, we determined that the optimum groove depth for push-pull tracking is about $\lambda/(8n)$; but recall from Chapter 5, Section 4, that the optimum depth for detecting embossed pits (i.e., reading preformatted information) is about $\lambda/(4n)$. These optimal conditions cannot be achieved simultaneously in a master for on-groove recording with wide grooves, but they can be achieved for on-land recording, as shown in Figure 10.5. The resist layer is chosen so that the fully exposed and developed preformat marks are optimized for readout. But the tracking grooves are underexposed, so they do not develop all the way through the resist layer. The narrow, shallow tracking grooves will be rough; but if the data are recorded on the wide, smooth lands, the groove roughness is not very apparent in the readout signal. The recording surface between grooves can be even smoother (less noisy) than within wide grooves, because there is no residual resist there. A practical demand of the on-land format is also apparent in Figure 10.5; a two-beam mastering system is required. Separate beams with a fixed relative spacing on the disk allow for acurate registration of the preformat marks relative to the grooves, and for independent optimization of the groove and mark widths.

Sampled-Servo Format

The principal alternative to push-pull tracking, as described in Chapter 7, Section 2, is sampled tracking. This scheme relies entirely on servo offset areas with preformatted wobble marks like those used in the continuous/composite format (Figure 10.3), except that very many offset areas are required. The necessary servo bandwidth, described in Chapter 7, Section 3, requires about 1000 measurements of the tracking error per track. Steenbergen (1986) describes a *sampled-servo* format proposal for the 130-mm write-once optical disk. This format divides the entire track into groups of eighteen bytes, two bytes dedicated as servo offset areas and sixteen bytes filled with other format information or left blank for user data.

Figure 10.6 illustrates the data area of a sampled-servo disk with data written on three tracks. The servo offset area includes two parts: a pair of marks offset to either side of the centerline of the track, which generate the tracking-error signal, preceded by an in-track synchronization pattern, which ensures that the servo's sample-and-hold circuit finds the correct offset signals. The preformatted synchronization patterns are also important in ensuring the fidelity

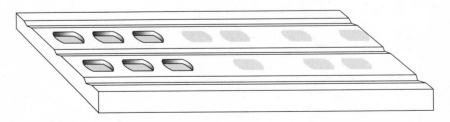

Figure 10.5 *Optimal conditions can be achieved for on-land recording on a two-beam mastered disk.*

data fields

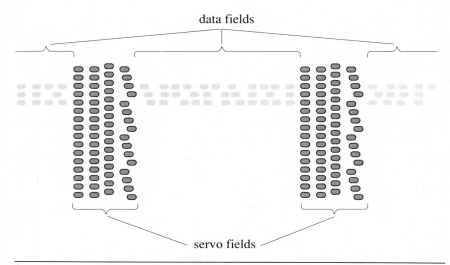

servo fields

Figure 10.6 *This data area of a sampled-servo disk has data written on three tracks.*

of data in the sampled-servo format. In a continuous/composite format, user data and other information written by the drive are recorded as a single, relatively long block. This information need not be synchronized closely to the rest of the sector and track format; resynch features and a gap separate written information from preformatted information. But in the sampled-servo format, resynchronization before each block of user data would require wasteful gaps and resynchs every few bytes. Instead, all data in the sampled-servo format must be recorded synchronously with the format pattern. This is possible because the timing features in the servo offset areas represent a constant, accurate system clock. However, a clock that is updated once for each block is not as accurate as a clock that is updated every few bits via an RLL code.

The synchronization patterns give rise to the concept of sample servo marks as a global map by which the drive maintains accurate (better than 0.1 μm) locations, both cross-track and in-track, anywhere in the recording zone. The in-track timing information is available continuously, whether the head is holding steady on a track or seeking rapidly across the disk. The absolute radial location is somewhat more tenuous. As discussed in Chapter 7, Section 4, the servo marks are too sparse for reliable track counting during high-speed seeks. If the marks are spaced every 18 bytes and the data rate is 5 Mbit/s, the interval between offset observations is at least 29 μs. If the disk has 18,000 tracks (i.e., a 130-mm disk) and the drive has a 30 ms seek time (one third full stroke), the maximum cross-track velocity is about 2 (6000 tracks)/(30 ms), or 12 tracks per servo offset interval. The track ambiguity could be eliminated by adding track address information to each servo area, but this would increase each area by two bytes, doubling the extra overhead associated with the sampled-servo format. It is more practical to add just a few bits of radial information with some kind of "gray code," a repeating series of servo area patterns (see Mitsubishi, 1987). In Figure 10.7, the pattern repeats with every fourth track, allowing the track location to be checked and revised with every servo update, as long as the counting error is never greater than one track.

The servo areas in a sampled-servo format add considerably to the disk overhead. But the absolute synchronization they provide increases the potential packing density. Non-self-clocking modulation codes like NRZ and (especially) 4/15 are compatible with these formats.

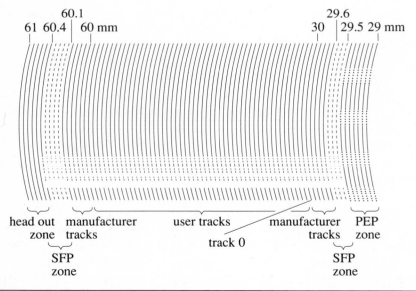

Figure 10.7 *The diagram shows the different types of tracks on a 130 mm optical disk.*

   Because the mark timing and radial offsets must be particularly accurate, servo offset areas must be preformatted. But this does not mean that they must be mastered and replicated into the substrate. Written marks can serve as well as molded pits. The disk is said to be *servo-written* when the format is recorded into the medium rather than molded in; this process is analogous to the method by which magnetic disks are formatted. A servowriter must have particularly good mechanical characteristics, especially for a sampled-servo format. Errors at this step contribute to runout errors for the rest of the disk's life. And the time required for servowriting raises the manufacturing cost of a disk. However, servowriting increases the flexibility for format adjustments and widens the choice of substrates (e.g., plain glass or aluminum could be used). Written servo and header patterns also simplify the signal-decoding circuitry, because data marks and format marks "look" the same. At least two companies, (ISI and Kodak) manufacture servowritten optical disks with sampled-servo formats.

10.3   Specific Format Features

The format of an optical disk covers more than the annulus of the recording zone where user data are recorded. Figure 10.7 is a diagram of the various bands of tracks provided on a 130-mm optical disk, according to the ANSI erasable, continuous/composite proposal (X3B11, 1987). The recording zone is filled with ordinary tracks, including sector headers and grooved data fields (which are blank until the user records data there). Usable sectored tracks extend beyond the recording zone at both the inside and the outside. The extra tracks are available for the media manufacturer to execute tests (necessarily destructive for write-once media) and to record useful information specific to the product. As implied in Figure 10.7, it is desirable to assign the manufacturer more space at the inside rather than at the outside of the recording zone, because an encroachment into the recording zone at the outside causes a greater reduction in the user capacity (recall Eq. 10.1). In a CAV system, accurate recording is most difficult at the inner tracks, where the data packing density is high; but the manufacturer can be assumed to have better-quality recording systems than the worst-case user has.

Each sectored track is assigned a number, which is noted in all its sector headers. In most optical disk formats, the tracks are numbered consecutively, starting with zero at the innermost user track. The manufacturer's tracks at the inside are assigned negative track numbers. This is the reverse of the convention for magnetic disk formats, where track zero is at the outermost radius. However, the track-numbering scheme is seldom a major issue, because it is a simple matter for the controller to convert between requested and physical track numbers.

Two types of control tracks, the *standard format part* (SFP) and the *phase encoded part* (PEP), are used by the manufacturer to present certain basic information to describe the optical disk. This important information can include media reflectance, the format type (e.g., sampled-servo vs. continuous/composite), whether the media is erasable, how much readout power is permissible, and so on. Neither standardization activities nor market demand are likely to result in a single, consistent optical disk format anytime soon, so control tracks will continue to be important. In the SFP zones, the media description is presented in the same format used for user data. The SFP is usually mastered and preformatted into the substrate as read-only information (pits and spaces). In the PEP zone, the same data are encoded and preformatted in the most obvious possible way so that virtually any disk drive can read it. In order for a drive to make the necessary adjustments to handle a particular disk (or reject it as incompatible), the drive first scans one of the SFP or PEP bands to read the media description.

Each track in the PEP zone has just three sectors with only 177 bits per sector. At the innermost radius of 29 mm, the bit length is longer than 300 μm. In a variant of bi-phase encoding, a high-frequency tone fills half of each bit cell; the bit value is 0 if the tone fills the first half of the bit cell and 1 if it fills the second half. The length and redundancy of the PEP data patterns make them quite immune to defects. Furthermore, all of the control tracks contain the same information. Since the PEP band is wider than the total radial runout, it is possible to read the PEP information whether or not the tracking servo is operating. The pattern is essentially unaffected as the optical stylus skips from track to track. This feature is especially important if a continuous/composite drive is presented with a sampled-servo disk or vice versa. In such cases, the SFP tracks are unreadable and the tracking servo will not function.

The *head out zone* shown in Figure 10.7 is comprised of featureless grooves. They allow for overshoot after a very rapid seek; they provide an area for testing or servo adjustment which is free of interruptions; and they serve as a coarse-tolerance lead-in for setup of the mastering machine before the format is recorded.

Figure 10.8 illustrates a data track and the various types of format features required in each sector. Each sector begins with a special feature, the *sector mark,* which warns the drive that a sector is about to begin. Sector marks are particularly important when the drive accesses a new track; the drive can probably pick up any subsequent sector without such a warning, using residual timing information from the preceding sector. Each sector mark is followed by the header, which contains synchronization fields and information to identify the track number and sector address uniquely. The servo offset fields required for a continuous/composite format are located near or within the headers. The header is followed by an initially blank groove, where the data field will be written. In a continuous/composite format, the data field must be separated from the surrounding preformatted regions by short gaps (also grooved). And if

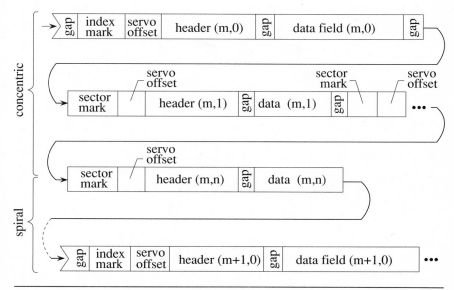

Figure 10.8 *This schematic track format shows the various types of format features required in each sector.*

any part of the track format is servo-written, it must also be separated by gaps from any replicated features. The gaps represent the tolerances required to accommodate slight timing variations between drives and the original formatting system. In a sampled-servo format, gaps are not required, because the servo offset areas maintain continuous drive synchronization.

After a drive seeks or jumps to a new track, it will have lost synchronization; the clock will not precisely match the data rate on the disk, and the digital decoding circuitry will be inoperative. The channel can be restarted using synchronization fields in a header, but first a header must be found. The sector marks are patterns that can be reliably detected without recourse to the regular data channel. The sector-mark pattern recommended in the ANSI format proposal is shown in Figure 10.9. It consists of a pattern of five "short" and "long" preformatted pits with special spacings. Actually, all the marks and spaces are quite long; the lengths correspond to three, five, and seven data bits. The shortest mark must be long enough to ensure detection, and the difference between the lengths must be at least two bits so that they can be reliably distinguished whatever the phase of the decoding clock. Identification of sector-marks is accomplished as shown by the flowchart of Figure 10.9. While the mark is

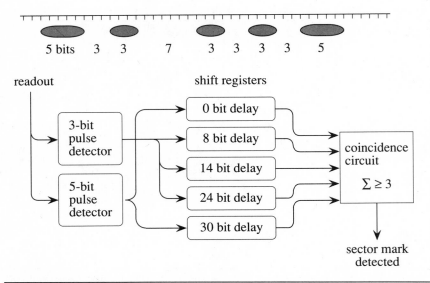

Figure 10.9 *Detection of a sector mark is accomplished as shown in this flowchart.*

being sought, a pair of detection circuits check for possible "short" and "long" pulses. Each detection event feeds pulses into five delay circuits which correspond to the spacings of the sector-mark pattern. As the optical stylus scans the sector mark, detection signals emerge from the delay circuits. At most, one signal is high at any given time, except immediately as the fifth mark is scanned. Then, a coincidence of five (delayed) signals identifies the end of the sector mark. Media defects can result in false coincidences or missed pulses. To provide some fault-tolerance, the coincidence threshold is lowered from five to three. The long mark length (five bits) and the long space (seven bits) are so long that they cannot occur legally in the header or data areas, assuming that the modulation code is at least as restrictive as (2, 7) code. Consequently, there is little chance of triggering a false sector-mark detection within a data or header field.

The sector-mark pattern in Figure 10.9 is relatively long, about 4 bytes. This length is required to allow for reliable detection and some fault-tolerance. Longer sector marks could enhance the reliability but at the cost of increased overhead. And very long sector marks could be susceptible to phase slippage, since the detection clock is not synchronous with the pattern.

In magnetic disk formats, the first sector is preceded by a different pattern called an "index mark." The index mark is similar in design to the sector mark and is detected with the same circuitry, except that different delays are used. This feature is not included in optical-disk format proposals for spiral tracks. Index marks are needed on concentric tracks to identify the beginning of each track. But identification of an arbitrary starting point for each track is unimportant when the tracks form a continuous spiral. Index marks on concentric tracks can be lined up with the same orientation, or they can be skewed by a fixed azimuthal offset from track to track. The purpose of a "sector skew" is to minimize the latency delays associated with single-track steps when large files are handled.

A sector header has four primary purposes:

1. it locates the subsequent data field;

2. it identifies the physical address (sequential track and sector numbers);

3. it establishes (predicts) the starting time for the data field for recording (readout); and

4. it can include features that generate corrective servo offsets.

The fourth header function is performed by the servo offset fields discussed in Section 10.2. Figure 10.10a is an illustrative header format, including the various features that perform these functions. This header format corresponds in most details to the X3B11 proposal for 130-mm erasable disks.

The first header function (locating the sector) is performed by the sector mark. But the sector mark does not prepare the drive to decode any digital information in the header. First, the clock must be accurately reset; this is done using a *variable frequency oscillator,* or VFO, field, which consists of a periodic sequence of marks at the highest frequency allowed by the demodulation code. If mark-length encoded (2, 7) is the modulation code used in the header, the VFO pattern is the *3T pattern* (which has a period of six channel bits or three data bits). Next, the byte synchronization must be established in order to predict which channel bit begins the next (preformatted) byte of data. Another peculiar pattern, called the address mark, is used for this purpose. The address mark is generally a pattern that is illegal under the rules of the modulation code but that can nevertheless be detected by the decoder. The ANSI format proposal defines a 1-byte address mark with the following channel-bit pattern: 0100100000000100. Note the nine channel-bit delay between the second and third transitions; this makes this pattern illegal under

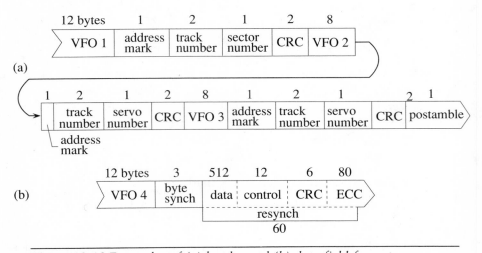

Figure 10.10 *Examples of (a) header and (b) data-field formats are shown here.*

(2,7) code rules, but it provides an unambiguous marker for the beginning of the data bytes that follow.

Once byte-synch is established, the preformatted sector address is read. This consists of a track number followed by a sector number. Two bytes are sufficient for the track number on most disks; two bytes can count up to $256 \cdot 256 = 65,536$ tracks per disk. At a track pitch of 1.6 μm, a 14" disk with a recording zone 105 mm wide would have over 66,000 tracks, so three bytes would be required for the track number. One byte is always enough information to store the sector number.

Finally, the sector identification information is followed by a cyclic redundancy check (CRC). This short field is an easily implemented error-detection code that gives a reliable indication of whether the address information is contaminated by errors. In Chapter 11, Section 2, we will discuss powerful codes that can correct as well as detect digital errors, but no attempt is made to provide error correction for short header fields; the required overhead would be excessive and there might not be enough time for true error correction. Nevertheless, it is necessary to make the address information fault-tolerant. A 130-mm CAV disk can have as many as 600,000 sectors (31 sectors, 19,000 tracks). For a raw error rate of only 1 byte in 10^5 and a header size of 6 bytes (ignoring the VFO field), we would expect to lose about 36 sectors from each disk to media defects located in the headers. The usual solution to this problem is to repeat the header information. Figure 10.10a shows triple redundancy.

The VFO field preceding the first address area is longer than the VFO fields for the second and subsequent address areas. This is because part of the first VFO is used to set up the automatic gain control (AGC) in the readout channel for preformatted information. In addition, the RLL patterns in the first address area provide some synchronization information, even if defects are present. Other than the VFO length, the sequences in a redundant header are identical.

The user data fields contain some features similar to those found in the headers. A data field cannot be recorded exactly synchronous with the preceding header (in either frequency or phase), so another VFO field and byte-synchronization pattern are required. The data area also includes CRC check-bytes.

Compared to the header, much more fault tolerance is required in every feature of a data field. In terms of overhead, it would be far too costly to improve reliability by duplicating the data fields. The data fields are so large that as many as 1% of them will contain errors at a byte error rate as low as 10^{-5}. Even if the data were replicated three times, we would still expect a net failure (all three duplicates in error) about once per disk. Therefore, in addition to CRC error detection, the data field also includes overhead from a powerful error-correction code (ECC). The amount of ECC overhead is usually in the range of 10% to 25%. The overhead of 16% in this example results from use of a (122,106) Reed-Solomon code interleaved to depth 5. (A description of Reed-Solomon codes is given in Chapter 11, Section 2; interleaving is described in Chapter 11, Section 3.)

The ANSI format proposal includes an optional provision for "resynch" fields, special one-byte patterns placed after every ten data bytes. The resynch patterns are similar to the address marks (0010000000100100 in the ANSI proposal) and are detected similarly. The resynch field is not a legal pattern under the modulation code rules. If the disk contains very large defects, or if the drive performance is marginal, it is possible for the digital channel to lose synchronization when a defect is encountered. The defect may be short enough for the ECC to correct the corresponding errors; but if the channel loses synchronization, then all the subsequent data will be decoded incorrectly. The purpose of resynch bytes is to limit such error propagation. At an interleave depth of 5, a 10-byte error burst (terminated by the next resynch) requires only 2 bytes of error correction from each ECC block. Resynch bytes are similar in purpose to the servo areas used in sampled-servo formats. They serve to unambiguously map the entire data field at the channel-bit level. Like servo areas, resynch bytes exact a significant penalty in overhead (an additional 10%). Therefore, they should be used only if sufficient media quality cannot be assured.

The signal from the data field is synchronized for readout in a manner similar to the signal from the header, using a VFO field followed by a byte-synch pattern. The byte synch serves the same function as an address mark, but it has sufficient redundancy to accommodate several errors. A channel-bit representation of the specific 3-byte pattern recommended in the ANSI proposal is shown in Figure 10.11a. This particular pattern can be generated in the drive as the (2,7) representation of 89 EA CB (see Table 9.3). The decoding circuit looks for the byte-synch pattern by passing the data through a buffer, dividing it into groups of four channel bits (two data bits),

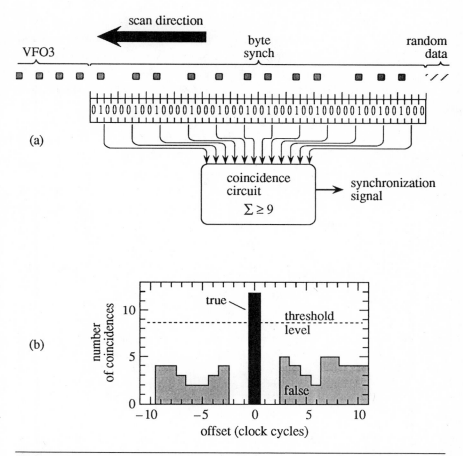

Figure 10.11 (a) Detecting a fault-tolerant byte-synch, and (b) setting a safe coincidence threshold are shown here.

and counting the number of groups that coincide with the expected pattern. As shown in Figure 10.11b, the autocorrelation of the byte-synch pattern is very sharply peaked. For a pattern misalignment up to ten channel bits, the expected number of coincidences is no more than five, compared to twelve when the pattern is perfectly aligned. Therefore, a coincidence threshold of nine will positively identify the timing for pattern synchronization, provided there are no more than three errors in the three-byte pattern. Like the other special patterns recommended in the ANSI format proposals, this byte-synch pattern is not absolutely optimal. Other patterns can be found which offer slightly more ruggedness and tolerance to errors.

The example data field shown in Figure 10.10b includes a few control bytes—nonuser data included within the data field and protected by the CRC and ECC. These bytes allow the controller to convey additional information about the sector, such as directory pointers or preferred relocation areas if the sector is of questionable quality. The controller pads the control bytes with zeros if such information is not needed.

━━━━━ MAJOR CONCEPTS

- A CLV layout maximizes the data capacity of an optical disk compared to a CAV layout, but at the expense of slower access (Eqs. 10.2 and 10.3).

- A QAV layout has characteristics intermediate between CLV and CAV. In the future, MCAV products will use a variable-data-rate channel to combine the speed of CAV with the maximum capacity of CLV.

- Noise from tracking grooves is minimized by recording on relatively wide, shallow grooves or on wide lands between the grooves (Figure 10.4 and 10.5).

- The greatest difficulty for sampled servo formats is accurate track counting during rapid access. A gray code within the servo fields can aid in track counting.

- For media standardization, the manufacturer must master or prerecord several special patterns such as SFP and PEP tracks, which identify specific media characteristics.

- Sector headers on a high-density optical disk are more vulnerable to errors than the data. They must be protected by redundancy and fault-tolerant sector marks. The synchronization pattern leading into the data field must also be very fault-tolerant.

━━━━━ REFERENCES

IBM, "Fault-tolerant synch byte for run-length-limited codes," *IBM Technical Disclosure Bulletin*, **29**, 151 (1986). Some considerations for designing synchronization patterns consistent with the constraints of RLL modulation codes.

Ishihara, A., T. Yoshimaru, and A. Chikamori, "The new application of MCAV method to the optical disk memory," *Topical Meeting on Optical Data Storage, Technical Digest Series 1987,* **10,** 168 (1987). A disk format that optimizes the disk capacity by varying the data rate, not the rotation rate.

Mitsubishi Electric Corp., "Proposal for servobyte layout of 130 mm sampled servo disk," ANSI document # X3B11/87-082 (1987). A proposed gray code that adds track-counting information to the sampled-servo areas.

Ohta, K., Y. Murakami, T. Inui, A. Takahashi, T. Deguchi, and S. Katoh, "Relation between groove shape and signal quality in magneto-optical disks," *IEEE Translation Journal on Magnetics in Japan,* **TJMJ-2** no. 8, 710 (1987). Wide, shallow grooves minimize media noise from magneto-optical disks.

Steenbergen, C, "Description of the format in the ATG/OSI/PDO/Sony standards proposal," ANSI document # X3B11/86-164 (1986). The version of the 130-mm alternative format that uses sampled tracking, the 4/15 modulation code, and a product code ECC.

X3B11, "Proposed American national standard 130mm reversible optical disk cartridge part 4; recorded format, tracking and servo technique," ANSI document #X3B11/87-094R1 (1987). A format proposal for a 130-mm reversible optical disk using push-pull tracking and a long-distance Reed-Solomon ECC.

CHAPTER 11

Error-Management Strategies

Optical recording systems generally have good-quality channels. The signal-to-noise ratio does not depend strongly on the data density except very near the optical resolution limit. Systems are usually designed to operate slightly below the resolution limit, where the SNR is still quite high. Therefore, soft errors due to electronic noise are inconsequential. Instead, the error rate is dominated by media defects. The surface area associated with each bit on an optical disk is an order of magnitude smaller than on the highest-density magnetic disk. Submicron defects that might not affect the signal from a magnetic disk can cause hard errors on an optical disk. After years of experience with various types of substrates, we have come to understand that the number of small defects cannot economically be reduced below about $1/mm^2$. Instead, an optical recording system must employ an error-management strategy to eliminate the *effects* of defect-induced errors. As the areal data densities of magnetic recording systems increase, these systems are also encountering increased problems with defect-induced errors. And the same error-management strategies developed for optical recording systems are proving effective there. The powerful interleaved error-correction code (ECC) employed in R-DAT systems is a good example.

In this chapter we will examine the typical characteristics of defect-induced error bursts, techniques for smoothing the effective error distribution, and error-correction codes that remove errors from the digital channel. Some special techniques for certifying media quality and verifying the fidelity of the recording channel are also presented.

11.1   Error Rates

The bit-error rate (BER) is the most common statistic used to describe the probability of errors from an optical disk. The BER is loosely defined as the number of bits recovered in error divided by the total number of bits checked. Even with the most careful handling, it is difficult to consistently manufacture optical disks in which the defect-induced error rate is less than 10^{-6}. Optical recording systems are typically designed to handle a BER in the range 10^{-5} to 10^{-4}. (The upper limit applies particularly to low-end applications such as CD and CDROM.)

In a well-designed system, almost all errors are defect-induced. Yet the BER is not purely a media characteristic: It must be specified for and measured on a particular recording system. Digital errors can be identified only after data are encoded, recorded, recovered, and decoded using a specific modulation code and channel hardware. The error rate will be affected by the channel margin, which is in turn affected by all aspects of the system. And many of the errors will be soft (occasional), even though they are associated with identifiable media defects. Some defects create such a marginal signal disturbance that the data are *almost always* decoded correctly. Slightly smaller defects might induce errors *hardly ever.* In sector headers or other format areas, the channel is essentially different than in the data areas (different modulation code, circuitry, data density, etc.), so BER measurements should be restricted to bits from the data area, except when the specific intent is to examine the header's reliability.

As a measure of media quality, the BER has a general deficiency: It measures the number of errors but not their distribution. Information about the distribution of errors is essential for designing an error-management strategy. Many of the errors from an optical disk occur in bursts. Figure 11.1 is a typical burst-length histogram; the ordinate is the number of bursts of a given length per bit of total data. This distribution is an average of burst-length histograms for a variety of injection-molded optical disks from Hitachi (1985). In this example, the BER is $5 \cdot 10^{-5}$, the average burst length is about 3 bits, and only 20% of the errors occur as isolated, single-bit events. Frequently, the burst-length histogram is plotted in terms of the corresponding distribution function, $N(x)$, which is the number of error bursts $\geq x$ bits in length.

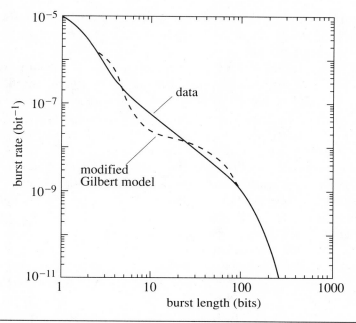

Figure 11.1 *This histogram describes a typical bit burst-length distribution.*

The powerful error-correction codes described in Section 11.2 treat information as 1-byte characters. Any pattern of errors within a byte is as easy/difficult to handle as any other. Therefore, it is usually more useful to know the byte-error rate (ByteER), defined as the fraction of bytes decoded with some error (one to eight wrong bits). Burst-length statistics collected with 1-bit precision can easily be converted to byte-error statistics, using the assumption that the byte boundaries are oriented randomly with respect to the error bursts. The ByteER for the distribution in Figure 11.1 is $1.4 \cdot 10^{-4}$. If the bit errors were distributed independently (no bursts), the ByteER would be 8·BER. But for typical error distributions, long bursts are about as important as one or two bit bursts, and ByteER $\cong$ 3·BER.

Some "correct" bits might occur within any long error burst, because of the vagaries of the channel code or because some of the errors are soft. So the error bursts counted in a burst-length histogram are usually identified using a *guard space* factor. An error burst always begins with an error, but ends only when a string of correct bits equal to the guard space is encountered. An 8-bit guard space is long enough to cover any soft errors yet short enough not to affect the byte-error statistics.

The BER average is often used improperly as a global descriptor of media quality. If the defect density is not uniform, the BER can seriously underestimate the worst-case error rate. In designing the system, it is very important to know how much the error rate fluctuates, since the error-correction code and overall error-management strategy must accommodate the worst-case error rate. One method of gaining this information is to measure the BER on many small but statistically significant samples, i.e., a few Mbytes each. For instance, BER sampling may indicate that the error rate depends on the recording radius. This could be due to changes in the data density or other channel characteristics, or the distribution of media defects could be radially dependent.

Another method for detecting clumpiness in the error rate is the *gap-length distribution,* the length distribution of the error-free passages between consecutive error bursts. The error distribution in Figure 11.1 has a burst density of $b = 2 \cdot 10^{-5}$ (per bit). Figure 11.2 is

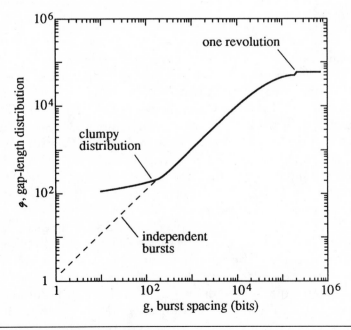

Figure 11.2 *This histogram describes burst spacings.*

a possible gap-length distribution for a $5\frac{1}{4}''$ optical disk with this
error rate and a (raw) capacity of $N = 3 \cdot 10^9$ bits. If the error bursts
were independently distributed, the number of gaps $\geq g$ bits would
be

$$G(g) = N b (1 - e^{-gb}). \qquad (11.1)$$

This Poisson distribution is plotted as a dotted line in Figure 11.2.
Note a discontinuity in the actual distribution at $2 \cdot 10^5$ bits, corresponding to one revolution. Sometimes a defect that crosses more
than one track can begin and terminate the same error-free gap.

For small g ($<< 1/b$), the gap-length distribution should drop
linearly with g, $G \cong N b^2 g$. Any significant excess indicates clumpiness in the error rate. Figure 11.2, shows a substantial deviation for
$g < 200$ bits, suggesting that there might be some sub-millimetre
regions with higher than average defect concentrations. An excess
number of short gaps can also be caused by servo or synchronization
problems in the drive. A sizable defect or error burst can create a
transient focus or tracking error, or upset the decoding clock, reducing the channel margin temporarily in the wake of any media-induced error and increasing the local rate of soft errors.

Error maps are another source of information about the error distribution. Maps with coarse resolution will highlight areas where the
defect density is clumpy. High-resolution maps are useful to guide
microscopic identification of specific defects. Such maps can sometimes distinguish between media and drive problems. For example,
synchronization or servo problems create streaks of errors that affect
only a few tracks.

In order to model the function of an ECC or predict the effectiveness of an error-management strategy, we sometimes need an analyti-
cal model for the error distribution. Since burst-length histograms
(Figure 11.1) usually seem roughly linear over some range on a log-
log plot, it is tempting to fit them to a power-law distribution, like
$N(x) \propto x^{-\alpha}$. The simplest function which asymptotes to a power-law
while converging at $x = 0$ is

$$N(x) = k(1 + x/(L (m - 1)))^m. \qquad (11.2)$$

L is the average burst length in bits; k is the BER; and m is the best
fit to the asymptotic slope on the log-log plot. This heuristic model
for optical-disk errors has been used widely, especially in standardization discussions (Nugent, 1986). Unfortunately, the power-law

distribution supports no useful physical interpretation and it can be misleading in some cases.

The Gilbert model is more useful as an analytic approximation to the error distribution. The *Gilbert model* supposes that error bursts are independently distributed based on only two stationary parameters: ρ—the probability of beginning an error burst following any correctly decoded bit; and γ—the probability of ending an error burst following any incorrectly decoded bit. Figure 11.3a is a state diagram describing this statistical model. We will see that ρ is the density of error bursts (or media defects) and $1/\gamma$ is the typical length of an error burst (defect length).

The BER was previously defined as the probability of any decoded bit being in error. This is also equal to the probability of an error burst continuing plus the probability of a new burst just beginning:

$$\text{BER} = \text{BER}\,(1 - \gamma) + (1 - \text{BER})\,\rho, \qquad (11.3)$$

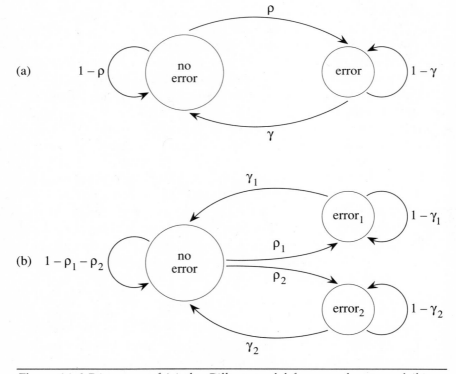

Figure 11.3 *Diagrams of (a) the Gilbert model for error bursts and (b) a modified Gilbert model are shown here.*

or

$$BER = \rho/(\rho + \gamma).$$

Define the distribution function N_j as the likelihood of bursts with length $\geq j$ bits. The total number of bursts (per bit) equals the probability of a given bit being decoded correctly times the probability of a burst beginning with the next bit,

$$N_1 = (1 - BER)\,\rho \qquad (11.4)$$
$$= \gamma\,\rho/(\rho + \gamma).$$

The probability N_{j+1} is less than N_j by a factor $(1 - \gamma)$, because whenever a burst of length j has developed, the likelihood is only $(1 - \gamma)$ that it will reach length $j + 1$ or greater:

$$N_{j+1} = N_j\,(1 - \gamma). \qquad (11.5)$$

Combining Eqs. (11.4) and (11.5), we can solve for the distribution function:

$$N_j = (1 - \gamma)^{j-1}\,\gamma\,\rho/(\rho + \gamma). \qquad (11.6)$$

The probability of a specific burst length is given by differencing N,

$$n_j = N_j - N_{j+1} \qquad (11.7)$$
$$= (1 - \gamma)^{j-1}\,\gamma^2\,\rho/(\rho + \gamma).$$

The average burst length for this distribution is

$$L_{avg} = \Sigma\,(j\,n_j)/\Sigma n_j \qquad (11.8)$$
$$= 1/\gamma.$$

Combining Eqs. (11.3) and (11.8) in the usual limit of small BER ($\rho << \gamma$), we confirm that the parameters of the Gilbert model should be physically interpreted as

$$\gamma = 1/L_{avg} \qquad (11.9a)$$

and

$$\rho = BER/L_{avg}. \qquad (11.9b)$$

That is, ρ is just the rate of error bursts.

The two-parameter Gilbert model does not fit the error-burst distributions measured from most optical recording media over a wide range of burst length. If a measured value for L_{avg} is used to fix γ (usually $L_{avg} \sim 3$ bits), the predicted distribution N_j falls off much too rapidly for large j. However, an extension of the Gilbert model produces a satisfactory fit. The modified Gilbert model, illustrated in Figure 11.3b, assumes that there are two independent classes of error bursts, each characterized as in the simple model by (γ_1, ρ_1) and (γ_2, ρ_2). These parameters can be interpreted using Eqs. (11.9), with the understanding that separate burst-length statistics (BER_1, BER_2, $L_{avg,1}$, $L_{avg,2}$, etc.) pertain to the two classes of bursts. The overall burst-length probability is just the sum

$$n_j = (1 - \gamma_1)^{j-1} \gamma_1^2 \, \rho_1/(\rho_1 + \gamma_1) + \qquad (11.10)$$
$$(1 - \gamma_2)^{j-1} \gamma_2^2 \, \rho_2/\rho_2 + \gamma_2).$$

The dotted line in Figure 11.1 shows a fit using the modified Gilbert model with $BER_1 = BER_2 = 2.5 \cdot 10^{-5}$, $L_{avg,1} = 1.6$ bits, and $L_{avg,2} = 32$ bits. The distribution looks like two populations divided at about $x = 10$ bits. Note that the Gilbert model gives a sharp cutoff for long error bursts. This is indeed the usual situation in the absence of handling damage to the media.

The modified Gilbert model is appropriate whenever several types of defects contribute to the error rate, and multiple error sources seem to be the rule for optical disks. Takeda, Saito, and Itao, (1988) found that the two-level Gilbert model gave an excellent fit to the error statistics from magneto-optic media. Upon microscopic examination, they were able to identify two distinct classes of defects: sub-micron contaminant particles, which were responsible for many small error bursts, and larger areas of substrate damage (from the substrate replication process), which caused long bursts.

11.2   Detecting and Correcting Errors

From the perspective of a computer system, the error distributions discussed in Section 11.1 can appear quite discouraging. The principal requirement for a computer-memory peripheral is that it have a *net error rate* below 10^{-12} or 10^{-13}. As data throughput and the memory requirements of computer applications grow, it is likely that the system-level requirements for channel reliability will become even more stringent than this. The purpose of the error-management strategy is to satisfy the system-level requirements using a data channel with a BER in the range of 10^{-5}. This job is accomplished by various methods of defect and error detection and (most importantly) by powerful error-correction codes (ECC). The success of optical recording systems in this regard has been remarkable.

The net error rate is *not* defined analogously to the BER. Rather, it is defined as the number of decoder failures per data bit. The nature of a failure could be an excessive number of errors, so that the ECC is insufficient to perform the required correction (uncorrectable errors). Or the error pattern could present a confusing aspect, interpreted by the ECC subsystem as a correct or correctable pattern. Undetected or miscorrected errors are sometimes called crypto-errors. In most applications, crypto-errors are much more serious than uncorrectable errors, because the user receives no clear warning that the data are tainted. Each decoder failure involves many bytes in error, and the entire ECC block (hundreds of bytes) must be considered questionable. Hence, the BER associated with the net data channel is many times larger than the net error rate.

Error-detection methods are based on the concept of parity. Figure 11.4 illustrates how one parity bit, appended to and recorded with a data sequence, can detect any 1-bit error. The circled addition symbols in the encoder represent the binary exclusive-or operations used to calculate the parity bit, p. At readout, the exclusive-or operations are repeated, and the recovered parity is compared with the newly calculated value. A difference indicates that an error has occurred (although the data might be error-free if the error affected the parity). A correct parity match does not guarantee that no error oc-

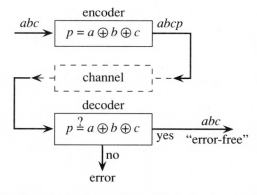

Figure 11.4 *Parity bits can be used for error detection.*

curred, only that if errors occurred there must have been an even number of them.

Generalized parity sequences can be defined which provide much more powerful error-detection capability than a 1-bit parity. Cyclic redundancy check (CRC) codes reliably detect multiple-error patterns without adding much overhead. CRC codes are usually configured to detect any error burst that is not longer than the parity sequence appended to the data. Alternatively, CRC codes can be configured to detect multiple error bursts (with a lesser number of total errors). Detection of more extensive error patterns cannot be positively guaranteed, but the probability of detection is usually very high. In earlier magnetic disk systems, CRC codes served as the only form of error management, but in optical recording systems, CRC codes play a secondary role. Short CRC sequences are used to verify the accuracy of header information, and longer CRC sequences are used to ensure the accuracy of the user data, preventing crypto-errors (see Chapter 10, Section 3).

Error detection is useful to verify the reliability of a good data channel, but that reliability can be achieved only with the aid of an error-correcting code. The simplest kind of ECC would be to record the data multiple times and employ majority logic to correct any discrepancies. However, this approach is extremely inefficient. In order to correct a 1-bit error, three duplicates of the data are required; $2t + 1$ duplicates are required to ensure correction of all t-bit error patterns. Any approach that requires such a high level of overhead is self-defeating, because the overhead greatly increases the number of errors associated with a given amount of data.

Much more efficient ECCs can be constructed using the same parity concepts used for error detection. The idea that parity bits can detect errors is intuitively convincing. That redundant parity information can also be used to identify and correct specific errors might not be so obvious. Table 11.1 is an example of a simple ECC that exemplifies most of the characteristics of useful, high-level codes. This table describes a (6, 3) code using 1-bit characters, so-called because the bits are treated independently and each code word is six bits long, including three data bits. Table 11.1 is also an example of a *systematic* ECC, because the parity information is appended without altering the data. The encoding rules are quite simple. If we write a code word as *abcdef,* the parity bits are calculated as

TABLE 11.1 An Error-correction Code of Distance 3

DATA AND PARITY	1 ERROR	$\geq$ 2 ERRORS
	100 000	000 111
	010 000	
	001 000	001 001
000 000	000 100	
	000 010	010 010
	000 001	
		011 100
	101 011	
	011 011	100 100
001 011	000 011	
	001 111	101 010
	001 001	
	001 010	100 001
010 101	.	
011 110	.	111 111
100 110	.	
101 101		
110 011		
111 000		

$$d = a \oplus b,$$
$$e = a \oplus c,$$
$$f = b \oplus c,$$

(11.11)

where the circled addition symbol again represents the exclusive-or operation. More powerful codes usually handle the data as m-bit characters; most commonly, $m = 8$ and the characters are bytes. More complicated arithmetic is used to calculate the m-bit parity characters.

After recording and playback, the code in Table 11.1 allows any 1-bit error to be detected and corrected. Here, as with any ECC, error correction is possible because of the "distance" between the code words. In this case, the distance is three because none of the legal code words can be transformed into another without changing at least three of the characters (bits). Any single-bit error leaves the (altered) code word "closer" to the original value than to any other legal code word. Error correction is just a matter of deciding which legal code word can be obtained by altering only one bit. In general, if the ECC has a distance of $2t + 1$, it is possible to correct error patterns involving up to t characters. And again, the error-correction technique is essentially a means of finding the closest legal code word.

The example is not the most efficient use of three parity bits for error correction. The Hamming (7, 4) code also has a distance of three and the ability to correct 1-bit errors. The overhead is only $3/4 = 75\%$, less than the $3/3 = 100\%$ overhead in the example. A (7, 4) code has $2^4 = 16$ legal code words and $16 \cdot 7 = 112$ correctable code words corresponding to 1-bit errors. This leaves no "unused," illegal code words. The Hamming (7, 4) code is as efficient (4 data bits) and effective (1-bit error correction) as is possible using 3 parity bits, but sometimes it is desirable not to use an ECC in its most efficient form. In a *shortened* ECC, the number of data characters is reduced without changing the rules for calculation of the parity characters. The example in Table 11.1 is a shortened version of the Hamming (7, 4) code. The benefit from this procedure is that some of the possible code words do not correspond to correct or correctable data patterns. In the example, eight word values correspond to at least two errors. If they turn up, they indicate to the system that an uncorrectable error has occurred. Shortened versions of high-level ECCs have many more illegal, uncorrectable code word values than correct or correctable values. If an uncorrectable error occurs, it is likely to generate one of these illegal code words, triggering an error warning rather than a crypto-error.

Some powerful error-correction codes were designed to detect and correct long error bursts. Such codes are used, for instance, in magnetic tape systems. Other codes were designed to handle multiple single-bit errors. Since optical disks usually have both large and small defects, it is fortunate that ECCs (and the corresponding circuitry) exist which are simultaneously optimized for both long and short error bursts; these are the Reed-Solomon (RS) codes. RS codes can be defined for any m-bit characters, but usually the characters are bytes ($m = 8$). An RS code is parameterized by (n, k), where k characters of data are contained in an n-character code word. Additional restrictions for these codes are $n < 2^m$ and an even number of parity characters, $n - k = 2t$. For $m = 8$, the code word can be no longer than 255 bytes. Because of the restricted length of the code word, one character is sufficient to address any other character in the code word. The 2*t* parity characters can be thought of as containing information equivalent to the address and correct value of up to *t* errors. And indeed an RS ECC provides enough redundant information to correct any error pattern affecting *t* characters or less. See Golomb (1986) for a discussion of Reed-Solomon codes compared to other types of ECCs.

A generic flowchart for RS encoding and decoding is shown in Figure 11.5. Data entering the encoder must be buffered and padded with trailing zeros, which hold the place for the parity bytes (or syndrome). The stream of *n* bytes is passed through a syndrome generator, which calculates the parity bytes using a pipeline architecture of shift registers, exclusive-or gates, and other simple digital logic. The

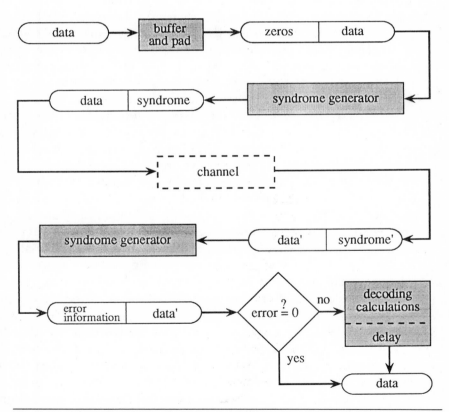

Figure 11.5 This flowchart shows the general procedure for Reed-Solomon encoding and decoding.

finished code word, data plus syndrome, emerges from the syndrome generator and passes through the data channel (modulation code, etc.) to be recorded on the disk.

Upon readout, the code word is digitally reconstructed and then passed back through the syndrome generator, both data and syndrome. The trailing sequence of $2t$ bytes now represents a unique pattern of up to t byte errors. The data is error-free if the error sequence is zero. But in general, it is not easy to convert the error sequence into a useful form (i.e., a list of 1-byte addresses and error patterns). And there are too many possible error patterns to use a look-up table. If there are errors, the RS decoding system invokes a microcomputer to find the error pattern. The error pattern is then "added" to the recovered data pattern to correct it.

The computational delay for error correction usually increases with the number of errors. For instance, an RS decoder might handle one or two byte errors in less than 1 ms, but 10 ms or more might be required to compute patterns of seven or eight byte errors (assuming, of course, that $t \geq 8$). Usually a data buffer is interposed between the disk and the decoder so that readout can continue while decoding of extensive error patterns proceeds.

If the recovered code word has errors in more than t bytes, accurate decoding is impossible. In this case, the RS syndrome generator usually produces an illegal pattern, indicating an uncorrectable error. For $m = 8$, there are 2^{16t} possible syndrome values, but the number of correctable data patterns is approximately equal to the number of t-byte error patterns, about $2^{8t} n^t / t!$. Illegal values far exceed the number of correctable values, especially if t is large or the code is shortened ($n << 255$). Therefore, in RS codes, the likelihood that an uncorrectable error pattern is a crypto-error is indeed small.

Two types of RS codes are sometimes distinguished. Long-distance RS codes have large t and n. For example, an 8-byte correcting (122, 106) code is used in the 512-byte sector format described in Chapter 10, Section 3. Long-distance codes have very good efficiency (k/n) and an ability to handle many errors per code word. Short RS codes have smaller t and n. Section 11.3 explains how two short codes can be combined to provide a high level of error correction, even though each code alone can correct only two errors. The primary advantage of systems using short RS codes is that decoding is rapid (because only a couple of errors are handled at a time).

11.3 Interleaving, Concatenation, and Product Codes

The most powerful available ECC can correct only 8 bytes per code word. We have seen that error bursts as long as 100 bits are encountered occasionally on some optical disks (Figure 11.1). Even in the absence of any other errors, a burst as short as 58 bits could be an uncorrectable error pattern within a $t = 8$ RS code word. However, if several code words are interleaved before recording, a very long burst is reduced to a manageable number of errors within each recovered code word.

A sector usually is structured around 512 or 1024 bytes of user data. Since the maximum size of an RS code word is 255 bytes (including the $2t$ syndrome bytes), at least three code words are required for a 512-byte sector, and at least five code words are required for a 1024-byte sector. In practice, even more code words are used (five and ten, respectively, for 512-byte and 1024-byte sectors) because the RS codes are substantially shortened. Each sector includes enough code words for very effective interleaving.

The data layout for a 512-byte sector using a long-distance ($t - 8$) code and depth-5 interleaving is illustrated in Figure 11.6. Recall from Chapter 10, Section 3, that control bytes and CRC bytes are usually appended to the data, a total of eighteen extra bytes in this example. The 530 bytes are divided among five code words, so $k = 106$, and $n = 106 + 2 \cdot 8 = 122$. As each of the code words is calculated, it is stored in a buffer. During recording, the system draws one byte at a time from each of the code words.

Any subsequent error burst of length b (bits) will affect no more than $\mathrm{INT}[(b + 46)/40]$ bytes in any code word. So the effect of interleaving is to reduce the number of byte errors in any one code word caused by a large defect. Table 11.2 shows how the burst-length distribution (measured in bytes) is changed by interleaving. These burst statistics correspond to the error distribution of Figure 11.1, with the assumption that all bursts ≥ 100 bits have been eliminated (by quality control) or otherwise avoided (by certification or fencing). The number of long bursts drops sharply as the depth of interleaving increases. The corresponding trade-off is that the number of shorter bursts increases somewhat as the long bursts are spread over many code words, but this is not a drawback for RS codes. For an interleaving depth of 5, 10, or more, no individual

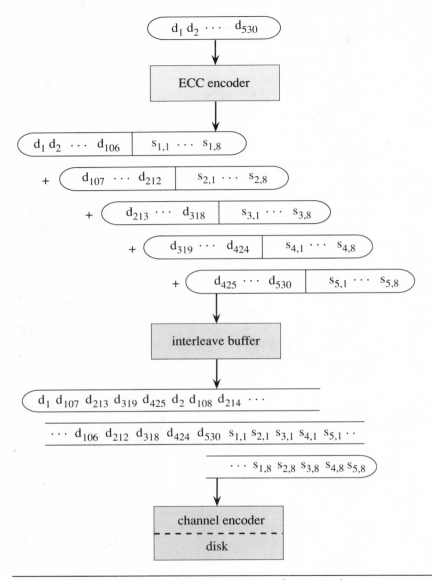

Figure 11.6 *This illustrates data organization for a 512-byte sector interleaved to depth 5.*

TABLE 11.2 Effect of Interleaving on the Burst-length Distribution

BURST LENGTH (BYTES)	INTERLEAVE DEPTH =	FREQUENCY (byte⁻¹)			
		1	3	5	10
1		$1.5 \cdot 10^{-5}$	$2 \cdot 10^{-5}$	$2 \cdot 10^{-5}$	$2 \cdot 10^{-5}$
2		$1.7 \cdot 10^{-6}$	$5 \cdot 10^{-7}$	$7 \cdot 10^{-7}$	$2 \cdot 10^{-7}$
3		$3 \cdot 10^{-7}$	$3 \cdot 10^{-7}$	$2 \cdot 10^{-7}$	0
4		$1.5 \cdot 10^{-7}$	$2 \cdot 10^{-7}$	0	
5		$7 \cdot 10^{-8}$	$3 \cdot 10^{-8}$		
6		$3 \cdot 10^{-8}$	0		
7		$3 \cdot 10^{-8}$			
8		$3 \cdot 10^{-8}$			
9		$3 \cdot 10^{-8}$			
10		$3 \cdot 10^{-8}$			
11		$3 \cdot 10^{-8}$			
12		$3 \cdot 10^{-8}$			
13		$2 \cdot 10^{-8}$			
14		$5 \cdot 10^{-9}$			
>14		0			

error burst places much of a demand on the ECC. Hence, several large defects can be accommodated in the same sector, even against a background of occasional small defects.

With sufficient interleaving, no defect causes more than one (byte) error per code word and all errors are effectively independent. Modeling of the ECC performance is particularly simple in this case. Consider a system using a well-interleaved, long-distance RS code. The net error rate is approximately equal to the probability of finding $t + 1$ independent errors in any code word, divided by the number of user bits per code word.

$$\text{net error rate} \cong \binom{n}{t + 1} \beta^{t+1} (1 - \beta)^{n-t-1}/(m\,k); \qquad (11.12)$$

where β is the ByteER and the parentheses represent the combinatorial function. For $n = 122$, $t = 8$, and $\beta = 10^{-4}$, the net error rate is $\sim 10^{-26}$. At $\beta = 10^{-3}$, the error rate is nearly 10^{-17} and the code cannot tolerate any local increases in β. But given the usual specification, BER $< 10^{-4}$ (therefore β much less than 10^{-3}), this ECC system would be very effective.

Concatenation is a technique whereby data are protected by multiple layers of ECC. For instance, the data could be encoded using an ECC designed for easy correction of single, long error bursts. The resulting code words would then be processed through a high-efficiency, low-performance ECC (e.g., an RS code with low t) before recording. The second, inner code layer would correct isolated single-byte errors, but any long burst or coincidence of multiple errors could result in the incorrect decoding of the entire subcode. The outer ECC layer would be desinged to correct such a burst.

The CRC error-detection bytes appended to the data bytes prior to ECC encoding (Figure 10.10) are another example of concatenation. One short parity sequence serves to verify that the ECC has recovered the data correctly, relieving concern about crypto-errors. With appropriate software, the CRC information can also be used to extend the power of the ECC.

Cross-interleaving is a more effective way to implement two layers of ECC. The cross-interleaved Reed-Solomon code (CIRC) from the CD format encodes the data first, using a (32, 28) RS code, which we will call C_1. Twenty-four of the C_1 code words are interleaved and then encoded using a (28, 24) RS code, C_2. The resulting matrix of data and syndrome bytes is illustrated in Figure 11.7. Bytes from the 32 × 28 matrix, or code block, are recorded and subsequently recovered in a diagonal order, as indicated by numbering in the figure. (Actually, two code blocks are generated together and interleaved during recording.)

Both C_1 and C_2 are capable of detecting and correcting two errors per row or column. Even if a row or column is initially uncorrectable, subsequent correction of alternate columns or rows may clean it up to a correctable state. The cross-hatched area in Figure 11.7 represents a huge 224-byte error burst (112 byte errors per code block) corresponding to a defect length of 1mm on the disk. Initially, only columns 9 through 13 are correctable, but by following the decoding sequence numbered on the edge of the matrix, the system can correct the entire error burst. Cross-interleaving and the diagonal recording sequence turn the weak $t = 2$ RS codes into a powerful ECC system.

The CIRC system has several drawbacks. One code block has 28 × 32 = 896 bytes with a data content of 28 × 24 = 672 user bytes.

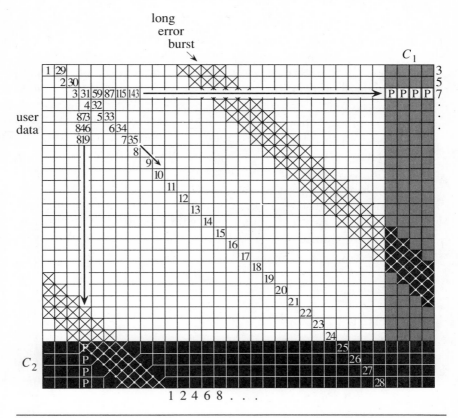

Figure 11.7 *This matrix shows the correspondence between ECC layers and data order in the CIRC scheme.*

The code was designed for the CD system, not computer applications, and the data content of a code block is not commensurate with any useful sector size. Furthermore, the CIRC overhead is $224/672 = 33\%$, compared with $16/106 = 15\%$ for a $(122, 106)$ long-distance RS code.

Two layers of cross-interleaved, or *product,* codes are used in the CDROM format. In the inner ECC layer, C_1 is a $(52,48)$ RS code and C_2 is a $(45, 43)$ RS code. The code block contains 2064 data bytes, enough for a 2-kbyte sector. The entire CDROM code block, along with some format information, is then concatenated within the standard CIRC system, where it fills four code blocks. The result is a very reliable error-correction system with very low efficiency. For

2048 actual data bytes, the system records $4 \cdot 896 = 3584$ bytes of information. Thus, the effective ECC overhead is $1536/2048 = 75\%$.

Experimental verification of working ECC systems is difficult because, by definition, the failures must be very infrequent. But a number of calculations and simulations have been performed to compare long-distance codes (interleaved as described above) with product codes for optical recording applications. Generally, the long-distance codes are superior in efficiency, reliability, and throughput, at least in nonstressful error environments (Nugent, 1986). Performance predictions for long-distance codes are more reliable than for product codes, because product codes can be pattern-sensitive. The major advantage of product codes is that they handle extensive error patterns more simply and quickly, because the errors are corrected one or two bytes at a time.

11.4 Certification and Verification

An error-detection-and-correction code (EDAC) is the necessary foundation for error management in any optical recording system. But the EDAC should be supported by other techniques that place guaranteed limits on the error distribution (certification) or check the data fidelity after recording (verification). Certification and verification techniques have been developed and widely utilized for magnetic recording systems. In addition to the conventional techniques, optical recording systems can make use of certification and verification methods unique to this technology.

Certification usually is used to qualify media as part of the manufacturing process. It generally has two purposes: to assure that the media-induced error rate (BER) falls below a specified maximum, and to assure that all error bursts and defects are smaller than some critical limits. Almost all error-causing defects are visible as scratches, pits, rough areas, pinholes, etc. This is particularly true of the defects that cause long error bursts. Although the burst length may be longer than the defect length, because of synchronization problems, an approximate correspondence between defect size and burst length can usually be obtained (experimentally). Hence, the surface of an optical disk can be examined optically for large defects and potential error bursts. Figure 11.8 illustrates a simple scanning technique in which an image of the disk surface is focused on a CCD array. Defects of almost any type scatter light out of the beam, reducing the signal at the corresponding element of the sensor. Defect size can be inferred from the number of sensor elements affected (radial extent of the defect), how long the signal is reduced as the disk rotates (azimuthal extent), and the amplitude of the signal change (for defects smaller than the optical resolution). The entire disk surface can be examined in one revolution. This kind of scanner can reliably detect defects smaller than 20 μm in diameter (Shojima and Yoshinaga, 1987). Since the critical defect size is usually in the range 50 to 100μm, the scanner is a very efficient means of finding unacceptably gross defects. Once a gross defect is detected, either the disk is marked to warn of an unusable section or (preferably) the disk is rejected (and studied for failure analysis).

In conventional disk certification (i.e., Winchester disks), data patterns are written to every sector on the disk. This trial data is reread (multiple times) to check for errors. Sectors with data errors or faulty headers are "fenced" so that they cannot be addressed as locations for user data. This kind of fencing can also be used to rid erasable optical disks of bad sectors. The only difference is that sectors with just a few errors may not be considered as bad in an optical disk. More errors are anticipated from optical recording media, and the ECC is well suited to handle a limited number of errors. The role of

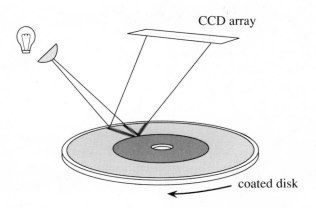

CCD array

coated disk

Figure 11.8 *Gross defects can be found by focusing an image of the disk surface on a camera or CCD array.*

certification for an optical disk is not to avoid all raw errors, but to guarantee a substantial margin for the ECC.

Figure 11.9 illustrates the format implications of fencing on an erasable disk. Each bad sector must be "relocated" to a good sector elsewhere on the disk. An initial list of the bad-sector addresses and the corresponding relocation addresses are written in a primary defect list, or *P-list,* at a predetermined location on the disk. Since there can be no guarantee that the P-list locale is free of bad sectors, the list should be duplicated at several separate locations. Each time the drive starts up, the controller or operating system reads the P-list into active memory. If part of the P-list is unreadable, the drive reads the next copy. Subsequently, anytime a user tries to write or read in one of the bad sectors, the system controller substitutes the relocated sector instead.

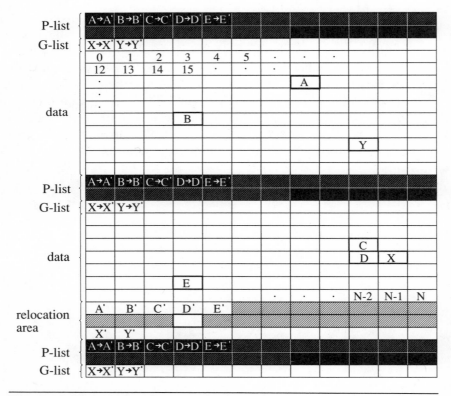

Figure 11.9 *An implementation of sector relocation used to fence defects is diagrammed here.*

During ordinary data readout or during special verification checks, the system can identify additional bad sectors (possibly caused by damage to the disk or growth of a defect). These can also be relocated to good sectors. An additional look-up table (the defect growth list, or *G-list*) is appended to the P-list to allow for this contingency. The number of entries in the P-list and G-list is limited by the amount of time required to sift through them (required every time any sector is accessed), the extra media capacity set aside for relocation, and the likelihood that an excessive number of errors implies that there is something dangerously wrong with the media (or system). P-list and G-list candidates are not necessarily unreadable; for purposes of fencing, a sector is bad if the number of errors *approaches* the ECC limit (say, five errors per subcode with a $t = 8$ RS code). See Glinka and Brown (1988) for a detailed certification proposal for erasable optical disks.

Conventional certification is not possible on write-once media, because a digital certification pattern would fill up the entire disk. The data areas could be read without writing (essentially, a high-resolution optical scan), but the correspondence between defects and errors is not as reliable for short error bursts as it is for long bursts. Even with erasable optical disks, a certification operation is very time-consuming. Consider a $5\frac{1}{4}''$ erasable optical disk with 20,000 tracks operating at 1800 rpm. Certification requires at least two passes per track, and therefore takes longer than 25 minutes per disk. This is not to say that certification is more difficult on optical disks than on magnetic disks. On the contrary, the track patterns formed onto most optical disk substrates makes the certification process particularly reliable, because the tracking location is independent of the certification equipment and environment. Ordinary drives can be used to certify optical disks. But although a slow certification process may be justifiable for Winchester disks (only one certification event per drive), the cost will become prohibitive for removable optical disks (many disks certified per drive).

The alternative to conventional certification is statistical certification. Given a powerful ECC, the goal of certification is to set limits on the error distribution, not to identify and eliminate all possible errors. An accurate statistical description of the error distribution can be obtained by examining, say, 100 error bursts at various locations on the disk. At BER $= 10^{-5}$ and $L_{avg} =$ bits, we could find this many error bursts by examining (writing and reading) only 4

Mbytes. This represents less than 1% of the capacity of most write-once optical disks. If the BER is lower than this, the sample might not yield so many error bursts, but the resulting statistical limits on the error distribution would be just as tight. So statistical certification should be a feasible method for qualifying any optical disk, provided that the typical BER is well within specification, the error distribution is spatially uniform, and very large defects are otherwise eliminated.

Conventional verification techniques are identical to those of conventional certification, except that they are performed subsequently by the user. Reformat commands usually check for errors and recreate the P-list (but only in erasable systems). And the user can always specify a verification option for every writing event. In this case, the drive executes a second pass after each writing command to check the recording for accuracy. The cost of conventional verification is added latency, at least one additional rotation of the disk for every write operation. Global verification can be performed using service software that checks all sectors for new errors, relocates marginal sectors, and updates the G-list accordingly. In addition, every readout event is an opportunity to check for error growth or marginal performance (although if error growth is a serious concern, readout events will not really be frequent enough).

Some unique verification techniques are possible in optical recording systems. Direct-read-after-write (DRAW) uses a secondary optical stylus to read the data almost immediately after they are written to check for errors (see Figure 11.10). Ordinarily, the readout stylus is focused about 10 μm downstream from the recording stylus, and the newly recorded data are read about 1μs after recording. For most types of media, this is long enough for the marks to form and stabilize completely, yet the delay is essentially instantaneous for purposes of comparing the input and output digital signals. DRAW provides the same reliability enhancement as conventional verification, but with no latency penalty.

A second optical stylus is not always necessary to sense recording errors as they occur. Read-while-write is a technique that offers some of the capabilities of DRAW with a single stylus. This concept is illustrated in Figure 11.11, which shows the detector signal observed during recording. As a recording pulse begins, the reflected light level increases dramatically. After a short delay, the reflected light level changes because the mark forms. (In the example, the mark reflec-

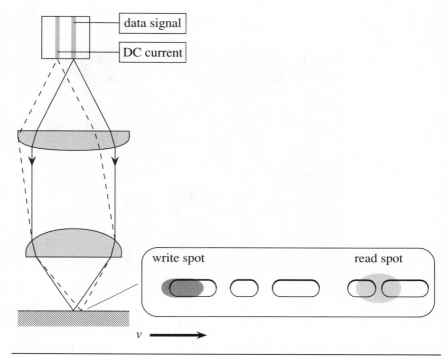

Figure 11.10 DRAW *can be implemented with a dual-source laser diode.*

tance is less than the land reflectance, so the mark formation reduces the detector current.) In the illustration, the second recording pulse does not show the two-level signal characteristic of mark formation; this indicates a drop-out, or missing mark. Large amplitude glitches (up or down) observed between recording pulses are indicative of media defects that could appear as false marks, or drop-ins, during subsequent readout.

Read-while-write is not an ideal verification technique. In order for us to verify the writing process accurately, the marks must have very high reflectance contrast; M-O systems, for instance, have signal levels that are much too small. It is much easier to verify the creation of a mark than to verify its length. Therefore, read-while-write is most effective with mark-position encoding. Finally, true verification uses the actual readout channel to find digital errors. Read-while-write uses (questionable) amplitude criteria to qualify the analog waveform. It is not an unambiguous way to sense all hard or soft errors as they are encountered, but it may be an effective way

recording pulses

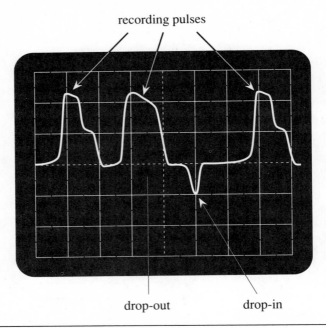

drop-out   drop-in

Figure 11.11 *The read-while-write technique for defect sensing uses a single stylus.*

to monitor the average defect rate, to look for large defects and error bursts, or to verify that recording is actually happening.

MAJOR CONCEPTS

- The high data density on an optical disk leads to a high error rate. The typical raw error rate is greater than BER $\sim 10^{-5}$.

- Error-causing defects on an optical disk are usually very small, affecting one or two bits. But there is usually a secondary distribution of very large defects, which cause long error bursts.

- An error-correction code records generalized parity bits along with the data. The parity is used to detect and correct a limited number of errors. An ECC overhead of 10% to 20% is sufficient to reduce the net (user) error rate from an optical disk to less than 10^{-12}.

- Reed-Solomon ECC codes are optimized for both long and short error bursts. All optical disk systems incorporate RS codes.

- Interleaving is a technique that makes a long error burst equivalent to multiple short bursts.

- Two ECCs can be combined by concatenation or in a product code for additional error-correction power.

- Techniques like direct-read-after-write (DRAW) can be used to guarantee data integrity in write-once systems. Conventional reliability techniques like certification, verification, and fencing are also useful in optical recording systems (Figure 11.10).

REFERENCES

Glinka, W., and M. Brown, "Proposal for a defect mapping scheme for reversible optical media," ANSI document X3B11/88-58 (1988). A detailed proposal for defining and fencing defective sectors on an optical disk.

Golomb, S., "Optical disk error correction," *BYTE*, May 1986, 203. An understandable introduction to the use of Reed-Solomon error correction codes.

Hitachi, "Proposal for 5″ optical disk standardization," ANSI document X3B11/85-113 (1985). Includes burst-length statistics for several varieties of optical disks.

Nugent, W., "Error detection and correction systems for optical disk: Issues of media defect distribution, defect growth, error management, and disk longevity," *SPIE Proceedings*, **695**, 10 (1986). A user's perspective on how the ECC can make optical disks reliable.

Shojima, T., and K. Yoshinaga, "Production system for optic memory disk substrate (2)—development of optic measuring system," *Idemitsu Sekiyu Gijutsu*, **30**, 558 (1987). A description of optical disk inspection equipment, including a CCD defect scanner.

Takeda, T., M. Saito, and K. Itao, "System design of 90 mm optical microdisk subsystem," *SPIE Proceedings*, **899**, 16 (1988). Description of the modified Gilbert model for error distributions on M-O media.

PART IV

MEDIA TECHNOLOGY

Many physical phenomena have been explored as mechanisms for optical recording. "Prime Evil," an anonymous columnist for *Optical Memory News,* once claimed that virtually any material—even peanut butter—could be used for write-once optical recording. It is just a matter of supplying enough laser power and heating the material enough to induce rapid physical change.

However, a practical recording medium must fulfill many stringent practical requirements. Some of these requirements have little to do with the sensitive recording layer or the marking mechanism. The media design must provide mechanical support, format information, and protection against dust and other hazards. And the entire media package, both coatings and substrate, must be (economically) manufacturable. This section examines some important requirements and concepts for designing and manufacturing optical recording media.

We will not attempt a comprehensive description of the details of specific marking mechanisms (other than those discussed in Chapters 3 and 4) or the trade-offs between them. Much of the optical recording literature is devoted to these topics. Bell (1987, referenced in Chapter 4) has reviewed and summarized this material comprehensively.

Chapter 12 discusses the function, design, and manufacturing of optical disk substrates. The substrate typically performs multiple functions: mechanical support, dust and handling protection, and formatting. Although special designs optimize one or another aspect of the substrate, the most-manufacturable substrates (injection-molded plastic) perform all the functions adequately.

A recording layer and (usually) several auxiliary layers must be coated on the optical disk substrate. Chapter 13 presents the general optical and thermal concepts used to design such layers. The characteristics and limitations of practical coating methods are also described.

Media designs often include features that stabilize the recording material and/or protect it from environmental factors. Chapter 14 discusses the important subject of media lifetime and the operating environment. Although any new technology invites concern over reliability, the evidence indicates that optical disks can be rugged and stable.

CHAPTER 12

Optical Disk Substrates

12.1 Basic Mechanical Requirements

The basic role of a substrate is to afford mechanical stability to the recording layers it carries. The important mechanical specifications include positioning, runout, and acceleration in both the radial direction (perpendicular to the motor's spindle axis) and the axial direction (parallel to the axis).

Warp, Tilt, and Axial Runout

Disk warp is a general term describing deviations from flatness. The nominal location of the recording surface is defined as a plane parallel to the spindle reference surface against which the disk is mounted. Deviations from this plane are tolerable but only to the extent that the focus servo can follow them to maintain the tight focus tolerance. Since the servo gain is nearly infinite at zero frequency (see Chapter 7, Section 3), a large degree of warp can be accommodated if the axial displacement is constant around any track. Symmetrical, cup-shaped deformation resulting from differential thermal expansion or inherent film stresses might be tolerable (though it can be a problem if the disk surface is tilted excessively), but asymmetrical warp is more problematical, because it produces axial runout, which the focus servo must follow.

Axial runout is measured by the *total indicated runout* (TIR) at a fixed radius as the disk spins. A component of axial runout at the rotation rate means that the disk surface is tilted relative to the rotation axis (because of a bent spindle, foreign material at the mounting surface, etc.) But generally, the largest component of axial runout occurs at twice the rotation rate. This indicates that the disk surface has a saddle-like shape, or some combination of saddle and cup shapes, resulting from asymmetrical stresses in the substrate, coated films, or other components of the disk.

Specifications usually limit the axial runout below 200 μm (TIR). This requirement is determined by the gain of the focus servo (about 50 dB at twice the rotation rate, c.f. Chapter 7, Section 3) and the need to stay in focus with a precision better than ± 0.5 μm. The physical limits (disk interference or the range of the focus actuator) are usually much wider than the servo capability. The axial runout can be affected by the rotation rate because centrifugal force at high rpm flattens the disk somewhat, especially if the disk is large. Therefore, axial runout should be tested dynamically, not measured from the static profile of the disk.

Disk tilt is the angle by which the recording surface deviates from the nominal plane. Excessive tilt aberrates the optical stylus and misaligns the return beam. For most systems, the maximum acceptable tilt is about 5 mrad. Higher-performance systems (higher NA) could require even tighter tolerances. Consider a saddle-shaped disk with (twice-around TIR) axial runout of α at the outer recording radius, r. The axial location of the disk surface around the outer track is

$$z(\phi) = \sin(2\phi) \, \alpha/2, \qquad (12.1)$$

where ϕ is the angular coordinate around the track. The component of tilt tangential to the track is

$$\delta z/r\delta\phi = \cos(2\phi) \, \alpha/r. \qquad (12.2)$$

The maximum tangential tilt (α/r) occurs at four points around the track. If z is proportional to r^2 (surface curvature independent of radius), the radial component of tilt is

$$\delta z/\delta r = \sin(\phi) \, \alpha/r. \qquad (12.3)$$

In this case, the magnitude of the tilt is constant around a track, though the tilt orientation rotates as the disk spins. Note that α/r is an underestimate of the tilt associated with axial runout because higher-frequency runout components and local variations in disk curvature can increase the tilt dramatically at some locations. Plugging in some typical numbers, we can predict that a 130-mm disk with an axial runout of 100 μm will have a tilt of at least 2 mrad. Unless the axial runout can be kept below 100 μm, an independent measurement of the disk tilt is advisable.

Disk warp is minimized in double-sided disk designs. The double-sided construction is often used even when only one side has an active recording layer, because the symmetrical placement of materials and layers creates an approximate balance between the forces of thermal expansion and film stress.

Radial Runout

The absolute radial position of tracks on an optical disk need not be controlled very precisely. On magnetic disks with open-loop tracking, any change in track radius must be much smaller than the track pitch. But this condition cannot be met in optical disk systems, because the track pitch is so small. Consider, for example, a 130-mm polycarbonate substrate in a tightly controlled operating environment spanning just 10°C. The expansion coefficient of polycarbonate is 0.01% / °C, so the position of the outer tracks is uncertain to $10 \cdot 10^{-4} \cdot 60$ mm = 60 μm. Even if the expansion coefficient of the drive and substrate are closely matched, the relative track location will still be uncertain by more than the track pitch. Fortunately, all optical disk systems use closed-loop tracking servos and read the track address directly from the headers. Therefore, changes in track radius on an optical disk (e.g., due to thermal expansion, centrifugal strain, or plastic deformation) are not a problem as long as they are radially symmetric.

The radial runout is defined as the TIR of the track radius under operating conditions. Most of the runout is due to track decenter, which includes imprecise centering of the track pattern on the disk and centering errors between the disk and the spindle. If the center of a track is a distance δ away from the rotation axis, the TIR is 2δ. All tracks on a disk are equally decentered, so the radial runout is essentially independent of radius.

Media specifications usually limit the radial runout to below 100 μm (TIR). This restriction arises from the low-frequency gain of the tracking servo (about 60 dB at the rotation rate, c.f., Chapter 7, Section 3) and the need to stay on track with a precision of ± 0.1 μm or better. Sometimes alignment issues arising from the optical design of the tracking servo further reduce the radial runout budget (see Chapter 10, Section 2).

Decenter of tracks with respect to the inner diameter of the disk is seldom a major contributor to the total radial runout. Even in the complex processes for manufacturing plastic substrates, concentricity can be maintained better than 25 μm (a TIR contribution of 50 μm). The largest contribution to radial runout occurs during operation, at the disk/spindle interface. Runout due to disk mounting and recentering depends on the details of this interface.

There are two competing design philosophies for the disk/spindle interface: the clamp method, which uses a relatively complex and precise mechanism in the drive; and the magnetic hub method, which requires a more complex disk structure. A clamping mechanism is shown in Figure 12.1. The clamp is a passive part that holds the disk on the spindle. The clamping force is provided by a permanent magnet in the spindle which attracts a permeable keeper in the clamp. As the disk is clamped to the spindle, a cone centers the disk. In order to accommodate variations in the inner diameter of the disk, the cone must be retractable. The cone—its surface quality and its fit to the spindle—are probably the most significant sources of decenter associated with the clamping method.

The alternate mounting technique using a hub is illustrated in Figure 12.2. A magnetically permeable metal hub is attached permanently to the disk. As with the clamp method, the mounting force is provided by a permanent magnet in the spindle. In some designs, the face of the hub mates with the spindle surface to define the axial reference plane. The advantage of referencing to the hub is that the metal hub probably has better wear characteristics than the bare substrate. However, by interposing another (albeit precision) part between the substrate and the spindle, this design reduces the nominal precision of the axial reference. In other designs, the spindle extends

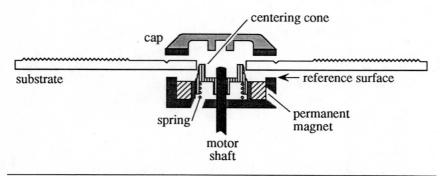

Figure 12.1 *A centering cone and clamp for mounting a hubless disk are shown here.*

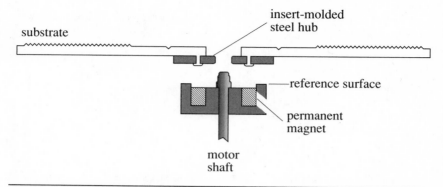

Figure 12.2 *Magnetic clamping of a disk with a precision hub permits a simpler spindle design.*

beyond the hub and mates directly with the substrate. In either case, the hub provides the radial reference. A precision hole in the hub mates "perfectly" with the spindle shaft, eliminating the play associated with a retracting cone. The potential precision of a hubbed disk can only be realized, however, if the hub is aligned very accurately to the tracks during assembly.

Axial and Radial Acceleration

Axial and radial runout are dominated by frequency components near the disk rotation rate. Higher-frequency components usually do not contribute much to the TIR in either case, yet they may present a significant problem for the servos because the servo gain drops rapidly as the frequency rises. Therefore, separate specifications are required to limit the components of runout at intermediate frequencies. These specifications are stated in terms of the net acceleration from all runout components below the servo cutoff frequency (a few kHz). This acceleration must be much less than what the servo can provide (a few g's). Servos do not respond at all to disturbances above the cutoff frequency, so the net amplitude of all high-frequency runout components must be much less than the tolerable residual error (i.e., $<< 0.1~\mu$m).

The runout and acceleration specifications clearly depend on the rotation rate. At higher rpm, the runout components shift to higher frequencies, where the servos cannot deal with them as effectively. A system cannot be redesigned for an increased rotation rate without either tightening the runout specifications, improving the servo performance, or both.

12.2 Substrate Materials

Magnetic disk substrates are aluminum, for high-performance Winchester disks, or plastic, for floppy disks. Recently, glass substrates have been considered for high-performance magnetic disks. The available materials for optical disk substrates are also aluminum, glass (both for high-performance applications), and plastic (for lower-cost designs). However, the quality factors for optical disk substrates differ considerably from those for magnetic disk substrates. Mechanical stability is less important for optical disks, while optical considerations are paramount.

Aluminum: Aluminum is a useful substrate material because it is stiff (a high ratio of strength to weight), it is easily machined, and it has a relatively low thermal expansion coefficient $(2.5 \cdot 10^{-5}/°C)$. Other drive components can be made to match the expansion coefficient of the aluminum substrate so that temperature changes have a minimal effect on the optical or mechanical alignment. The aluminum substrates developed for magnetic disks are about 1.7 mm thick. After initial forming, they are thermally annealed and then diamond-turned to create two new surfaces. The finished substrates are exceptionally flat, with very low axial runout and droop even for substrates 14″ in diameter. Because the disks are annealed, the flat shape is very stable (as long as the disk does not bump into anything).

Optical recording films generally are not deposited directly on a metal surface. The smoothest diamond-turned surface still has a large number of sub-micron pits or inclusions caused by local inhomogeneities in the alloy composition. Even if the aluminum substrate were perfectly smooth, it might not be suitable for direct application of the recording layers. The thermal conductivity of a metal substrate would conduct heat away from the recording layers, dramatically lowering the media sensitivity. For these reasons, a thick polymeric layer, or *surface smoother,* is coated on the aluminum surface before deposition of the recording structure. Thus, aluminum optical disk substrates actually have plastic surfaces.

Aluminum substrates have been used only for 14″ optical disks, for which mechanical precision is the dominant requirement. Figure 12.3 is a photograph of the 14″ Kodak optical disk. Conventional magnetic disk substrates have very large center-holes, but the Kodak disk has a relatively small center-hole, which leaves a larger recording area.

Glass: Glass is nearly as stiff as aluminum and even more stable. Most types of glass also have very low thermal expansion coefficients ($< 10^{-5}$ K^{-1}). As a substrate material, glass is inferior to aluminum only in the difficulty of machining and the danger of breakage. In almost all applications, the deficiencies of glass are more than compensated by its transparency, which facilitates dust protection (Section 12.3) and permits format replication. The risk that glass substrates might break is more of a safety concern than a problem of disk fragility. Most glass substrates are chemically tempered to increase their strength. Any impact likely to shatter a glass substrate would probably bend an aluminum disk or crack a plastic disk, rendering them equally useless. But should a glass disk shatter while spinning at high speed (possibly due to centrifugal stress or mechanical failure of the tracking actuator), it would create a very real and unpredictable hazard.

The photopolymerization (2P) method is the principal technique

Figure 12.3 *The 14″ Kodak optical disk uses an aluminum substrate similar to a magnetic disk substrate. Photo courtesy of Eastman Kodak Company.*

for formatting glass substrates. This method is illustrated in Figure 12.4. The mastering and preparation of formatted metal stampers is discussed in Section 12.4 in connection with molded plastic substrates. A solution of an organic monomer and an ultraviolet activator (no volatile solvents) is dispensed onto the formatted stamper surface or injected between the substrate and the stamper. The stamper and substrate are squeezed together to spread the monomer solution over the entire disk surface. The organic material is polymerized in place by a U.V. light shining through the substrate. Finally, the stamper is peeled away from the disk, leaving a thin organic coating which replicates the stamper pattern.

The conventional 2P process cannot be used with opaque substrates. However, transparent nonmetallic stampers can be made for 2P applications (Horigome, 1988). Such stampers could be used in an inverted 2P process to format opaque aluminum substrates.

The surface quality of the substrate underneath a 2P format layer is unimportant. The smoothness of the recording layer and the number of defects are determined by the stamper surface and the fidelity of its replication. The adhesion and chemical stability of the recording films are affected not by the glass but by the polymeric 2P layer.

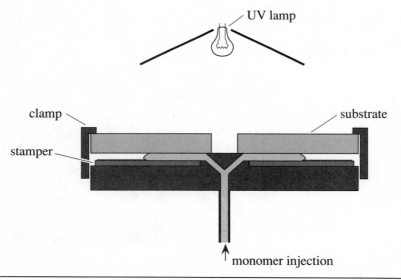

Figure 12.4 *The 2P method can be used to format any transparent substrate.*

But the glass substrate still determines the mechanical stability of the disk. And if a sandwich configuration is used (Figure 12.8), the glass still forms an effective barrier to moisture and other contaminants.

Ohta, Hirokane, Inui, Takahashi, Deguchi, and Okamoto, (1985) demonstrated that lower noise levels can be achieved on a glass surface than on conventional 2P or molded plastic disks. They produced grooved glass substrates (not 2P replicas) and coated them as M-O disks. The disks achieved about 5 dB higher CNR than equivalent plastic disks, because they had smoother surfaces and correspondingly lower noise. In essence, each grooved glass disk went through the entire photoresist master process (Section 12.4) plus additional glass-etching steps. Actually, only the land areas were smooth and suitable for recording; the etched grooves were quite rough. Better control of the groove geometry on an etched-glass substrate may be obtained by first coating the disk with a layer of SiO_2 (Miyagi, Iwasaka, and Yamazaki, 1987). This layer is removed with relative ease by reactive ion etching, exposing the native glass substrate within the grooves or preformat marks. When the photoresist is stripped off, the SiO_2 layer forms the land surface. Unfortunately, these processes for making etched-glass substrates are too slow and complex for practical manufacturing.

A potentially cheaper means of making formatted glass substrates has been investigated at Nippon Sheet Glass. A blank glass substrate can be coated (by spin-coating, dipping, or spraying) with a thin sol-gel layer, composed of silica suspended in a polymeric matrix. The gel surface is embossed by a stamper to form the grooved pattern. Heat treatment or hard U.V. exposure then drives off most of the organic component, leaving a hard, glassy surface.

Plastic: Plastic substrates are used for most optical disks. These substrates are usually manufactured using the injection-molding process described in Section 12.4. This technique is particularly efficient because it forms the disk, its center-hole, and the format pattern all in one step.

The first plastic material used for injection-molded optical disks was polymethylmethacrylate (PMMA). PMMA resin is inexpensive, easy to mold, and very transparent. (The index of refraction is low, $n \cong 1.48$, so the surfaces reflect relatively little light.) PMMA is still used in optical videodiscs, because moldability is so important for that product. However, PMMA is dimensionally unstable. It absorbs moisture readily from the air and tends to warp when wet. The glass transition temperature of PMMA is low, $T_g \sim 90°C$, and some relaxation (disk warp or groove changes) can occur even at 60°C. Consequently, PMMA disks cannot survive the widest ranges of operating, storage, and keeping conditions (see Chapter 14, Section 1).

Polycarbonate is now the preferred material for injection-molded optical disk substrates. In subsequent discussions of molded substrates, we will assume that this is the material. Polycarbonate is a good engineering plastic (stiff, strong, and stable) which is manufactured with optical purity. The T_g is over 140°C, so polycarbonate disks are much more stable than PMMA disks at elevated temperatures. Several manufacturers offer CD grades of polycarbonate resin developed specifically for compact disk substrates. These resins have low molecular weight (as low as possible without compromising strength) and narrow molecular-weight distributions. CD-grade polycarbonate is nearly as easy to mold as PMMA.

As a substrate material, polycarbonate could be improved in several ways. The principal defect of polycarbonate is the high level of birefringence in molded disks (discussed in Section 12.5); many other plastics, such as PMMA, have intrinsically low birefringence. An even higher T_g would be a desirable property for the substrate (though molding becomes more difficult for materials of high T_g). The thermal expansion coefficient of polycarbonate ($10^{-4}/°C$) is much higher than that of glass or aluminum. Although this expansion coefficient is typical of most plastics, much-lower thermal expansion is possible (i.e., Ultim). Polycarbonate has quite a high refractive index ($n \cong 1.58$ at $\lambda = 800$ nm); the surface of a polycarbonate disk reflects 5.0% of the incident light, compared to only 3.7% from PMMA disks (recall Eq. 3.2). Finally, although polycarbonate absorbs much less moisture than PMMA (and suffers much less humidity distortion), a substrate material that is truly hydrophobic would be desirable.

A number of "improved" substrate molding resins have been proposed: polymethylpentene, copolymers or blends of polycarbonate and other polymers, "polymer Z" from Mitsui (a polyolefin), and so on. Although none of these materials looks like an easy replacement for polycarbonate, we have no reason to believe that dramatically improved resins for injection molding cannot be developed. However, since a high level of investment is required to develop and scale up any new material, we should not expect major improvements in this area until the market for optical disks has grown significantly.

Casting of plastic substrates has been proposed as an alternative to injection molding. The casting process is similar to the 2P process, in that the substrate material is polymerized in place. Polymerization can be initiated using heat, chemical activators, microwaves, or UV exposure. The primary drawback to substrate casting is that the process is very slow and therefore costly. A 2P replication is five to ten times slower than injection molding; the curing time for a cast substrate is about 100 times slower than injection-molding. Substrates can be cast from a wide variety of precursor materials (Kudoh, Maruno, Ieki, Kawabata, and Yamamoto, 1987; Sudou, Miwa, Tajima, Horigome, and Ohta, 1988), but the final materials are similar, in that they are all heavily cross-linked. Cross-linking enhances the thermal stability of these materials, but it also inhibits the kind of rheological properties required for injection-molding.

12.3 Dust Protection

The large spacing between the objective lens and the recording layer permits optical disks to be designed with a transparent protective layer. If this protective layer is thick enough, it keeps dust, scratches, and minor surface imperfections out of focus while the optical stylus is positioned on the recording surface. Very thin layers of various sorts are used in optical recording media for other protective purposes (see Chapter 14, Section 3). However, the term *protective layer* is used specifically to describe a transparent layer that provides optical protection. Figure 12.5 illustrates how dust particles or scratches on the surface of a thick, transparent protective layer are much smaller than the laser beam. Small particles or defects do not change the optical stylus qualitatively, other than to reduce its intensity slightly (Chapter 5, Section 5). So if the protective layer is thick enough, surface defects or contamination only cause minor modulation of the signal amplitude.

A beam focused through a protective layer with thickness d and refractive index n has a diameter of

$$\Delta = 2\,d\,NA\,[1 - (NA/n)^2]^{-1/2}/n \qquad (12.4)$$

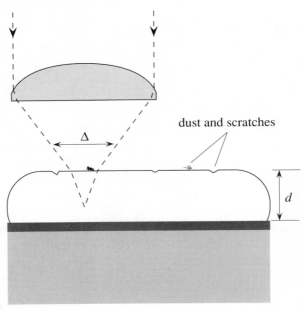

Figure 12.5 *A transparent protective layer keeps dust and scratches out of focus.*

at the surface of the protective layer. Since the numerical aperture, *NA,* is usually about 0.5, the approximation

$$\Delta \cong d/n \qquad (12.5)$$

is usually adequate.

The protective layer is effective only if Δ is very much larger than the size of the contaminating particles or surface defects. Almost all dust particles are smaller than 30 μm in diameter. (Larger particles fall out of the air too quickly to spread far beyond their source.) Typical scratches and airborne fibers are thinner than 20 μm, though they may be several millimeters long. On theoretical grounds, the necessary thickness of an in-contact protective layer has been estimated at about 0.5 mm (Marchant, 1984). The effectiveness of a protective layer has also been verified experimentally, as shown in Figure 12.6. The disk surface was covered with dust (carbon toner particles). The particle diameters ranged from 7 to 30 μm, similar to ordinary dust, and they covered (geometrically) about 1% of the surface. The BER was measured as a function of protective-layer

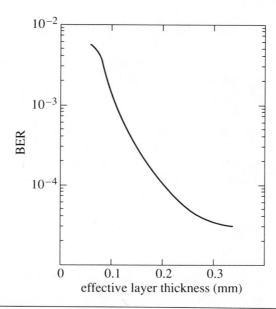

Figure 12.6 *If the protective layer is too thin, dust will cause errors.*

thickness. The effective protective-layer thickness plotted in the graph is the equivalent thickness of a layer with $n = 1$ and the same value of Δ. For a protective-layer thickness of less than 0.1 mm, the error rate approached the fractional coverage by dust and defects. Only for an effective thickness greater than 0.3 mm ($d > 0.45$ μm for $n = 1.5$) did the error rate approach the value associated with defects in the recording surface.

Practical methods for uniformly coating very thick layers (> 0.2 mm) do not exist. Several optical disk designs with spin-coated protective layers have been proposed (e.g., the STC 14″ optical disk). But these layers were not much thicker than 100 μm, too thin to protect against scratches or larger dust particles. Insufficient protective-layer thickness is also a problem for some optical card designs. Since the card is constrained to the total thickness of an ordinary credit card, its protective layer cannot be much thicker than 0.3 mm. This is probably not enough for adequate dust and scratch protection, especially if the *NA* in the card-reader is much smaller than 0.5. (Dust protection is less efficient at low *NA* precisely because the depth of focus is greater.) The protective-layer thickness is also a difficult challenge in the design of optical tape, which must be much thinner than 0.1 mm for flexibility.

Fortunately, there are a number of practical designs for thick protective layers on optical disks. Figure 12.7 is a cross-section of the 14″ Kodak optical disk, which uses a transparent cover sheet suspended over both surfaces of an aluminum substrate (Maher, 1987). The cover sheet is only about 0.1 mm thick, but the air gap beneath it is much thicker. The effective protective-layer thickness is about 0.4 mm. (A disk like this, with an adjustable air gap, was used for the experiment of Figure 12.6.) 3M has developed optical disks with a conceptually similar structure: a two-sided disk covered on each side by a rigid, transparent cover cap, with a substantial air gap over each recording surface.

If the substrate is transparent, and if the recording-layer structure permits efficient heating from a substrate-incident laser beam, the substrate itself can serve as a good protective layer. Plastic and glass substrates are relatively thick for reasons of strength (i.e., 1.2 mm), so they provide more than enough defocus protection against large dust particles and scratches. A transparent substrate used in this way can be coated only on one side. But a two-sided disk can be constructed by combining two coated substrates, as illustrated in Figure 12.8. Figure 12.8a is an air-sandwich construction in which the disks are bonded together with spacers at the inner and outer edges. The enclosed air gap has no optical effect, but it is required by some recording media to permit the free formation of marks. One drawback to the air-sandwich is that it is easily distorted by differential air pressure (inside and out) caused by altitude changes or centrifugal pumping as the disk spins. Small vent holes may be provided to bal-

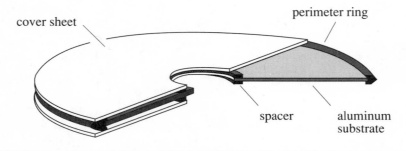

Figure 12.7 *Flexible cover sheets are stretched over spacers above the recording surface.*

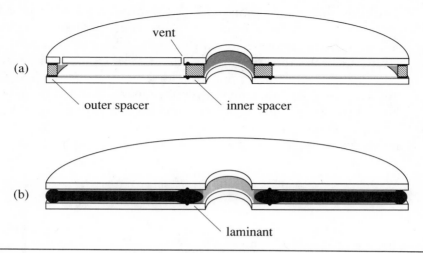

Figure 12.8 *Transparent substrates are configured as a two-sided disk using (a) an air-sandwich structure or (b) a solid sandwich structure.*

ance the pressure. If the marking dynamics permit, the more reliable solid-sandwich disk construction can be used (Figure 12.8b). In this design, the two disks are simply laminated together. The laminant bonds the disks and (it is hoped) helps protect the recording layers from the atmosphere (O_2, moisture, etc.).

In Chapter 5, Section 5, we described the basic optical effects of a transparent layer on the optical stylus. The optical effects are independent of vertical location, so it does not matter whether the transparent material is suspended above the recording surface (a cover sheet) or in intimate contact (a transparent substrate), but the thickness and refractive index of the layer are important. The objective lens is designed to provide diffraction-limited performance at a specific wavelength (800 nm) for a specific protective-layer thickness and index (usually 1.2 mm and 1.58, respectively). Deviations from the nominal design thickness create spherical aberration (in addition to substantial defocus). In most cases, thickness variations up to ±50 μm may be tolerable.

Spherical aberration can also result if the protective layer does not have the nominal refractive index. For practical purposes, a change in refractive index can be treated as an equivalent change in thickness. If the index is increased, the layer "looks" thicker in terms of spherical aberration. (This result is counter-intuitive because high-index layers visually appear thin.) Therefore, changes in refractive index can be compensated by corresponding changes in the protective-layer (substrate) thickness (Marchant, 1986). Figure 12.9 shows the adjusted protective-layer thickness that best compensates for variation in refractive index in a system designed to use 1.2-mm polycarbonate substrates. The necessary thickness correction is a very nonlinear function of the refractive index. An approximate equation for reoptimizing the protective-layer or substrate thickness for alternate materials is

$$d(n) = d_{\text{polycarbonate}}\ 0.423\ n^3\ (n^2 + 0.259)/(n^2 - 1)/ \qquad (12.6)$$
$$(n^2 + 0.577)$$

given an objective lens with $NA \sim 0.5$ designed for use with polycarbonate at $\lambda = 800$ nm.

The question of variation in refractive index is important because the available and potential substrate materials cover a wide range in refractive index. For instance, $n_{\text{PMMA}} \cong 1.48$, $n_{\text{polycarbonate}} \cong 1.58$, and $n_{\text{glass}} \cong 1.50$, all measured at $\lambda = 800$ nm. Polymethylpentene, a proposed substrate material, has an index as low as 1.46. Fortunately, even if the objective lens is designed specifically for use with polycarbonate, any of these materials can be used with good results, provided that the nominal substrate thickness is reoptimized for the

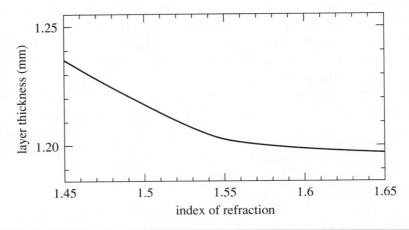

Figure 12.9 *This graph shows the protective-layer thickness equivalent to 1.2 mm of polycarbonate.*

specific material used. Several X3B11 standards interpret the protective-layer or substrate thickness using the equivalent of Eq. (12.6) in order to permit the use of a broad range of materials.

12.4 Manufacturing Plastic Substrates

This section describes the usual techniques for making molded plastic substrates. Plastics possess a few advantages as materials for optical disk substrates—low materials cost, low inertial mass, and ruggedness—but overall, glass is a preferable material. Instead, plastic substrates are generally preferred precisely because they are more manufacturable. They are formed and formatted in one (relatively quick) step.

The manufacturing sequence consists of three groups of processes: mastering, matrixing, and molding. Mastering produces the original format profile. Matrixing copies the surface of the formatted master onto a material hard enough for mass replication. Injection molding is the mass replication process that turns plastic pellets into formatted substrates. See Figure 12.10 for a representation of this sequence.

Photoresist Mastering

Mastering generally refers to any process used to form the original format pattern for replicating substrates. In the LP mastering process, the grooved pattern is machined directly into a metal master (e.g., soft copper). A very sharp tool attached to a high-frequency piezoelectric driver cuts a spiral groove with a modulated depth. Because of the tight track pitch, a fairly deep layer of metal is eventually removed, but the remaining grooves are rather shallow, because with each pass the tool cuts away most of one wall of the preceding cycle. The direct machining method was refined and adapted for mastering capacitive videodiscs. Because it is well known and relatively inexpensive, this method has also been suggested as a viable technique for mastering CD and perhaps CDROM disks (Redlich and Joschko, 1987), but a lack of flexibility makes it inappropriate for write-once and erasable optical disks. For example, direct machining cannot be used to make concentric tracks, nor can it produce format patterns with ungrooved regions (mirror areas).

In the usual process, the master begins as a polished glass disk.

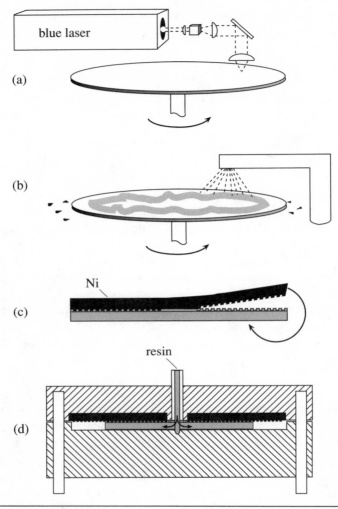

Figure 12.10 *Manufacturing steps for plastic substrates are illustrated here, where (a) shows laser exposure of a photoresist master, (b) shows wet development of the master, (c) represents electroplating to make stampers, and (d) shows injection molding.*

The optical characteristics and quality of the glass blank are not important, but it must be quite flat and perfectly smooth. Any dirt, scratches, or inclusions will be replicated as corresponding defects in the finished disks and could lead to even larger coating defects. The format is not created directly in the glass surface but rather in a photoresist layer. A thin layer of positive photoresist is spin-coated on the clean glass master from a solvent solution. Spin-coating, which is described in more detail in Chapter 13, Section 4, is a highly reproducible process that creates very uniform coatings. The format pattern consists of voids where the photoresist is solubilized by exposure to short-wavelength light and subsequently developed away. The depth of these marks is determined by the thickness of the photoresist layer. The coating thickness should be slightly greater than the desired depth of the tracking grooves or format marks, to compensate for profile reductions that accumulate in the subsequent process steps. In principle, negative photoresist could be used instead of positive resist; this would produce patterns in which the background is the glass surface and the marks consist of raised areas where the exposed resist remains. But positive resist is chosen because it gives higher resolution and sharper definition.

The format exposure is made on a mastering machine, which is a specialized optical recording system (see Figures 12.10a and 6.1). A gas laser must be used for mastering because photoresist is sensitive only to short-wavelength light. The typical resist sensitivity drops rapidly for wavelengths longer than 400 nm. The most commonly used lasers for mastering are HeCd and argon iron gas lasers; they can be adjusted for reasonably powerful emission at 442 nm and 458 or 488 nm, respectively. In addition to a gas laser, a modulator, and an optical head, the mastering system must have very precise positioning systems. Any position errors, focus errors, or vibration during mastering are passed through to every drive that plays the replicated disks; therefore, extraordinary mechanical precision is needed in the mastering system. A fairly ordinary closed-loop focus servo is usually used in the optical head of the mastering system. However, the tracking must be open-loop, since no tracking pattern of any kind is visible on the predeveloped master. An interferometer provides highly accurate radial positioning and pitch control. High-quality vibration isolation is also necessary to eliminate track runout and pitch irregularity.

After exposure, the master is developed in a wet process, usually by spinning it under a stream or spray of developer (Figure 12.10b). As the developer dissolves away exposed resist, the track pattern becomes visible. Ideally, all areas that received more than a critical exposure (laser energy per unit area) should be etched clean away, while the original resist coating remains elsewhere. For an intermediate range of exposure, however, the resist will be only partially developed. Moreover, if the developer is allowed to act long enough, all the resist will dissolve (since the solubility change associated with exposure is only a matter of degree). As mentioned under *Format Testing,* below, the optical characteristics of the pattern can be used as a real-time check on the completeness of developing.

Mastering includes many other steps in addition to those described here—washing, priming, baking, and so on. Itoh, Hamada, and Ohtaki, (1987) give a more detailed summary of the mastering and matrixing processes.

Matrixing

The master surface has the profile that is desired on the substrates. But photoresist is a fragile material, not rugged enough for molding plastic parts. An intermediate step is needed to transfer the master pattern into a material hard enough for repeated replication under conditions of high temperature and high pressure. Nickel metal is chosen as this material because it is quite hard and durable; but most importantly, nickel can be electroplated as a thick, conformal layer on the photoresist master. After separation from the glass master and photoresist, the electroformed nickel part can serve as a tool, or *stamper,* for molding.

Stamper-making begins with metalization of the photoresist master. Since resist is an insulator, electrical current cannot be passed directly into the master surface. Therefore, a thin metal layer (evaporated silver, electroless nickel, etc.) is deposited on the master surface to make it conductive. Then the master is connected as the cathode in a plating cell and immersed in a solution of nickel salts. Nickel metal is reduced on the surface of the master at a rate proportional to the current density. The electroplating system carefully controls the current density and the cleanliness, temperature, and composition of the plating solution in order to form hard nickel parts of uniform thickness and low defect density.

The electroplating process was originally developed for LP record manufacturing. The thick electroformed replicas were called *matrices* (to distinguish them from thin electroplated coatings); hence the term *matrixing* to describe stamper-making in optical disk manufacturing. In LP manufacturing, the stampers are used for embossing (pressing a pattern into a heated plastic surface). For optical disk manufacturing, they are usually used for injection molding, but they can also be used in alternate manufacturing methods (i.e., casting or the 2P method).

It is possible to make many stampers from a master. The photoresist surface is destroyed when the first electroplated part is separated from it (Figure 12.10c). But the matrixing process can be used to create a second-generation replica. Unlike the photoresist master, the nickel part is not appreciably damaged by subsequent electroplating; therefore several second-generation parts (mothers) can be created from a single first-generation part (father). In CD manufacturing, third-generation parts are used as stampers. Twenty or more good CD stampers can be made from each master. Note that the stamper surface has the same shape as the father, a shape opposite to that of masters, mothers, and molded substrates.

For more demanding applications (i.e., substrates for M-O disks), the first-generation nickel parts are used as stampers. These first-generation stampers have a finer surface finish and less contamination than third-generation stampers. The drawback in this case is that a new master must be processed for each new stamper; and mastering is considerably more costly than matrixing.

Stampers are treated as replaceable parts in the molding system. Depending on the required disk quality and molding schedule, a stamper surface may produce 5,000 to 30,000 substrates before it collects too much damage or wear. But in every other respect, the molds last for millions of cycles. For this reason, the stamper must serve as a replaceable mold surface. A center hole, punched in the stamper concentric with the format pattern, centers the stamper within the mold, where it is clamped against one face of the mold. Injected resin forces the stamper back against the mold surface so that it behaves like an integral part of the mold. But when it is worn out, the stamper can be removed and replaced with a new stamper.

Stampers are usually about 300 μm thick. They have the strength and appearance of thick metal foil. Because they are fairly flexible, any large scratch, protrusion, or particle on the back side of the stamper will deform the stamper surface under the high pressures of injection molding, resulting in small dents and local thickness variations on the substrates. For this reason, the finish and cleanliness of the mold and stamper are critical. The absolute thickness of the stamper is also important. Since the stamper occupies space in the mold, variations in stamper thickness result in corresponding variations in substrate thickness. The average stamper thickness can be controlled by following a precise current/time profile in the plating process. Thickness uniformity around the stamper is achieved by rotating the part within the plating bath to maintain a symmetric plating profile, but it is not unusual to see thickness variations from center to edge. These must be controlled by an empirically designed aperture between the anode and cathode in the plating cell. There is no practical method to machine or polish a stamper down to a thin, uniform profile, so the plating process must be carefully controlled by baffling, solution control, and current control to maintain the requisite uniformity.

The edges of the plated part are quite irregular, but the rough edges are trimmed away during stamper finishing. Trimming is the reason why the glass master is always much larger in diameter than the substrate. The accuracy of the outer diameter of the stamper is not critical, but the inner diameter of the finished stamper determines the orientation of the stamper during replication. If the inner diameter is not concentric with the format pattern, the substrate center holes will not be concentric either, and the disks will exhibit unnecessary radial runout. Usually, the stamper is mounted on a precision turntable for punching the center hole. A fiduciary track is viewed through a microscope, and the stamper position is adjusted until no runout is observed, then the center hole is punched. Centration accuracy as fine as 10 μm can be achieved by this method.

Injection Molding

Injection molding is the process of forcing molten plastic to fill a mold, as illustrated in Figure 12.10d, where it cools and hardens to form the molded part. The plastic is fed to the molding machine in the form of small resin pellets. A heating jacket surrounding the injection barrel melts the resin. Then a "plasticating screw" pumps it toward the injection nozzle. Shear friction from the screw further heats the resin to a temperature of 300 to 400 °C, making it fluid enough to squirt into the mold when the gate is opened. Shear heating is required because heat cannot be conducted into the resin fast enough, and because the plastic material will begin to decompose if it is heated too early and too long. Once in the mold, the resin cools rapidly by conduction into the steel mold. This cooling step is relatively rapid because the disk is so thin; nevertheless, cooling and resolidification account for most of the time in the injection-molding cycle.

A modified type of injection molding (*injection-compression molding*) is usually used for optical disk substrates. The mold is not clamped firmly shut as the molten resin is pumped in. It is held closed with a certain clamp force but allowed to open slightly as the resin is forced in. Then a higher clamp force is applied to pack the mold. This compression step helps force the resin to conform more perfectly to the stamper surface. Filling and replication can also be enhanced by pumping the air out of the mold as the resin is injected. An exaggerated form of injection-compression molding called *variable cavity volume molding* has been proposed as a means to minimize substrate birefringence. See Shimojo (1987) for more detail on injection-molding of optical disk substrates.

In most applications of injection molding, multiple-cavity molds are used to create many parts with each cycle. But multiple-cavity molds for high-quality optical disk substrates have not yet been successful. Instead, single-cavity molds are used, with cycle times greater than 10 seconds. In a single-cavity optical disk mold, the resin is injected through a gate at the center. The radial flow pattern minimizes asymmetrical stresses, which would otherwise result in deformation, thickness variations around the disk, and irregular birefringence patterns.

Format Testing

Features much smaller than 1 μm can be replicated by injection molding (e.g., the 0.3-μm Moth Eye pattern described in Chapter 13, Section 2). Nevertheless, the replication is not perfect. The pattern contrast (groove depth and edge definition) can be reduced at each step of substrate manufacturing: over-development dissolves some resist off the land areas; under-development leaves a sloping profile at the edges; the resist tends to shrink during post-baking; the conductive coating tends to fill in the features; chemical passivation and the mechanical stripping operation after electroplating wear down any sharp features; wear occurs (at a much slower rate) within the mold as each molded disk is ejected off the stamper; and shrinkage or relaxation of the plastic material following molding further reduces the pattern definition. Each of the process and handling steps (especially the wet processes) also add discrete defects that will be replicated into each substrate.

Discrete defects must be examined microscopically or by the certification techniques discussed in Chapter 11, Section 4. The tracking-groove profile can be tested more directly using an optical technique called *diffraction spectrometry*. The principle of diffraction spectrometry is illustrated in Figure 12.11. The grooved surface is illuminated by a laser beam at near-normal incidence. If the grooves have a regular pitch, they diffract the reflected beam into discrete orders (recall the discussion in Chapter 7, Section 2). The angle between adjacent diffraction orders depends only on the track pitch and the laser wavelength (Eq. 7.5). The relative intensities of the orders are an indication of the groove profile.

For the purposes of a simple analysis, assume that the groove profile (or rather its reflective phase profile) is perfectly square, with width w and phase depth ϕ. The groove width determines the ratio of the 1st and 2nd orders. From Eqs. (7.7) we can derive

$$w = p \arccos(\sqrt{f_{21}})/\pi, \qquad (12.7)$$

where p is the track pitch and f_{21} is the ratio of the intensity of the 2nd-order beam divided by that of the 1st-order beam ($f_{21} = I_2 / I_1$). The ratio f_{21} goes to zero when the groove and land widths are equal ($w = p/2$). So the solution to Eq. (12.7) can be ambiguous, though an independent estimate of w (i.e., from microscope observation) will usually resolve any question.

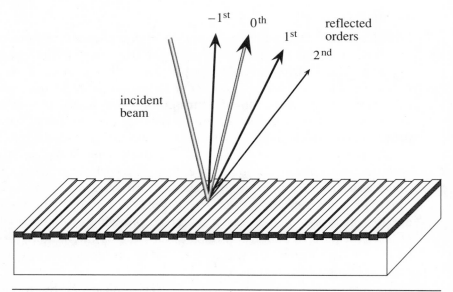

Figure 12.11 *Diffraction intensity is an indication of groove depth and width.*

Given a value for w from Eq. (12.7) or other means, we can calculate the phase depth from the ratio of the 0th and 1st orders:

$$\cos \phi = 1 - (p/w)^2 / \{2[f_{01} \operatorname{sinc}^2(w/p) + p/w - 1]\}, \quad (12.8)$$

where $f_{01} = I_0/I_1$. If scalar optics applies, the relationship between the phase depth, ϕ, and the physical groove depth, δ, is

$$\phi = 4 \pi \delta \cos \theta / \lambda, \quad (12.9)$$

where θ is the angle of incidence and λ is the laser wavelength. Eqs. (12.7) and (12.9) are discussed in Sekizawa, Yamada, and Iwamoto, (1984); Eq. (12.9) corrects an error in that reference.

Diffraction spectrometry gives information about two other aspects of the grooves. Scattering between the orders usually indicates that the pitch is not uniform. The 1st and -1st orders should have the same intensities (for near-normal incidence). If f_{-11} does not equal 1, the grooves are asymmetrical from side to side—a serious condition because it creates a false push-pull tracking-error signal.

Diffraction spectrometry is only an indirect means of measuring the groove dimensions. However, it is the optical character of the format pattern which affects the disk performance, not the physical dimensions per se. Diffraction spectrometry is a reproducible means to measure those characteristics of the format which really matter to the readout and servo systems.

Diffraction spectrometry can be used to inspect the format pattern at any stage of manufacturing. It can be used to monitor the photoresist development process in real time (Dil and Wesdorp, 1979), to inspect electroformed parts, or to examine coated disks. But note that in each case, the laser beam should be air-incident on the grooved surface. Any secondary reflections from additional transparent layers will confuse the analysis.

12.5 Birefringence

In contrast to substrates made of glass or PMMA, injection-molded polycarbonate disks have a high degree of birefringence. Birefringence is a condition in which the refractive index is polarization-dependent. In general, a birefringent material has three principal axes and three corresponding refractive indices, which apply when the polarization (E-field) is parallel to one of the axes. Because of mold symmetry, the principle axes in an optical disk usually are closely aligned with the radial direction (r), the azimuthal direction (ϕ), and the thickness direction (z). Any light ray incident on the disk is divided into two components which sense different refractive indices. Figure 12.12 illustrates a light ray at nonnormal incidence in the (r, z) plane. The light ray is divided into an s-polarized component with $n = n_\phi$ (because the E-field is parallel to ϕ), and a p-polarized component with n intermediate between n_z and n_r. The two component rays travel through the disk following different optical paths. The difference in total optical-path length is called *retardation*. Retardation varies with the incidence angle and the incidence direction.

Much of the light from an objective lens impinges on the disk at near-normal incidence. In this case, the double-pass retardation is approximately proportional to the *normal birefringence,*

$$\delta = 2\,d\,|\,n_r - n_\phi\,|, \qquad (12.10)$$

where d is the substrate thickness. The normal birefringence is due to anisotropy in the in-plane stresses within the disk, coupled with the stress-optical coefficient of the polycarbonate material. Because retardation has detrimental effects on optical disk readout (as described in Chapter 8, Sections 3 and 4), the molding process is adjusted to minimize and balance the in-plane stresses, thus reducing the retardation at normal incidence.

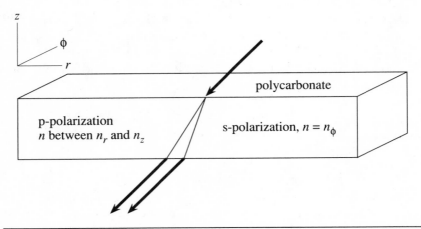

Figure 12.12 *Lateral birefringence alters the apparent refractive index for obliquely incident, p-polarized light.*

Even if the normal birefringence is perfectly balanced out, polycarbonate disks still exhibit substantial retardation at non-normal incidence. Figure 12.13 shows the measured retardation vs. incidence angle at three radii on a very good injection-molded polycarbonate disk. The normal birefringence is very low; the double-pass substrate retardation at normal incidence is less than 20 nm. However, the retardation increases sharply at higher incidence angle; at 30° incidence (the margin of an 0.5 *NA* objective lens), the retardation exceeds 150 nm double pass.

The large value of retardation at non-normal incidence is due to *lateral birefringence,* a condition in which n_r and n_ϕ are approximately equal but n_z is dramatically different. Theoretically, we expect any retardation due to lateral birefringence to increase as θ^2, a relationship that looks linear in Figure 12.13 because the abscissa is is also scaled as θ^2 (see Marchant, 1986).

Lateral birefringence in polycarbonate is not due to stress. Rather, it is due to preferential alignment of the molecular constituents in the polycarbonate material. As shown in Figure 12.14, the structure

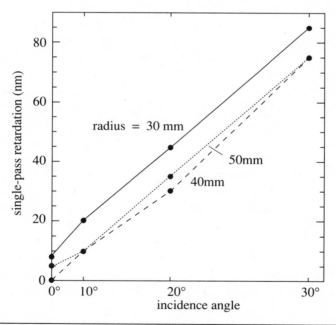

Figure 12.13 *Retardation of a typical injection-molded polycarbonate substrate is graphed here.*

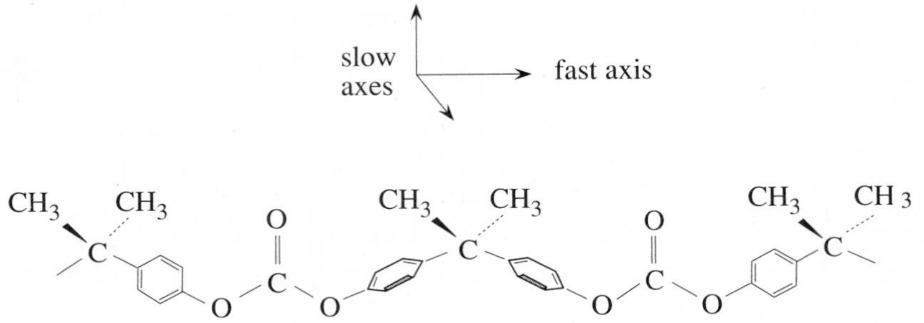

Figure 12.14 *The chemical structure of bisphenol-a polycarbonate is dominated by phenyl rings.*

of polycarbonate is dominated by phenyl rings (six carbon atoms with three double bonds). The polarizability of the rings, and thus the refractive index, depend strongly on whether the rings are aligned parallel or perpendicular to the E-field of the light. Stress-induced birefringence in polycarbonate is related to molecular alignment caused by strain. Lateral birefringence, on the other hand, is due to a preferential, in-plane orientation of the polymer chains. If the polycarbonate polymer chains are aligned roughly parallel, then the direction of alignment corresponds to the "fast" optical axis. That is, the refractive index is higher when the E-field of the light is parallel to the polymer chains because the benzene rings are all nearly parallel to this direction. If the E-field is perpendicular to the polymer chain, roughly half of the rings are aligned face-on, so the medium is not as polarizable and the refractive index is lower. Fluid shear during injection molding acts to align the polycarbonate chains in the plane of the disk. Therefore, n_z is much larger than n_ϕ or n_r. The large values of retardation shown in Figure 12.13 are due to a refractive index difference of about $5 \cdot 10^{-4}$ between n_z and n_ϕ or n_r. This is very much larger than typical values of normal birefringence: $|n_r - n_\phi| < 5 \cdot 10^{-6}$. Lateral birefringence in polycarbonate is less sensitive to the molding conditions than is normal birefringence. Note in Figure 12.13 that the retardation is virtually independent of radius except for an offset due to normal birefringence. Normal incidence retardation in polycarbonate can be virtually eliminated by tuning the molding cycle, but some lateral birefringence is inherent to injection-molded polycarbonate; a double pass retardation less than 100 nm at 30° incidence may not be possible. The lateral birefringence can be removed by annealing near the glass transition temperature (145°C), but this ruins the substrate's flatness and the format pattern (Okada, Nakada, Toki, Gokan, Iwanaga, and Inada 1987). Dramatic improvements in this regard probably are contingent on the future development of new plastics.

━━━ MAJOR CONCEPTS

- Radial and axial runout are consequences of optical disk removability. Low-frequency runout is easily compensated by the tracking and focus servos.

- Glass and aluminum substrates are used for large, high-performance optical disks. But for reasons of cost and manufacturability, injection-molded polycarbonate is preferred in most cases.

- Dust contamination on the surface of an optical disk does not cause errors because the dust particles are held out of focus on a thick protective layer (transparent substrate, cover sheet, etc.) (Figures 12.5 and 12.6).

- Optical disk mastering is essentially non-real-time optical recording in photoresist. Short-wavelength (blue) gas lasers are used for mastering (Figures 6.1 and 12.10).

- Birefringence is the most troublesome characteristic of injection-molded polycarbonate substrates. Birefringence is due to internal stress and/or molecular orientation. Optical retardation due to birefringence depends strongly on the angle of incidence (Figure 12.13).

━━━ REFERENCES

Dil, J., and C. Wesdorp, "Control of pit geometry on video disks," *Applied Optics,* **18,** 3198 (1979). Diffraction spectrometry for process control during the development of masters.

Horigome, S., Y. Miyamura, K. Katou, M. Itou, and N. Ohta, "Novel stamper process for optical disk," *SPIE Proceedings,* **899,** 123 (1988). Plastic 2P replicas used as stampers for subsequent 2P manufacturing.

Itoh, K., M. Hamada, and S. Ohtaki, "Replication master for optical disk substrates," *Fujitsu Sci. Tech. J.,* **23,** no. 1, 44 (1987). A review of substrate replication technology, especially photoresist mastering and stamper making.

Kudoh, Y., Y. Maruno, M. Ieki, H. Kawabata, and K. Yamamoto, "Magneto-optical disc with casting substrate," *Japanese J. Appl. Phys.,* **26** suppl. 26–4, 27 (1987). Substrates cast from vinylester monomers and cured by microwave.

Maher, J., "The rigid optical disk assembly by Eastman Kodak Company," *Topical Meeting on Optical Data Storage, Technical Digest Series,* **10,** 82 (1987). Description of the design of a 14″ optical disk based on an aluminum substrate.

Marchant, A., "Cover sheets for dust protection," *OSA Topical Meeting on Optical Data Storage Technical Digest,* FC-A4 (1984). A theoretical and experimental demonstration of the minimum spacing requirements for protective layers.

Marchant, A., "Index variations in cover sheets," *Applied Optics,* **25,** 490 (1986). A description of how the substrate thickness should be adjusted to compensate for materials of different refractive index.

Marchant, A., "Retardation effects in magneto-optic readout," *SPIE Proceedings,* **695,** 270 (1986). A description of substrate retardation at non-normal incidence.

Miyagi, M., A. Iwasaka, and H. Yamazaki, "Pregrooved disk formed by dry etching technique," *Japanese J. Appl. Phys.,* **26** suppl. 26–4, 105 (1987). SiO_2 used as a secondary resist layer for controlled etching of glass substrates.

Nakajima, M., M. Hamada, M. Moribe, H. Hirano, K. Itoh, and S. Ogawa, "Reduction of media noise in optical disks," *OSA Topical Meeting on Optical Data Storage, Technical Digest,* ThCC5 (1985). Descriptions of several types of media noise arising in the mastering process.

Ohta, K., J. Hirokane, T. Inui, A. Takahashi, T. Deguchi, and T. Okamoto, "Magneto-optical disk substrate prepared by reactive ion etching," *Journal of the Vacuum Society of Japan,* **28,** 77 (1985). A grooved format was etched directly into a glass substrate. Good CNR was observed, but only for on-land recording.

Okada, M., M. Nakada, K. Toki, H. Gokan, T. Iwanaga, and H. Inada, "Magneto-optical disks using PC substrates," *OSA Topical Meeting on Optical Data Storage, Technical Digest,* **10,** 123 (1987). Thermal annealing was used to reduce the lateral birefringence in polycarbonate substrates and increase the CNR by 3 dB.

Redlich, H., and G. Joschko, "The Teldec direct metal mastering process for compact disc," *Memoires Optiques,* no. 14, 13 (1987). A proposal for mastering CD's by physically cutting the pattern into a metal master.

Sekizawa, H., K. Yamada, and A. Iwamoto, "Disk-memory pregroove inspection," *Applied Optics,* **23,** 2830 (1984). The use of diffraction spectrometry to measure grooves on optical disk substrates.

Shimojo, S., "Ultra-precise injection molding of optical disk blanks," *Plastic Age,* **33,** 159 (1987). A description of injection molding of optical disk substrates.

Sudou, R., H. Miwa, T. Tajima, S. Horigome, and N. Ohta, "Optical disk substrate using photocurable casting resin," *SPIE Proceedings,* **899,** 129 (1988). Photopolymerization used to accelerate casting of plastic substrates.

CHAPTER 13

Practical Recording Layers

General Physics of Optical Recording

Recording in optical media is always effected by an intense laser beam, but there are many alternative physical mechanisms that convert the laser exposure into a visible mark (recall Chapter 3, Section 1). There are also many mechanisms for erasable optical recording, including phase-switching and thermo-magneto-optics, which we discussed in detail in Chapter 4. Optical recording physics is too broad a topic to be treated in detail in this book, but see Bell (1986, referenced in Chapter 4) for a comprehensive review of optical recording materials and the diverse physics of optical recording.

In most cases, the marking processes follow a common sequence.

1. The recording layer absorbs light from the focused laser beam. The greater the absorption, the greater the efficiency of recording. Design techniques that reduce the media reflectance (and increase absorption) are discussed in Sections 13.1 and 13.2.

2. The absorbed energy is thermalized rapidly. Photons absorbed by dye molecules generally are converted into thermal energy on a picosecond timescale. Thermalization is even more rapid in metals.

3. A (time-dependent) temperature profile is established. The temperature is directly proportional to the laser power. It also depends (sometimes subtly) on the scanning velocity, pulse length, absorption profile, thermal conductivity, and so on. Heat flow and the resulting temperature profiles are discussed in Section 13.3, along with the design factors that influence heat flow.

4. When and where the temperature exceeds some threshold value, the heat (or the associated temperature gradient) drives a marking mechanism. Sometimes the heat only triggers another energy source, e.g., in write-once bilayers that alloy exothermically after melting, and in M-O recording, where the bias magnetic field actually switches the magnetization.

5. After the laser pulse is switched off (or the optical stylus has moved on by), the recording layer cools quickly as heat flows vertically into the substrate or laterally across the layer. The marking mechanism turns off as the temperature drops below the threshold, freezing the mark into its final shape. The thresholding character of (most) optical recording mechanisms prevents subsequent damage to previously recorded marks during repeated readout.

13.1 Reflectance and Interference

The reflection of light and its absorption within a layered structure depend on the refractive indices and thicknesses of the layers, the wavelength, the sense of polarization, and the angle of incidence. Eq. (3.1) give the (complex) reflectance coefficients at a boundary between semi-infinite layers (e.g., air and a transparent substrate) or at the surface of an opaque layer. These formulae are complicated, and when multiple layers are involved, the reflectance calculations are even more elaborate.

If the layers are thick, reflections from each interface add incoherently, meaning that the beam intensities from multiple reflections add together without any dependence on relative phase. This situation is illustrated in Figure 13.1a. Eqs (3.1), (3.3), and the corresponding equations for transmittance can be used to calculate the reflectance (R_1, R_2) and transmittance (T_1, T_2) at each interface. If just two interfaces contribute, and if the intermediate layer (layer 1) is transparent, the net reflectance is

$$R_{net} = R_1 + T_1^2 R_2 + T_1^2 R_2^2 R_1 + \ldots \qquad (13.1)$$
$$= (R_1 + R_2 - 2R_1 R_2)/(1 - R_2 R_1).$$

This equation makes use of the fact that R and T at an isolated interface are the same for light incident from above or below. If the inter-

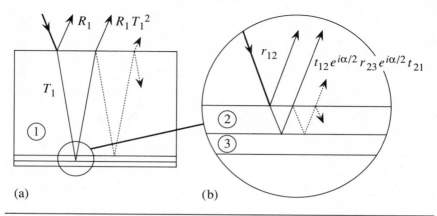

Figure 13.1 *Multiple reflections from thick layers (a) add incoherently; reflections from thin layers (b) interfere coherently.*

mediate layer is slightly absorbing, additional terms are needed to account for power loss during each pass.

The condition of incoherent reflection (Eq. 13.1) obviously applies if the thickness of the film layers exceeds the coherence length. Lasers used for optical recording usually have coherence lengths of at least several cm. But reflection is *effectively* incoherent if the optical path length within the layers varies with incidence angle by much more than λ. Thus, Eq. (13.1) can be used to predict the net reflectance of transparent substrates. Consider an uncoated polycarbonate substrate with $R_1 = R_2 = 5\%$. The net reflectance (e.g., measured by a spectrophotometer) is about 10%. If one surface of the substrate were coated with aluminum ($R_2 = 90\%$), the net reflectance for illumination through the substrate is still just 90%. But note that the reflected intensity observed by an optical head differs from the net reflectance measured in typical test instruments, because only the light reflected from one surface is focused onto the detectors. In the example of the aluminized substrate, the effective reflectance observed by a head is

$$R_{\text{focused}} = R_2 T_1^2, \qquad (13.2)$$

about 10% less than the nominal surface reflectance.

Optical recording media are composed of films that are typically thinner than 0.1 μm ($<< \lambda$). If the structure is a single opaque film, Eq. (3.1) may be used to calculate the reflectance; but generally, the structure includes multiple layers, which are transparent or only partially opaque. Reflections from the several interfaces interfere constructively or destructively; the net reflectance therefore depends strongly on the thicknesses of the component films. Figure 13.1b illustrates reflection from a thin film, layer 2, sandwiched between materials 1 and 3. As in the incoherent reflection case, the net reflectance involves a converging series of reflection terms. But in this case, the addition of the complex amplitudes depends on a propagation phase factor, $\alpha \cong 4\pi \, d \, n \cos \phi' / \lambda$, where n is the complex refractive index of layer 2, d is its thickness, and ϕ' represents the beam direction within layer 2 calculated from the incidence angle ϕ using Snell's law (Eq. 5.1). The net reflectance coefficient from a single film with two visible interfaces is

$$r_{net} = \frac{r_{12} + r_{23} \, e^{i\alpha}}{1 + r_{12} \, r_{23} \, e^{i\alpha}}. \qquad (13.3)$$

In Eq. (13.3), the subscripts 1, 2, and 3 identify the incident medium, the thin film, and the material (or structure) beneath the film. The symbol r_{12} is the reflectance coefficient corresponding to light incident from material 1 to material 2 (from Eq. 3.1), and r_{23} is the reflectance coefficient for light incident at the 2/3 interface. Eq. (13.3) is applicable at any incidence angle and with either polarization state. (The equations for r_{ij} are polarization-dependent. As long as the materials are optically isotropic, without birefringence, Kerr rotation, and so on, the reflected and transmitted light have the same polarization, s or p, as the incident beam.)

If layer 2 is transparent $[\mathrm{Im}(n_2) = 0]$ and $|r_{12}| = |r_{23}|$, there exists some film thickness at which $r_{23} \, e^{i\alpha} = -r_{12}$ and $r_{net} = 0$. For example, for a low-index dielectric film ($n_2 \sim 1.3$) on polycarbonate ($n_3 \sim 1.6$) we have $r_{12} \sim r_{23} \sim 0.1$ at normal incidence from air ($n_1 = 1$). Precise equality between r_{12} and r_{23} is achieved when

$$n_2 = \sqrt{n_3}, \qquad (13.4)$$

if an appropriate coating material is available. An antireflection condition is created when $\alpha = \pi$, or $d = \frac{1}{4}\lambda/n_2$. It is generally true that a *quarter-wave* coating of a transparent film reduces the reflectance from any surface. Coatings like this are used to minimize reflection losses from lenses, prisms, and beam-splitters.

The propagation factor, α, has a maximum at normal incidence and asymptotes to a minimum at grazing incidence. As a result, when a thin-film coating is viewed obliquely, its appearance is similar to that of a thinner film viewed at normal incidence. This useful fact runs counter to the intuitive idea that one looks through a greater depth of material at non-normal incidence.

We can apply Eq. (13.3) in an iterative procedure to calculate the reflectance from more-complex optical stacks. Eq. (3.1) gives the reflectance coefficient from the lowest interface; Eq. (13.3) gives the net reflectance coefficient at the next interface. Repeated applications of Eq. (13.3) (using successive values of α and $r_{i,i+1}$) eventually generates the net reflectance coefficient for the complete stack. Another simple computational method for modeling multilayers is the matrix method described by Heavens (1955). Because they mix the polarization states, magneto-optic or birefringent layers require more-elaborate modeling calculations. Li, Sullivan, and Parsons, (1988) have described a practical computational approach to modeling more general thin-film situations.

13.2 Antireflection Structures

Optical recording media are designed to have low reflectance. Or rather, they are designed to absorb as strongly as possible at the laser wavelength within the recording layer, and thus increase the recording sensitivity. Some reflectance, at least 10%, is necessary to provide large-enough servo signals and readout signals from molded format marks. The optical design parameters that increase absorption are usually adjusted to provide reflectance in the range 10% to 30%.

A single-layer coating is the simplest optical media design. Figure 13.2 illustrates a moderately absorbing (dye-containing) organic film with a refractive index $n = 1.5 + 1i$ coated on a transparent substrate. In this and the subsequent figures in this section, the reflectance is calculated for normal incidence at $\lambda = 800$ nm. The absorption curves plot the fraction of incident light absorbed *within the recording layer.* For a given recording material, the only free parameter in the single-layer design is the recording-layer thickness. In the example of Figure 13.2, an antireflection minimum is achieved for a film thickness of about 25 nm. This minimum differs from the quarter-wave thickness discussed in Section 13.1, because the two reflectance coefficients (r_{12} and r_{23}) have nearly opposite phases. This reflectance

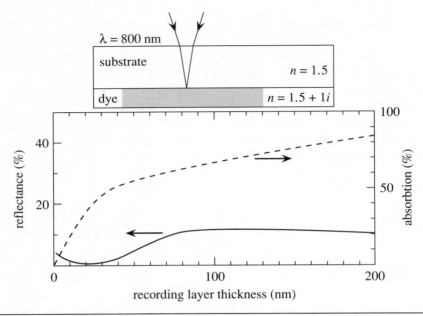

Figure 13.2 *Reflectance and absorption vs. film thickness for a single-layer organic recording medium are graphed here.*

minimum would not be a good media design, because the net reflectance is insufficient for readout and because the absorption is very low (most of the incident light is transmitted and lost). A film thickness in the range 50 to 70 nm provides both higher reflectance and more absorption. Note that marks (pits) recorded in a film of this thickness are darker than the surrounding land areas.

With a greater film thickness, the absorption increases still further, but the absorbed energy is shared over too much film volume. Wrobel (1983) has described a figure of merit, called the *specific absorption,* which is the absorption divided by the heated depth of the recording medium. This concept must be invoked in the thermal/optical optimization of organic recording media.

An alternate way to use an organic recording material is to coat it in a bilayer structure with a reflector. Figure 13.3 shows a recording film (again with $n = 1.5 + 1i$) coated on an opaque aluminum reflector and used in an air-incident configuration. In this case, the reflectance minimum and absorption maximum occur at about the quarter-wave thickness. The design thickness is usually around 100 nm for such media. The signal contrast for the bilayer organic media

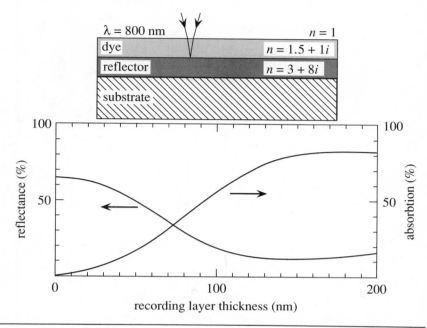

Figure 13.3 *Reflectance and absorption vs. recording-layer thickness for an organic bilayer recording medium are graphed here.*

design is opposite to the single-layer design: Bright marks form on a darker background.

In Section 13.1 we discussed how transparent coatings can be applied to reduce the reflectance from the surfaces of transparent optical elements. Transparent coatings can also be used to reduce the reflectance from, and increase absorption within, reflective films. For instance, M-O recording layers are usually undercoated with a high-index dielectric layer, which serves this purpose. An undercoat of silicon ($n \cong 4$) gives an almost-perfect antireflection match for an M-O film (RE/TM composition) that has a refractive index $n \cong 3 + 3i$ (Hunt, 1969). Most undercoat materials have n in the range 2 to 2.5. Figure 13.4 shows how an undercoat with $n = 2.5$ reduces the reflectance from 40% to about 10%. It increases the absorption of the recording layer accordingly. The reflectance minimum occurs for an undercoat thickness slightly less than a quarter wave.

Media sensitivity can be further enhanced using the optical trilayer design. A trilayer consists of a thin, semi-transparent recording film, a transparent spacer layer (about a quarter-wave thick) and an

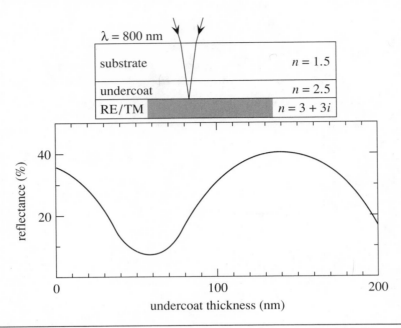

Figure 13.4 *Reflectance vs. overcoat thickness for a standard M-O recording medium is graphed here.*

opaque reflector layer (Au, Al, etc.). Most of the light transmitted through the recording layer is reflected by the reflector back through the recording layer, where destructive interference enhances its absorption. Figure 13.5 describes the optical characteristics of an M-O trilayer made up of a thin RE/TM film, a dielectric spacer, and an aluminum reflector. Arbitrarily low reflectance can be obtained together with very high absorption in the thin recording layer. An ideal antireflection condition is achievable for any spacer refractive index by slight adjustment of the recording-layer thickness.

The trilayer design is a very powerful method for enhancing media sensitivity. Because the absorbing layer is very thin, the specific absorption can be extremely high. Trilayer recording has been demonstrated in many materials with high melting points which are not usually thought of as recording materials—Al, Ti, and so on (Bell and Spong, 1978).

The most complicated media structure commonly used in optical recording is the M-O quadrilayer. The M-O recording layer is usually encapsulated by two dielectric coatings in order to enhance its

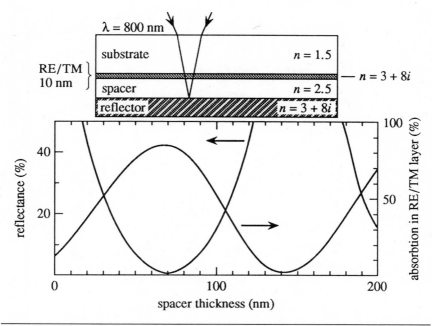

Figure 13.5 *Reflectance and absorption vs. spacer thickness for a trilayer magneto-optic recording medium are shown here.*

environmental stability (see Chapter 14, Section 3). The trilayer configuration illustrated in Figure 13.5 would have an undercoat added, for a total of four films, each of which affects the net optical characteristics.

The film thicknesses in M-O media (undercoated thick films or quadrilayers) are designed to enhance the magneto-optical signal, as well as the reflectance and sensitivity. The shot-noise-limited SNR from an M-O disk is proportional to $\theta_k \sqrt{R}$, where θ_k is the Kerr rotation and R is the reflectance. In general, the Kerr rotation and the reflectance are inversely related, but Figure 13.6 shows that slightly better overall performance is theoretically achievable from M-O media with low reflectance. Figure 13.6 also demonstrates that different dielectric materials (TiO_2, $n = 3.5$; Si_3N_4, $n = 2.5$; and Al_2O_3, $n = 1.7$) produce almost the same Kerr rotation angle at the same net reflectance (Bell, 1987). For a given recording layer, the M-O signal ($R \, \theta_k$) is virtually independent of the net reflectance and the media structure, except when interference effects exaggerate the

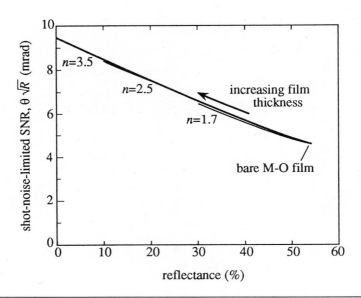

Figure 13.6 *The increase in the shot-noise-limited SNR of magneto-optic media depends on the reflectance of the structure, not the refractive index of the antireflection coating.*

ellipticity (see Eq. 4.3). The value of multilayer interference structures in enhancing M-O media performance is often overestimated.

A completely different antireflection technique that does not involve multilayer interference is used in the write-once Moth-Eye media made by Plasmon Data Systems. The reflectance at an interface is reduced if the refractive-index change is gradual rather than abrupt. The recording surface on the Plasmon disk is a thin film of platinum ($n_{Pt} = 3 + 6i$), which would ordinarily have a reflectance greater than 50%. But the film is deposited on the finely textured Moth-Eye substrate shown in Figure 13.7. The periodicity of the texture is much smaller than the wavelength of the light used for recording, so the incoming light encounters a gradual optical transition from the transparent substrate material to the platinum film. The texture reduces the media reflectance to 15%. Enhanced absorption accompanies the reduced reflectance. Preformatted marks are mastered so as to remove the texture, and recorded marks are formed by breaking the Pt film away from the textured surface; the untextured marks have a reflectance approaching 50% and good contrast compared to the background.

Figure 13.7 *The surface of a Plasmon substrate, shows the Moth-Eye texture interrupted by recorded marks. Photo courtesy of Plasmon Data Systems.*

13.3 Thermal Efficiency

The temperature profile during a recording event depends on the laser exposure (Chapter 5, Section 3), the efficiency of optical absorption (Section 13.2), and the thermal properties of the materials comprising the recording medium. Two independent thermal parameters must be considered—the volume heat capacity, η, and the thermal diffusivity, κ. The heat capacity is defined as the ratio of an incremental increase in the thermal energy density to the corresponding increase in temperature:

$$\eta \equiv \Delta \mathscr{E} / \Delta T. \qquad (13.5)$$

Over the temperature range of interest, η is relatively constant; therefore, it can be used as a conversion factor between temperature and energy density. The diffusivity is the diffusion coefficient for thermal energy. It relates the energy flux, $\mathscr{F}$, to the gradient in the energy density or temperature:

$$\begin{aligned} \mathscr{F} &= -\kappa \, \nabla \mathscr{E} \\ &= -\kappa \, \eta \, \nabla T. \end{aligned} \qquad (13.6)$$

In the reference literature, materials are often described by the specific heat (η/ρ where ρ is the density) and the conductivity ($\kappa\,\eta$). Representative values of η and κ are listed in Table 13.1 for plastics, inorganic glasses and dielectrics, and metals. The heat capacity does not vary dramatically among different materials, but the diffusivity varies by several orders of magnitude. Consequently, the thermal phenomena during optical recording depend both quantitatively and qualitatively on the composition and structure of the recording medium.

The diffusivity determines how far heat can flow during a laser exposure or recording event. In a time τ, heat diffuses a typical distance Λ:

$$\Lambda = (\kappa\,\tau)^{1/2}. \tag{13.7}$$

The effective length of a recording pulse, as seen by the recording medium, is approximately equal to the scan time for the optical stylus. For typical values of the stylus f.w.h.m. and the scanning velocity ($s = 1\ \mu\text{m}$ and $v = 10$ m/s), this interval is

$$\tau \sim s/v = 100 \text{ ns}. \tag{13.8}$$

Eq. (13.8) is applicable during readout and erasure because the laser is unmodulated. It is also applicable during recording when mark-length modulation is used (Chapter 9, Section 2), because the marks and corresponding recording pulses are longer than the optical stylus. If the recording channel uses mark-position modulation, the la-

TABLE 13.1 Thermal Properties of Various Materials

MATERIAL	DIFFUSIVITY, κ (cm^2/s)	HEAT CAPACITY, η (J/cm^3/K)
Dielectrics		
Plastic	0.001	1.5
Ordinary glass	0.01	2
Ceramics	0.02–0.2	2
Metals		
Tellurium	0.02	1.5
RE/TM alloys	0.1	3
Silicon	0.5	2
Aluminum	1	3

ser pulse is shorter than s/v, and τ should be interpreted as the actual pulse time. In principle, the thermal efficiency of recording is enhanced by very short recording pulses, because less heat is lost through diffusion. But in practice, τ is seldom much shorter than 100 ns because of media sensitivity and laser-power limitations.

Three heat-flow phenomena account for most of the thermal behavior of optical recording media: thermal equilibration between and among the thin-film coatings; lateral heat flow; and heat loss into the substrate (see Figure 13.8).

Equilibration: The optical energy is usually absorbed in one film, or even a specific layer of one film, but the resulting heat spreads quickly among the several layers of the recording structure. Diffusion creates a uniform temperature distribution through the entire depth of the recording layer if the diffusivity is greater than

$$\kappa > d^2/\tau, \tag{13.9}$$

or

$$\kappa > 10^{-3} \text{ cm}^2/\text{s}$$

for a typical layer thickness $d \sim 100$ nm. From Table 13.1, we see that only plastic (organic) layers insulate well enough to support a substantial temperature gradient. A recording medium composed of

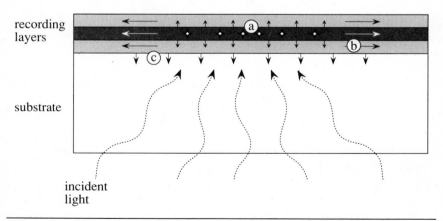

Figure 13.8 *Three phenomena account for heat flow during optical recording: (a) equilibration within the recording layers, (b) spreading across the surface, and (c) loss into the substrate.*

inorganic films usually has enough diffusivity to maintain a uniform temperature profile through its depth.

If a film stack is isothermal in the vertical direction because of high diffusivity, the thermal parameters of the several layers can be combined into two effective values for the stack,

$$\eta_{\text{eff}} = \Sigma \, \eta_i \, d_i \, / D \qquad\qquad (13.10)$$

and

$$\kappa_{\text{eff}} = \Sigma \, \kappa_i \, \eta_i \, d_i \, / \, (\eta_{\text{eff}} \, D), \qquad\qquad (13.11)$$

where D is the total thickness, Σd_i. Using these parameters, the film stack can be modeled as a simple homogeneous structure. Because η is very similar for most materials, η_{eff} does not depend strongly on the media design. On the other hand, κ_{eff} is dominated by any metallic or high-conductivity ceramic layers that might be present.

As an application of Eq. (13.10), consider an M-O medium with a reflectance of 25% composed of 60 nm of an RE-TM alloy protected by an inorganic dielectric undercoat and overcoat (70 nm each). The isothermal stack has a net thickness $D = 0.2 \ \mu$m. With the parameters from Table 13.1, the stack has an effective heat capacity of $\eta_{\text{eff}} = 2.3 \ \text{J/cm}^3/\text{K}$. For $s = 1 \ \mu$m, $v = 10$ m/s, and $P = 10$ mW, the maximum exposure at the center of the track is about 0.1 J/cm^2 (see Eq. 5.34). In the absence of any other thermal losses, the maximum temperature rise would be about 75% 0.1 J/cm^2/η_{eff} / $D \sim 1600$K. However, we will see in a more detailed model below that lateral diffusion and substrate losses reduce this temperature rise by nearly an order of magnitude.

Lateral Flow: In 100 ns, heat flows about 0.1 μm in organic materials, 0.3 to 1 μm in inorganic dielectrics, and 0.3 to 3 μm in metals (from Eq. 13.7 and Table 13.1). Clearly, there is no appreciable lateral heat flow during recording in organic media. The simple application of Eq. (13.7), which proved unsatisfactory for M-O media, works quite well for organic media (with an appropriate estimate of the heated depth D). But when the media structure includes metal films or high-conductivity ceramic layers, substantial lateral spreading can occur.

For some purposes, it may be satisfactory to estimate a spreading distance and the corresponding decrease in the thermal energy density. In our M-O example, the effective diffusivity is $\kappa_{\text{eff}} = 0.07 \ \text{cm}^2/\text{s}$, and the spreading distance is $\Lambda \sim 0.8\ \mu m$. The initial exposure region has a diameter of $s \sim 1\ \mu m$, but the heat eventually spreads over a diameter of about s + 2Λ (2.6 μm), and the energy density is reduced by a factor of $1/(1 + 2\Lambda/s)^2$, about $1/6\times$. This explains qualitatively (but not quantitatively) why our first heating estimate was so much too high.

Substrate Losses: In almost all media designs, the substrate is made of plastic or covered with an organic layer. Heat conducted out of the media films diffuses only a short distance into the substrate. Because of low conductivity, there is no appreciable lateral diffusion within the substrate. Some media designs include an organic protective layer on top of the recording films or an adhesive layer between two substrates. The amount of heat lost to these auxiliary layers is about the same as the amount lost to the substrate.

Heat flow into the substrate and auxiliary layers is an important factor in most optical recording systems. Substrate heating has two qualitative effects. (1) The additional heated layers increase the thermal mass of the medium and reduce the overall heating rate. But (2) vertical heat flow out of the more conductive films also slows down lateral heat flow. In some cases, these two effects are counterbalancing.

Substrate losses can be estimated in the context of Eqs. (13.10) and (13.11). Suppose, in our M-O example, that the media is coated on a plastic substrate and covered with an organic lacquer layer. Two organic boundary layers about 0.1 μm thick are thermally involved. The heated region has a total thickness of $D = 0.4\ \mu m$ and effective thermal parameters $\eta_{eff} = 1.9\ J/cm^3/K$ and $\kappa_{eff} = 0.04\ cm^2/s$. The distance of lateral heat flow is $\Lambda \sim 0.6\ \mu m$, so the exposure density is reduced by a factor of $1/(1 + 2\Lambda/s)^2 = 0.2$ from 0.1 J/cm^2 to 0.02 J/cm^2. The estimated maximum temperature is now 75% 0.02 J/cm^2/η_{eff} /D $\sim$ 200 K. This value is close to results obtained from detailed calculations and experiments (see below).

When more-accurate thermal predictions are required, several calculational methods are available. The basic heat equation is

$$dT/dt = A/\eta - \kappa \nabla^2 T, \qquad (13.12)$$

where A is the local rate at which energy is absorbed from the laser beam (power per unit volume). A unique solution to this differential equation is constrained by the boundary conditions of temperature continuity at each interface between layers and an asymptotic match to the ambient temperature. Analytic solutions of the heat equation are possible in some specific cases, but analytic results seldom provide satisfying insight into the physics. In principle, a direct difference-equation approach can be used to solve Eq. (13.12) numerically; however, this method is usually time consuming and/or unstable.

A Green's-function approach is always stable, and usually more efficient, because it makes use of the linearity of the heat equation. See Mansuripur and Connell (1983) for a good example of this approach. It is often helpful to recognize that heat flow is a linear diffusion process, except to the extent that η and κ depend on T. Energy deposited in the recording medium at one location and time will diffuse in a pattern that is independent of subsequent heat inputs. One consequence of this principle is that thermal calculations need only be done for one laser power, because the thermal profiles are strictly proportional to the laser output.

The thermal problem can also be solved by numerical simulation. For each short time interval, Eq. (13.6) is used to calculate $\mathcal{F}$ and redistribute $\mathscr{E}$; a detailed energy balance is enforced; and Eq. (13.5) is used to re-compute the temperature distribution. The results of a detailed thermal simulation of the M-O recording problem (our extended example) is illustrated in Figure 13.9. The media structure

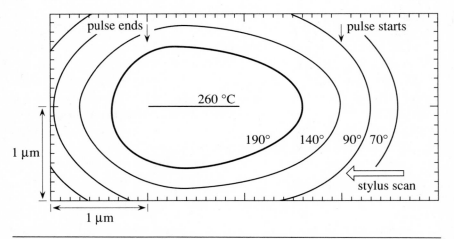

Figure 13.9 *Contours of maximum temperature on an M-O disk for a 10-mW, 0.2-μs laser pulse at 10 m/s are plotted here.*

consists of a plastic substrate, a 70-nm ceramic undercoat, a 60-nm RE-TM recording layer, a 70-nm ceramic overcoat, and an organic lacquer or lamination layer. The thermal properties of these materials are taken from Table 13.1, with $\kappa_{ceramic} = 0.05$ cm^2/s. The substrate-incident reflectance is assumed to be 25%. Figure 13.9 shows profiles of the maximum temperature achieved at each point during a 10-mW, 0.2-μs pulse of an optical stylus (s $= 1$ μm). The maximum temperature (240 K above ambient) is quite close to the third simplistic estimate above.

Figure 13.9 also displays some qualitative features that are not apparent in any of the qualitative thermal models. The heavy profile surrounds the region heated above the Curie point ($\sim 190°$C), the region expected to switch and form the recorded domain. The domain has an asymmetrical shape, wider at the trailing edge due to lateral heat flow. Wide, asymmetrical domains like this are observed in M-O recording (e.g., Takahashi, Niihara, and Ohta, 1988). The thermal profile has a rather broad maximum and a steep temperature gradient at the edge of the heated region; the thermal profile is much more "square" than the Gaussian laser-beam profile. This thermal profile explains why the carrier vs. recording-power dependence has such an abrupt character: the domain size increases very rapidly with a slight increase in power immediately above the marking threshold. It is also apparent from Figure 13.9 that the mark position is offset in the scan direction. This could cause a substantial timing error (~ 0.5 μm or 50 ns). But fortunately all marks are offset by about the same amount.

Throughout this section, we have tacitly assumed that the thermal and structural characteristics of the recording medium remain unchanged during the modeled event. This condition can be violated if the materials flow, decompose, or change their chemical structure (e.g., in write-once marking). Detailed thermal modeling becomes much more complex when such changes occur, but the simple principles are applicable in many cases: readout, write-once recording before the marking threshold is attained, and recording in most erasable media.

As an extra complication, the thermal conditions are sometimes modified by additional, nonoptical energy sources. M-O recording, because it occurs at relatively low temperatures, is sensitive to variations in the ambient temperature. When the recording medium has a high diffusivity, energy deposited during previous recording pulses can "preheat" the area of a subsequent mark, leading to data-dependent shape distortions similar in principle to the asymmetry observed in Figure 13.9 (inter-symbol interference). Some types of write-once materials react exothermically during the recording process, an addition to the thermal input that increases the media sensitivity. Suh and Craighead (1987) describe a medium composed of layers of selenium and bismuth, which melt and then react to form nearly-stoichiometric Bi_2Se_3. The heat of reaction aids hole-opening and lowers the critical recording temperature to near the melting point of Bi. The current write-once optical disks from SONY function similarly.

13.4   Media Coating Techniques

The coating of thin films is a very broad, cross-disciplinary technology. This section is just an introduction to the most common coating methods used in optical disk manufacturing. Practical process descriptions for these and other coating methods are accessible in references such as Bunshah (1982) and Chapman (1980).

Evaporation

Vacuum evaporation is probably the most adaptable method for making optical media coatings. Almost any material can be coated evaporatively. The composition and thickness can be carefully controlled and the resulting films can be kept free of defects. Evaporation cannot easily be scaled for volume manufacturing, but it is useful for early materials exploration and media development.

Evaporation systems are relatively simple and inexpensive. The basic components are shown in Figure 13.10. The evaporative coating process occurs in a high-vacuum bell jar with a heater, an evaporation source, and a film-thickness monitor.

The substrates and coating material are mounted in the bell jar, or vacuum chamber. The chamber is evacuated to a pressure of around 10^{-6} torr. (Atmospheric pressure is about 760 torr.) At such a low pressure, the mean-free-path is greater than the dimensions of the bell jar. The low pressure is maintained by a high-vacuum pump (preferably a cryopump or turbopump), backed up by a mechanical roughing pump.The material to be coated is held in some kind of

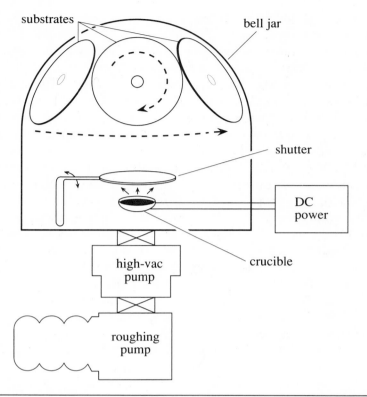

Figure 13.10 *Planetary substrate motion improves the uniformity from evaporative coating.*

heater: a resistively heated tungsten filament or boat, a ceramic crucible with an inductive heater, an electron-beam heater, and so on. For many applications, an e-beam source is preferred because it provides finer temperature control, causes less overheating, and prevents mixing of the coating material with its container. The coating material is covered with a rotating cover or shutter and then the heat source is turned on, raising the temperature of the coating material until evaporation begins to occur. The temperature of the coating material must be stabilized safely below the boiling point. Rapid evaporation is undesirable, because any semblance of boiling destroys the high-vacuum condition and contaminates the coating with particulates.

After the rate of evaporation is stabilized, the shutter is removed from the heater and evaporated atoms or molecules pass across the bell jar to the exposed substrate surface. They strike the substrate on a direct trajectory from the source. Surface transport is usually negligible, so the coated film is virtually conformal, with a thickness independent of the underlying substrate profile. Usually a crystal monitor is mounted near the substrate(s). The oscillation frequency of the crystal is a sensitive indicator of its mass. A change in the frequency is proportional to the coating mass, indirectly indicating the film thickness. When the intended coating thickness has accumulated, the shutter is closed again and the heat source is turned off.

The thickness uniformity of evaporated films depends on the distance from the source to the substrate, the angle of emission from the source, and the angle of incidence on the substrate. Excellent uniformity is easily achieved when the substrate is far from the source, but then the utilization of the source material is very inefficient. Figure 13.10 illustrates a *planetary* mechanism, which rotates the substrates through the evaporation pattern to produce good (time-averaged) thickness uniformity with reasonable efficiency.

Materials with very high vapor pressures and materials that decompose before evaporating are poor candidates for evaporative coating. However, the range of coatable compounds and alloys can be extended by *coevaporation* from multiple sources. The physical structure of the coating (crystalline, polycrystalline, amorphous) can sometimes be manipulated through the deposition rate and substrate temperature.

Sputtering

Sputtering, an alternative method of vacuum coating, is illustrated in Figure 13.11. The vacuum chamber is initially pumped down to high vacuum (at least 10^{-5} torr) to eliminate contaminants like O_2 and H_2O. But then the chamber is back-filled with a noble gas (usually argon) to the range 1–20 mtorr. A cathode covered with a slab of the coating material (the *target,* usually a few millimeters thick) is raised to a potential of several hundred volts to ignite a plasma in the sputtering gas. Positive ions (Ar^+) from the plasma are accelerated into the target surface. When they strike, they break loose individual atoms. The mean free path for neutral atoms in the vacuum chamber is greater than the distance from the target to the substrate (a few centimeters), so the target atoms follow essentially ballistic trajectories to the substrate surface, where they stick, forming the

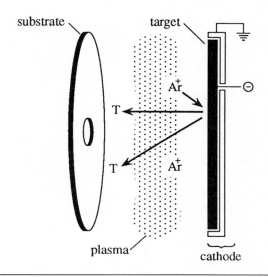

Figure 13.11 *Inert gas ions sputter individual atoms or molecules from the target surface.*

coating. The sputtering efficiency is enhanced by *magnetron sputtering,* in which a magnetic field from a magnet mounted behind the target confines the plasma and the energetic Ar^+ ions near the target surface. The ground shield shown surrounding the target serves to keep the plasma away from the target edge and prevents excessive erosion there. Neutral Ar atoms continuously strike both the target and substrate surfaces (with low energy). They increase atomic mobilities and help to densify the coating; but since noble gases are nonreactive, they are not incorporated into the coating except at very high deposition rates.

On the laboratory scale, sputtering systems are more expensive and difficult to operate than evaporation equipment; but sputtering has several advantages over evaporative coating which make it preferable for large-scale manufacturing. The coating process adds relatively little heat to the substrate as long as the target, shields, and vacuum chamber are kept cool. Sputtered films are generally denser and adhere better than evaporated films of the same composition. Large areas can be coated with one charge of coating material (one target). Very high sputtering rates can be achieved with high efficiency, especially for metal films. Systems can be configured to deposit multiple media layers, either sequentially or simultaneously without withdrawing the substrates from the vacuum. For example, a throughput of 300 M-O disks per hour ($5\frac{1}{4}''$-diameter substrates with up to four metallic and/or dielectric layers) has been reported from an in-line sputtering system (Schultheiss, Bäuer, Dicken, Müller, and Shieh, 1988).

In manufacturing systems, the distance between substrates and targets is always small, and any variation in plasma efficiency at the target leads to a variation in coating rate across the substrate. The targets, cathodes, and shields must be carefully designed and adjusted to achieve a high degree of coating uniformity. As with evaporation, substrate motion across the sputtering target (rotation or translation) is also effective in averaging-out rate variations.

Sputtered films are essentially conformal, just like evaporated films. However, when the sputtered atoms are incident over a wide angular range (and especially if the substrate moves past the target during coating), odd and undesirable features can form over any sharp edges on the substrate surface. Such an effect is illustrated in Figure 13.12.

The range of materials that can be sputtered is more limited than the range of materials for evaporation. Metals are usually easy to sputter, as long as they are conductive and can be machined into targets. Metallic alloys can be sputtered from prealloyed targets, by cosputtering (from two targets simultaneously), by sputtering from a mosaic target (a homogeneous target patterned with small slabs of the alternate elements), or by rapidly rotating the substrate through the sputtering zones of multiple targets. Different materials sputter at different rates and with different angular distributions. So the film composition does not necessarily correspond to the target composition (alloy targets) or the surface pattern (mosaic targets). Therefore, targets must be empirically optimized to produce the desired compo-

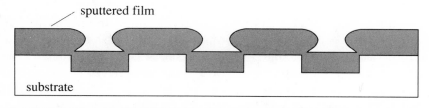

Figure 13.12 *Sputtered films are generally conformal.*

sitions. Magnetic materials are sometimes difficult to sputter in magnetron systems if the targets are highly permeable. Such materials require enhanced magnetron magnets or thinner targets (which shunt less field).

Nonconductive dielectric materials are much harder to sputter than metals. In conventional DC sputtering, if the target is not conductive, a surface charge quickly builds up, shielding the potential and shutting down the plasma. The charge buildup can be eliminated by RF sputtering, in which the target oscillates between a negative and a positive potential. Unfortunately, the efficiency of RF sputtering is much lower than that of DC sputtering. Some dielectric materials can also be coated by *reactive sputtering* from a conductive target in the presence of a reactive gas. For instance, sputtering from a conductive (doped) Si target can create an SiO_2 film if a little O_2 is added to the inert sputter gas. Si_3N_4 can be coated using the same target if N_2 is added instead of oxygen.

Spin Coating

Vacuum coating methods are particularly suitable for inorganic materials but not for most organic films. Spin coating is the best technique for coating thin, uniform, organic films on round substrates. This method is used widely with optical recording media to coat photoresist masters (Chapter 12, Section 4), to deposit organic recording layers, and to form auxiliary layers of various kinds.

Materials for spin coating must be in a liquid form. A solid organic material is prepared as a solvent solution (or dope) using a solvent with a moderate evaporation rate. Some inorganic materials can be spin-coated from sol-gel suspensions, but this technique usually includes a heat treatment, which is inappropriate for plastic or plastic-surfaced substrates.

The spin-coating process is a complex interplay of physical effects. As illustrated in Figure 13.13, the basic phenomena are centrifugal force, viscosity, and solvent evaporation. The coating process begins with the application of an excess amount of solution applied as a puddle at the center of the disk (if there is no center hole), or as a ring at the inside diameter of the coating zone. If a more-uniform starting condition is required, the solution can be applied as a closely spaced spiral while the disk spins slowly. After application of the solution, the disk is quickly accelerated to a high speed of rotation. The rotation creates hundreds, or even thousands, of G's of centrifugal acceleration acting to drag the solution off the edge of the disk.

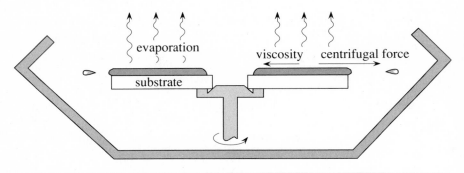

Figure 13.13 *Spin coating is a balance between centrifugal force, viscosity, and evaporative drying.*

Most of the solution is thrown off within a few seconds of the ramp-up, but as the coating layer thins, viscous drag sets in to balance the centrifugal force. This dynamic balance creates a vertical gradient in the radial fluid velocity distribution:

$$dv/dz = (\delta - z)\, \rho\, r\, \omega^2/\eta, \qquad (13.13)$$

where δ is the film thickness, ρ is its density, r is the radial location on the disk, η is the solution viscosity, and ω is the angular rotation rate. The radial fluid velocity is zero at the disk surface ($z = 0$) and increases toward the free (air) surface according to

$$v(z) = (\delta\, z - z^2/2)\, \rho\, r\, \omega^2/\eta. \qquad (13.14)$$

The average velocity is

$$<v> = \delta^2\, \rho\, r\, \omega^2/(6\eta). \qquad (13.15)$$

The volume of solution interior to a radius r,

$$\mathcal{M}(r) = \int_{x<r} 2\pi\, x\, \delta(x)\, dx, \qquad (13.16)$$

changes with time at the rate

$$d\mathcal{M}/dt = 2\pi\, \delta\, <v>. \qquad (13.17)$$

If the solution extends to the center of the substrate, Eqs. (13.16) and (13.17) can be satisfied by a thickness distribution $\delta(r, t)$, which is independent of r:

$$\delta(t) = [3\eta/(2\, \rho\, \omega^2\, t)]^{1/2}. \qquad (13.18)$$

Even if the initial solution thickness is irregular, the film thickness quickly asymptotes to this value after most of the solution applied at the center spreads past the outer diameter. To good approximation, t can be interpreted as the elapsed time from the beginning of the high-speed spinning cycle. The fact that the eventual thickness of the layer is nearly independent of radius and initial coverage is both remarkable and very useful.

As an application of Eq. (13.18), consider a U.V.-curable lacquer solution with $\rho = 1$ g/cm³ and a viscosity of 1 poise. This kind of solvent-free lacquer is used as the protective film on CDs. At 3000 rpm, the coating thickness will drop to about 15 μm after 10 s. In the lacquer-coating process, the disk rotation is stopped at the correct time, and then the disk is passed under a U.V. lamp to cure the film.

Solvent solutions such as those used to coat organic recording layers usually have a much lower viscosity, say 1 centipoise. At 3000 rpm, the solvent solution thins out rapidly to a thickness of 1 μm after about 20 s. At about this thickness, the solvent evaporates rapidly, the film dries out, and centrifugally-driven flow ceases. In the case of a solvent-free monomer solution, the final coating thickness is determined by the spinning time; arbitrarily thin coatings can be made using very long spin times, but when the coating is made from a solvent solution, the final thickness is determined by the drying time. Initially, the drying rate is insignificant compared with the rate at which solution spins off the disk. But as the coating becomes thinner, the drying rate increases, while the viscous flow slows down. Eventually, drying dominates and the entire film suddenly gels. Subsequent reduction in the film thickness (e.g., from 1 μm to 0.1 μm if the initial solids content is a few percent) is due solely to final drying. Continued spinning will not affect the final thickness (though it may speed the final drying by increasing the air flow over the disk).

During spinning, a thin, gel-like skin and a solvent concentration gradient form in the film. The subsequent drying rate is determined by the rate of solvent diffusion through the layer. Therefore, drying will become the dominant process at a critical time,

$$t_{\text{crit}} \sim \delta^2/D, \qquad (13.19)$$

where D is the diffusion coefficient for solvent through the layer (approximately the self-diffusion coefficient for the solvent). Substituting Eq. (13.19) into Eq. (13.18) we obtain an expression for the final film thickness:

$$\delta = f_{\text{crit}} (1.5 \, D \, \eta/\rho)^{1/4}/\sqrt{\omega}. \qquad (13.20)$$

The fraction f_{crit} is the percentage solids content at t_{crit}, somewhat larger than the solids content of the initial solution. The basic functional dependence of Eq. (13.20),

$$\delta \propto f/\sqrt{\omega}, \qquad (13.21)$$

is observed over a very wide range of spin speed for spin coating from solvent solutions. Note that the final film thickness depends only weakly on the solution density, viscosity, and diffusivity. The humidity and solvent content of the air in the spin coater can also affect the final thickness slightly by changing the drying rate.

Eq. (13.21) explains why standard photoresist solutions are not used to coat optical disk masters. These solutions are usually optimized for spin coated layers at least 1 μm thick on semiconductor wafers. To coat a master at about 0.1 μm, we would have to increase the spin speed by 100× (very dangerous for a large glass disk). Instead, a more dilute photoresist solution is used.

The main advantage of spin coating is that the film thickness is remarkably uniform and repeatable. The fact that a vacuum system is not needed is an advantage in some applications. And spin coating is a relatively quick procedure for making thick films (the process time for most other techniques is proportional to the film thickness). But spin coating also has disadvantages as a technique for mass production: Air flow can cause increased particle contamination; splashing solution could contaminate the disk; large flow patterns (thickness variations) form around and accentuate any substrate defects; solvent recovery systems may be required; and the process is inherently wasteful, with a lot of dope ending up (concentrated and contaminated) in a catch basin. The relative amount of wastage is greatest for thin coatings, when most of the solution is spun off the substrate.

When an organic recording layer is formed by spin coating, the substrate might have a grooved or formatted surface. If the coating thickness is greater than the groove depth, the entire process can be understood using the simple model presented above; but on a featured surface, the coating process does not result in a uniform, conformal coating. At the point of transition between centrifugal flow and dry-down, the surface of the gel/solution is nearly flat due to surface tension. Since the layer is thicker over the grooves than the lands, it will dry to a nonconformal film. This situation stands in direct contrast to thin vacuum-coated films (see Figure 13.14). If the

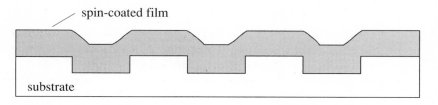

spin-coated film

substrate

Figure 13.14 *Solvent-coated films may be thicker in preformatted grooves or pits.*

groove depth is d, then the final film thickness in the grooves will be greater than the thickness of the lands by about df_{crit}. This effect is responsible for an apparent reduction in the groove depth on single-layer organic media.

━━━━━ MAJOR CONCEPTS

- The sensitivity of optical recording media can be enhanced by reducing its reflectance. Quarter-wave coatings, trilayer structures, and other techniques are used to reduce reflectance.

- Trilayer media can have extremely high sensitivity, but the performance of a trilayer depends critically on the thickness of each layer (Figure 13.5).

- In M-O media, reduced reflectance is accompanied by an increase in the Kerr rotation. However, the SNR increases only slightly and the signal itself is not enhanced.

- The thermal diffusivities of optical recording materials cover a range of several decades, from organic materials with very low diffusivity to amorphous glasses with moderate diffusivity and metals with high diffusivity. The volume heat capacity, on the other hand, is always about 2 J/cm^3/K (Table 13.1).

- Optical recording in organic materials involves little heat flow outside the illuminated region.

- Optical recording in a metal film is accompanied by significant heat loss across the film and into the adjacent layers and substrate. Lateral heat flow leads to asymmetrical mark shapes (Figures 13.8 and 13.9).

- Sputtering and spin-coating are the favored techniques for media manufacturing. Vacuum evaporation is frequently used for experimental or pilot-scale coatings.

■ REFERENCES

Bell, A., "Antireflection structures for magneto-optic recording," *Topical Meeting on Optical Data Storage, Technical Digest Series 1987,* **10,** 138 (1987). The shot-noise-limited SNR of overcoated M-O media depends primarily on the net reflectance of the media, not the refractive index of the coating.

Bell, A., and F. Spong, "Antireflection structures for optical recording," *IEEE Journal of Quantum Electronics,* **QE-14,** 487 (1978). Sensitivity enhancement using the trilayer design.

Bunshah, R., ed., *Deposition Technologies for Films and Coatings,* NOYES, Park Ridge, New Jersey (1982).

Chapman, B., *Glow Discharge Processes,* John Wiley & Sons, New York (1980). An accessible introduction to sputtering and other plasma treatment techniques.

Heavens, O., *Optical Properties of Thin Solid Films,* Academic, New York (1955). A detailed and comprehensible treatment of the optics of thin films and multilayers.

Hunt, R., "Magnetic storage medium for enhancing magneto-optic readout," U.S. Patent #3,472,575 (1969). Antireflection overcoats for M-O media with $n \sim 4$.

Li, Z., B. Sullivan, and R. Parsons, "Use of the 4×4 matrix method in the optics of multilayer magnetooptic recording media," *Applied Optics,* **27,** 1334 (1988). A computational method for evaluating the reflectance of magneto-optic thin-film structures.

Mansuripur, M., and G. Connell, "Laser-induced local heating of moving multilayer media," *Applied Optics,* **22,** 666 (1983). A Green's function method used to model thermal effects in magneto-optic recording.

Suh, S., and H. Craighead, "Optical writing characteristics of multilayered bismuth selenium thin films," *Optical Engineering,* **26,** 524 (1987). An example of optical recording assisted by an exothermic reaction.

Schultheiss, E., G. Bäuer, W. Dicken, S. Müller, P. Wirz, and D. Shieh, "Production technology for magnetooptic data storage media," *Solid State Technology,* **31** no. 3, 107 (1988). A mass-production method for M-O disks and a description of reactive DC sputtering.

Takahashi, M., T. Niihara, and N. Ohta, "Study on recorded domain characteristics of magneto-optical TbFeCo disks," *J. Appl. Phys.*, **64**, 262 (1988). Observations of domain shapes in M-O recording.

Wrobel, J., "The physics of recording in write-once optical storage materials," *SPIE Proceedings*, **420**, 288 (1983). A good description of the interplay of optical absorption, thermal diffusion, and marking mechanisms in many types of optical recording media.

CHAPTER 14

Environment and Lifetime

Many manufacturers of optical media quote a disk lifetime of ten years. Such lifetime estimates probably have more to do with the perceived market requirement than with scientifically rigorous projections. Generally, the supporting data cover a limited range of test conditions compared to the specified operating and storage limits. Short-term, high-stress tests (which usually violate the specified limits) are called upon for moral support. One company has variously quoted lifetimes of thirty, fifty, and one hundred years for a write-once optical disk product, basing these different estimates on exactly the same test data.

Actually, a ten-year lifetime is inadequate for archival applications. Printed matter (on good-quality paper) is expected to last for hundreds of years. Photographic microform should last for more than a century. To be useful for archival applications, optical disks and the information recorded on them must last much longer than ten years, and the lifetime limits must be accurately understood. On the other hand, the question of optical disk lifetimes might be moot, because system obsolescence could make the digital recordings unreadable long before they deteriorate. Most electronic hardware is not expected to function longer than ten to twenty years. For instance, many varieties of magnetic disk and tape recorders have become obsolete during the past thirty years. Software and documentation become obsolete just as fast. As pointed out by Zech (1984), only human-readable records are reliable for very-long-term archival purposes. Much more extensive system standardization will be required to qualify optical recording products for truly archival applications.

The discussions in this chapter presuppose nonarchival applications, where the lifetime requirements are measured in years or decades, not centuries. Even so, reliable system design requires a knowledge of the environmental restrictions (media and system), probable failure modes, and lifetimes. Few of these questions can be answered accurately in detail for optical disks until more actual experience has accumulated. But preliminary tests and qualitative studies are still valuable.

14.1   Indications of Aging

Optical disks must satisfy many constraints—mechanical, thermal, optical, magnetic, and so on. And they incorporate a wide variety of materials, designs, and manufacturing techniques. Consequently, optical recording media can, and sometimes do, fail in many different ways. Here are some examples:

Mechanical failure: A plastic substrate can relax slowly under conditions of high temperature and/or humidity. Relaxation of internal stress causes the substrate to warp, increasing its axial runout and the associated tilt. Radial runout usually does not worsen with time, because it is principally due to centration of the format pattern. But if the disk is mounted using an attached hub, any deterioration at the hub/substrate interface could increase both the axial and radial runout.

Optical efficiency: As we discussed in Chapter 13, Section 2, most optical media are designed for enhanced optical coupling into the recording layer. Any changes in the optical constants of the recording layers or substrate could alter the reflectance, reduce the recording sensitivity, or reduce the readout contrast. Optical degradation is not necessarily due to changes in the disk materials. For instance, a transparent substrate could become obscured by the accumulation of scratches, dust, or other contamination.

Recording performance: The channel quality depends on many media characteristics such as sensitivity, thermal conductivity, and surface roughness. Any physical or chemical change in the recording layers (e.g., corrosion, cracking, crystallization, etc.) is likely to degrade the channel characteristics. Although it depends on many factors, the recording performance can be monitored using time interval analysis or another measure of channel margin (Chapter 9, Section 3).

Data retention: The stability of recorded marks can be different from that of the unrecorded media. Pits in an ablative write-once medium could become obscured by debris generated during subsequent recording. In many types of media, marked regions are chemically altered, and the marks might age differently than the unrecorded regions. Therefore, aging tests must include channel measurements of patterns recorded both before and after the environmental exposure.

Error rate: Of all media characteristics, the defect level or hard error rate is usually the most sensitive to harsh environmental conditions. Local defects such as film cracking, delamination, or corrosion might not change the overall CNR or reflectance, but they are likely to create new hard errors. Figure 14.1 illustrates how a burst-length histogram can change with time. Existing error bursts will grow longer because the underlying defects are

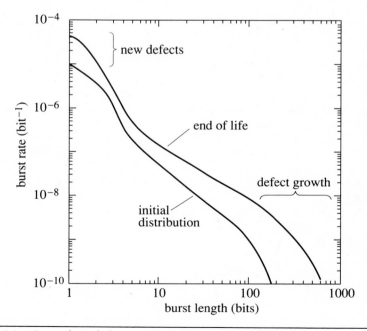

Figure 14.1 *Burst-length histograms showing the appearance of new defects and the growth of old defects.*

prime sites for corrosion or film delamination. Defects that start out too small to cause errors can also grow, creating new bursts.

In order to identify the major failure modes and the corresponding aging rates, we must start with a description of the anticipated media environment. Table 14.1 summarizes the standard environmental restrictions on 130-mm write-once optical disks (ANSI, 1987). These restrictions are typical of the goals for other optical disk products, and indeed for all types of recording media. Three environments are described: an operating range within which the media are expected to be fully functional, a storage range within which the media and recorded data should not undergo permanent changes, and a harsher shipping environment that the media are expected to withstand for only a brief time (e.g., only 14 days). The ANSI standard also specifies a benign test environment (23°C/50% RH) in which the detailed performance specifications must be demonstrated. Formal standards normally do not specify a necessary lifetime within the operating, storage, or shipping environments; such numbers are treated as quality features specific to individual products.

The environments in Table 14.1 include several interrelated restrictions on temperature and humidity. The absolute amount of moisture corresponding to a given percentage of relative humidity increases dramatically with temperature. But extremely high

TABLE 14.1 Environmental Restrictions on 130-mm Write-once Optical Disks

	OPERATION	STORAGE	SHIPPING
Temperature (°C)	10 to 50	−10 to 50	−20 to 55
RH (%)	10 to 80	10 to 90	5 to 90
Temperature Gradient (°C/hour)	10	15	20
General	No condensation on or within the disk		
	Wet-bulb temperature ≤ 29°C		
	Temperature RH gradient ≤ 10°C/hour		
	Air pressure from 0.75 to 1.05 bar		
	Air class 1,000,000		
	≥ 2 hours of conditioning prior to operation		

amounts of moisture are proscribed by the general wet-bulb restriction, which limits the maximum moisture content to the amount that would saturate the air at 29°C. This moisture content is about 29 g/m³, equivalent to about 30% RH at 50°C. The moisture is further restricted by the requirement of no condensation; the relative humidity must always be significantly below 100% everywhere around and within the disk structure. The conditioning requirement and restrictions on the rate of change of temperature serve partly to prevent unrealistic thermal shock and partly to facilitate the humidity restrictions. For instance, without sufficient time for equilibration, the interior of an air-sandwich disk will pass the dew-point whenever it is cooled near 0°C.

The temperature limits for shipping and operation are meant to reflect actual conditions that might be encountered. It is not hard to see that extreme temperatures (i.e., -20°C to 55°C) could be encountered during shipment by truck or train through harsh weather. But the need for high-temperature operation is more subtle. An optical disk must operate within a drive, and the drive is likely to be housed within a system enclosure (e.g., a desktop microcomputer.) The temperature in the system enclosure could easily be 10°C warmer than ambient. And the power dissipated by the mechanical and electronic components of the drive could raise the temperature of the disk by another 10–15°C. Thus an operating condition of 50°C is likely in an office environment of only 25–30°C. This circumstance also implies that the medium is expected to undergo frequent (rapid) temperature cycling through a range of 20°C or more.

The pressure restriction listed in Table 14.1 is an accommodation for disk designs, like the air sandwich, which have an enclosed air cavity. Large differences between the internal and external pressure could warp such disks or even split them open. Other disk designs, like a single-substrate, one-sided disk or a laminated solid sandwich, are insensitive to air pressure.

The adverse effects of dust contamination were discussed in Chapter 5, Section 5. During operation, an optical disk is always exposed to airborne dust. Even though the disk is housed in a cartridge, the cartridge door is open during operation. As the disk spins, it pumps air radially outward across its surface, increasing the rate of dust contamination if the air inside the drive is dirty. Fortunately, dust need not be a critical problem because (in principle) it can be cleaned off without permanent damage.

The air quality specified in Table 14.1, class 1,000,000, corresponds to a typical office or home environment. The class number refers to the number of particles per cubic foot larger than 0.5 μm in diameter. This single number is usually sufficient to characterize the particulate content of the air, because the size distribution function (number of particles with diameter larger than d) typically follows a power law, $N(d) \propto d^{-2}$, with a sharp cutoff beyond 25 μm. Solid particles much larger than 25 μm in diameter are seldom found in most computer environments because they cannot remain airborne without significant air turbulence. (Fuzzy fibers are the obvious exception.)

Although existing standards do not address this point, it is important for recording media to be resistant to, and/or protected from, atmospheric pollutants. To evaluate its media, SONY performs the following separate tests: ten days in an atmosphere including 4% ammonia; ten days in an atmosphere containing 5 ppm ozone; and an extended smog test in a 30°C/90% RH atmosphere including 2 ppm SO_2, 2 ppm H_2S, 2 ppm NO_3, and 1 ppm Cl_2. Although these test environments are unrealistically harsh, they give a good indication of the media's ability to withstand a range of industrial and urban pollutants.

The ANSI standards also include a specification for the impact resistance of optical media units. The disk, enclosed in its case, must survive drops from 760 mm (desk height) onto vinyl-covered concrete (i.e., linoleum) with impacts on each corner and each surface. Of course, the disk need not be perfectly rugged. Minimally, it must remain functional after fourteen drops, eight on the corners and six on the surfaces.

The media unit must also survive shock and vibration during operation and shipping. Figure 14.2 shows the range of maximum shock amplitudes experienced by products during shipment by rail, truck, and air freight. At low frequency, the shocks seldom exceed 1 G (10 m/s^2); otherwise the packages would have to be tied down. But fairly large transient shocks, up to 100 G, occur at high frequencies. Any loose components of the media unit could be subjected to severe rattling if not well packaged or solidly assembled. The shock and vibration conditions within an operating drive are qualitatively similar to the shipping conditions, in that transient high-frequency shocks are the strongest and most problematical. The drive design is constrained by shock and vibration more than the media or packaging

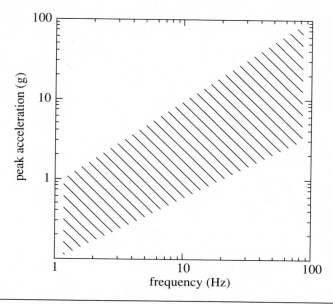

Figure 14.2 *The range of shocks experienced during product transport.*

designs are. Reliable system performance is impossible without a significant degree of shock damping and vibration isolation within the drive.

Optical disk systems are being considered for various aviation and military uses. These applications usually require even more environmental resistance (Collins, 1987). The disk should be expected to operate at high altitudes and low pressure. Greater shock and vibration amplitudes are expected. Active cooling might be required to keep the media within the operational temperature range within the drive. The overall drive efficiency is doubly important, because power dissipation heats the unit and entails additional cooling capacity.

14.2   Accelerated Aging Tests

In almost any technology, the time allotted for product development is insufficient for a straightforward demonstration of an acceptable product lifetime. This is especially true for information storage media. Somehow, the development staff must assemble convincing evidence of a product life of five, ten, or fifteen years during the one or two years between the initial invention and product introduction. With luck, the staff might have time to demonstrate that the media can survive the rigors of shipping and operate under the various conditions of pressure, temperature, vibration, and so on that can occur in the drive. But claims of operational and storage lifetime are always based on some form of prediction.

In component testing, it is sometimes assumed that failure occurs with a fixed probability, following an exponential decay. Under this assumption, the necessary testing time can be shortened by increasing the scale of testing, e.g., by monitoring the performance of many media units until 10% of them fail (about 10% of the *mean time before failure*, or MTBF). This approach is actually undesirable for recording media, because the claimed lifetime is supposed to refer to every individual media unit, not just a typical disk. Moreover, media failure is often caused by cumulative aging effects, with results that show up catastrophically only after some inductance period. When such fears arise, accelerated aging tests are usually called in for moral support.

If a single chemical or physical process is responsible for media aging, Arrhenius testing can be used to predict the functional failure rate based on short-term, high-temperature testing. The basic *Arrhenius relationship* states that the temperature dependence of a reaction is governed by a Boltzmann exponential:

$$\text{rate} \propto e^{-E/kT}, \qquad (14.1)$$

where E is the activation energy (per unit of reaction), T is the temperature (absolute Kelvin scale), and k is the Boltzmann constant ($8.6 \cdot 10^{-5}$ eV/K). Figure 14.3 is an Arrhenius plot, designed to display exponential relationships between the temperature and the reaction time, $\tau \equiv \text{rate}^{-1}$. If the aging process is governed by a single reaction with Arrhenius kinetics, then $\log \tau$ is proportional to $1/T$, and the corresponding Arrhenius plot is a straight line. The slope of the straight line is proportional to the activation energy:

$$-\Delta(\log \tau)/\Delta(1/T) = E/(k \ln 10), \qquad (14.2)$$

or

$$-\Delta(\log \tau)/\Delta(1/T) = 5\,E,$$

with T measured in units of 1000 K and E measured in eV as in Figure 14.3.

Arrhenius extrapolations of lifetime follow a lengthy and uncertain evaluation procedure. Representative media samples are stored in several (three or more) environmental chambers at constant temperature and humidity. The temperatures should all be much higher than the temperature corresponding to the lifetime estimate, but not so high as to activate unrealistic reactions. For example, the stability of films on plastic substrates can be tested only at temperatures well below the T_g, so that the substrates themselves do not warp or melt. Media samples from each environment are tested at intervals until the samples fail. The failure time, treated as an inverse reaction rate, is plotted as a function of temperature on an Arrhenius graph. If the data do not have a linear form (log τ vs. $1/T$), then a unique activation energy cannot be assigned and the Arrhenius model is not applicable. If the graph does look linear, it is extrapolated to the temperature range of interest to estimate the lifetime. Okino (1987) describes a specific set of keeping conditions and failure criteria used by the Japanese Standards Committee for optical disks to make Arrhenius projections of media lifetime.

As an example, consider the accelerated keeping data for the multi-layer SONY write-once recording medium shown in Figure 14.3 (data from Nakane, Sato, Makino, and Miyaoka, 1985). The solid-line segment on the left corresponds to interdiffusion between layers

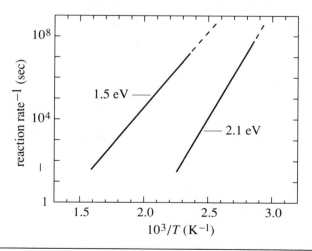

Figure 14.3 *Arrhenius plots for the temperature dependence of failure rates for a SONY write-once medium.*

of Sb_2Se_3 and Bi_2Te_3; the activation energy for this reaction is 1.5 eV. The solid-line segment on the right corresponds to crystallization of the Sb_2Se_3 layer; the activation energy of annealing is 2.1 eV. Interdiffusion, were it to occur, would "mark" the entire media surface, writing over any existing data. Annealing would reduce the sensitivity, making the media useless for further recording. Extrapolating both reactions to the upper operating limit (50 °C or 1000 K/T = 3.1), we can estimate a lifetime of 10^{12} s ~ 30,000 years for interdiffusion and 10^{10} s ~ 300 years for annealing.

This analysis of the SONY medium is encouraging, but not conclusive. Annealing is the dominant cause of degradation for temperatures between 100°C and 300°C, but it may be that another physical mechanism or chemical reaction actually dominates near room temperature. Localized catalytic contaminants *might* reduce the activation energy for corrosion nearly to zero, and a complete study of corrosion might reveal a third, nearly horizontal, line which crosses below the curves for interdiffusion and annealing at low temperatures. Then the Arrhenius projection would be quite misleading. Another risk with Arrhenius testing is oversimplification of the tests. It is tempting to simplify the media in order to obtain unambiguous results, e.g., by using a stable (glass) substrate or media units that are not completely assembled. But such simplification could eliminate important aging mechanisms and render the tests irrelevant.

Some aging mechanisms can be accelerated, without forcing the test environment to very extreme temperatures, by *cycling,* or rapid variation in the environmental conditions. In general, no "acceleration factor" can legitimately be applied to such tests. However, the failure mechanisms they reveal are usually important, and cycling durability is a practical indicator of overall media ruggedness. So media manufacturers use cyclic tests of one sort or another to quantify improvements in media quality and to internally qualify products.

The premier example of a cyclic test is the Z/AD cycle, shown graphically in Figure 14.4. Z/AD was initially developed as a means to test the integrity of electronic device packages. It is considered to be the most severe of several standard cyclic stress tests. (See the definitions and discussion in the referenced IEC document, 1974). Each 24-hour cycle consists of two hot subcycles and one cold subcycle, each followed by a brief return to a 25°C ambient temperature within the environmental chamber. The relative humidity is maintained near saturation. This means that the actual moisture

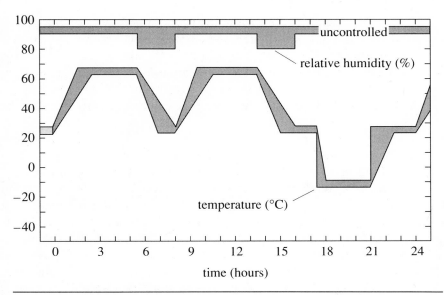

Figure 14.4 *Temperature and relative-humidity limits for one Z/AD cycle.*

content of the chamber varies dramatically. At 65°C, the air holds about 200 g/m³ of water; this will drop below 2 g/m³ at −10°C. A good-quality environmental chamber is required for Z/AD testing to control the high humidity at 65°C; because sub-zero control is so difficult, the RH during the freezing subcycle is not even specified, except that overt condensation should not occur.

Thermal cycling induces a variety of different mechanical stresses in the media which may cause mechanical failures such as cracking, warp, buckling, or delamination of coated layers or media components. The high-temperature/high-humidity subcycles of the Z/AD test enhance the transport of moisture (or oxygen) into the media structure. If a significant amount of moisture does penetrate, it may condense and freeze during the cold subcycle. Thus the cold subcycle aggravates and enlarges any microscopic defects or damage. The cold subcycle also increases the range of stress conditions (tensile and/or compressive) imposed within the media.

The Z/AD test is also quite appropriate as a shipping simulation. Except for its extreme humidity at high temperature, the Z/AD range is close to the standard shipping environment described in Table 14.1.

Less-aggressive cycling tests are sometimes used for initial media research and development. Some development groups use the Z/AD test without its freezing subcycle. Media always last much longer under such reduced temperature excursions. If the media can survive only a few thermal cycles anyway, a gentler test might quantify small differences in media stability more clearly than a harsh test, that destroys everything quickly.

As with any type of accelerated aging test, useful interpretation of cyclic test results requires an understanding of the overall media design and materials characteristics. Consider, for example, Z/AD testing of a read-only disk (polycarbonate coated with aluminum) compared to a "simple" magneto-optic disk (polycarbonate, dielectric, TbFe, dielectric). The read-only disk should survive cycling easily. The thermal expansion coefficient of the substrate is much higher than that of the aluminum coating, so temperature cycling will create significant tensile and compressive strains in the aluminum as the substrate expands and shrinks. But since Al is reasonably elastic, the strain should not cause catastrophic failure, provided that the film adheres well to the substrate. Slight cumulative degradation might be expected due to repeated damage to the passivating aluminum oxide surface or moisture penetration through film defects.

M-O media structures, though they can be quite stable under ordinary conditions, are much more sensitive to temperature cycling. The dielectric layers are relatively brittle, prone to cracking when the substrate expands at high temperatures and to buckling when the substrate cools and shrinks. The M-O layer is very prone to corrosion, and under humid conditions any damage to the dielectric layers grows quickly. Temperature cycling accelerates aging effects for M-O media on plastic substrates more than for simpler types of media, or even for the same M-O structure on glass substrates.

One of the difficulties in media aging studies is to establish the failure criteria on which the lifetime estimate is based. The actual end-of-life criteria can be very clear from system-level specifications; i.e., there are precise values for the maximum error rate, minimum CNR, and minimum sensitivity. But during testing it is not always correct to extrapolate small changes in the performance characteristics to predict the eventual failure time. Consider, for instance, the coercivity of M-O media. Coercivity is very important, because it affects the recording sensitivity, recorded noise level, and data stability. It is usually easy to measure coercivity because it can be treated as a global property, unaffected by local degradation (which should be measured via the hard error rate). However, coercivity is a poor choice as an aging criterion. Figure 14.5 illustrates typical coercivity changes during high-temperature aging of bare, unprotected TbFe films. For Fe-rich films (< 21 atomic % Tb) the coercivity decreases monotonically with time. Tb-rich films (> 23 atomic % Tb), however, show a more complex behavior: initially, the coercivity rises rapidly, but eventually it drops back below the original value. Detailed studies demonstrate that both of these films undergo steady oxidation and diffusion of Tb out of the film. Clearly, the initial rate of change of coercivity cannot be used to predict when overall media failure will occur. Similarly misleading results are seen with many other performance parameters: sensitivity, which can increase by a transient change in reflectance; CNR, which can drop quickly at first, but then stabilize; or short-term changes in substrate warp or birefringence due to humidity changes or structural relaxation.

14.3 Designing Stable Media

Stable vs. Unstable Materials

Tellurium was the first optical recording material that showed both high recording sensitivity and high performance (CNR), but its good reputation was quickly tarnished by its propensity to corrode. Tellu-

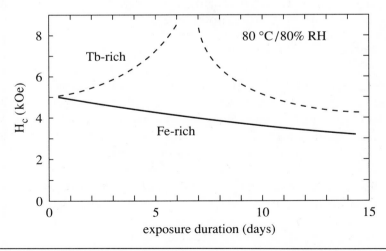

Figure 14.5 *Coercivity changes in oxidized TbFe films depend sensitively on the composition.*

rium reacts with water to form tellurium hydride (H_2Te, which is volatile and poisonous) and other ugly corrosion products. Several other high-performance optical recording materials also turned out to be chemically unstable or sensitive to corrosion, for example, M-O alloys, some phase-change materials, and cellulose nitrate. Consequently, optical recording gained a general reputation for media instability; but along with recognition of the aging problems came the inventions necessary to make sufficiently stable optical recording media.

A number of intrinsically stable optical recording materials have been demonstrated. The Plasmon disks mentioned in Chapter 13, Section 2 are a good example. After 2000 hours at 65°C/85% RH, these disks undergo virtually no change in their signal level, noise level, error rate, and physical characteristics (Kalstrom, 1987). This stability should be credited to the simplicity of the media design. It has only two components—a polycarbonate substrate (a very stable plastic) and a chemically inert, platinum recording layer. Under ordinary conditions, the only imaginable mode of failure for this medium would be delamination of the coating from the substrate. Possible adhesion failure is a weakness for any thin-film structure.

Organic single-layer optical disks represent another simple design that tends to be particularly stable. Adhesion of the organic-dye recording material to the organic substrate is usually good. Possible failure modes which remain include bleaching of the dye, dark-fade (if the dye itself is chemically unstable), and chemical attack from solvent vapors or other pollutants.

Barrier Layers for Corrosion Prevention

The first method used to stabilize a Te recording medium was to encapsulate it in an air-sandwich disk configuration to keep it dry. Moisture could not penetrate through the two glass substrates to react with the Te. Unfortunately, paths for moisture penetration can develop at the interface between the substrates. An air-sandwich really just delays the penetration of moisture; the media layer will seem stable for a while, then begin to corrode rapidly after moisture has had time to penetrate. Plastic substrates are more or less permeable to moisture, so they do even less to prevent eventual corrosion. And in fact, most air-sandwich disks are now vented; they are not expected to provide a hermetic seal.

The first investigators of M-O media noted keeping problems, such as corrosion and discoloration, which occurred even more rapidly than in Te. The typical corrosion behavior of a TbFe thin film is described in Figure 14.6. After rapid growth of an initial TbO_2 film (usually thinner than 10 nm), the oxide thickness increases proportionally to the square root of the exposure time, indicating that surface oxidation is very rapid and that subsequent oxidation is limited by diffusion through the developing oxide layer. These data represent accelerated corrosion under severe conditions. Slower, but qualitatively similar, behavior is seen under office conditions.

In order to make their samples last long enough for testing, M-O researchers learned to overcoat them with dielectric films such as SiO_2. The overcoats greatly inhibited oxidation and aging. However, oxides are not entirely satisfactory for protecting RE/TM films. Rare-earth elements such as Tb have such a high affinity for oxygen that they reduce otherwise stable oxides at the interface. Immediate changes in Kerr rotation, coercivity, and so on, are usually seen when TbFe or other RE/TM films are coated with SiO_2.

Oxygen-free dielectrics make better barrier layers for RE/TM recording materials. Robinson, Payne, and Bell, (1987) have described the effects of an amorphous carbon overcoat (*diamond-like carbon or DLC*) on the corrosion resistance of M-O films. Their samples were aged at 70°C/95% RH. A slight decrease in θ_k (interpreted as prompt oxidation at the media interface) occurred over the first few hours, but subsequently, θ_k remained stable for over 500 hours. Quite a few other oxygen-poor materials have been proposed as overcoats: AlN, Si_3N_4, oxy-nitrides, and metal-rich suboxides.

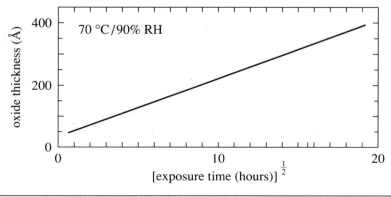

Figure 14.6 *Growth of an oxide layer on a TbFe film at 70°C.*

Whenever a protective overcoat is required, a similar undercoat is also needed. For instance, an RE/TM coating on a glass substrate will be partially oxidized by reaction with the glass. Plastic substrates are even more problematical, since they are permeable to oxygen and moisture. Corrosion can be prevented only by an impermeable undercoat. For substrate incident recording and readout, a transparent dielectric undercoat may serve the additional function of reducing the media reflectance, increasing the media sensitivity, and increasing the Kerr rotation (for M-O media). Transparency is not particularly important for overcoat layers, but undercoat materials are usually selected partly for their optical properties.

Figure 14.7 illustrates a duplex overcoat/undercoat design that provides more active corrosion protection (Frankenthal, vanDover, and Siconolfi, 1987). An active, self-passivating metal such as aluminum is used as a corrosion barrier for an RE/TM recording layer. Coated directly on or under the recording layer, the aluminum film could interdiffuse with the M-O film, reducing both the recording performance and the passivation efficiency. Therefore, the passivating layer is separated from the M-O film by a thin barrier layer of niobium. Nb does not passivate, but it is a particularly good diffusion barrier. In order to use a duplex film as an undercoat, the layers must be thin enough to be essentially transparent. Since overcoat transparency is not critical, the second duplex film can be thicker.

In order to avoid confusion with the transparent 'protective layers' described in Chapter 12, Section 3, we have referred to thin-film barrier layers as undercoats and overcoats. They are usually about 0.1 μm thick, always much too thin to serve any role in dust protec-

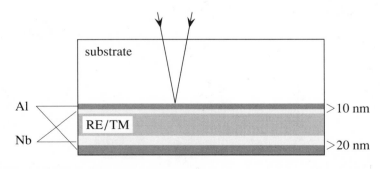

Figure 14.7 *Duplex coatings for passivation and diffusion protection.*

tion. On the other hand, the thick protective layers can play a significant (though not decisive) role in corrosion prevention. For instance, a glass substrate will prevent any ongoing permeation of moisture to the bottom of the recording film. And any relatively thick layer can effectively keep corrosive airborne contaminants away from the recording layers. The lacquer coating on the back of a CD serves this purpose, among others.

Alloys and Additives

The corrosion resistance of thin films depends on their chemistry and microstructure. Coating experiments often show a dependence of corrosion rate on the film thickness or deposition conditions. For instance, high-density, sputtered RE/TM films are much more stable than films of the same composition but with a loose, columnar structure. TbFeCo alloys tend to corrode locally, forming small pinholes, but with little global oxidation. Such observations indicate that slight local variations in composition or microstructure can have a dramatic effect on the corrosion resistance of thin films; hence it seems reasonable that minor additives could greatly increase film stability.

Te readily forms amorphous alloys, and it can be chemically stabilized by trace additives (Terao, Horigome, Shigematsu, Miyauchi, and Nakazawa, 1987). Se is particularly useful as a passivating agent for Te: Te oxidizes at the surface but leaves an Se-rich underlayer, which prevents further oxygen or moisture diffusion. Te can also be alloyed with metals such as In, Pb, or Sb. These elements improve the film's integrity, preventing cracking of the resolidified material after recording, and reducing oxygen and moisture diffusion at grain boundaries.

A variety of additives have been been shown to enhance the stability of TbFe. One reason TbFe corrodes so rapidly is that the oxide film that develops is not self-passivating—it does not inhibit further oxygen penetration or Tb diffusion. Co is effective in reducing corrosion, largely because it forms a passivation layer. Even better passivation is provided by additives like Al or Ti, but these materials reduce the magneto-optical performance of the material, while Co increases θ_k. Other additives to TbFe improve the stability by other mechanisms. For instance, Pt is a stabilizing additive, even though it is unreactive and does not form a barrier layer. Rather, Pt appears to fill in diffusion pathways and increase the film's integrity.

14.4 Functional Cycling

Discussions of the media environment usually refer only to the external conditions. But problems are also caused by transient local conditions occurring during use. Handling effects such as cartridge damage, disk contamination, or hub wear should be tested directly by repetitive use in real drives. The cumulative effects of intense laser exposure on the recording layers should be investigated. In addition to doing the usual keeping tests, it is necessary to determine the stability of marks and unrecorded areas after repeated readout. For erasable media, stability must also be demonstrated after repeated cycles of recording and erasure.

In Section 14.2 we discussed the problems inherent in thermal cycling when the expansion coefficients of the substrate and coated films are dissimilar. During recording and readout, the media temperature rises *locally*. Thermal gradients are established which, in turn, create large local film stresses. (In some types of media, these local stresses actually drive mark formation.) Repeated readout and recording take the media through rapid, localized temperature cycles. Brittle films might develop cracks; soft organic layers might gradually deform; adhesion failure might occur at weak interfaces; and chemical reactions might be accelerated locally.

Readout cycling of an optical disk can be tested by measuring media performance while continuously reading a single track. Systems with a spiral format usually have an automatic jump-back feature to provide this mode of operation. The stability of marks is measured by monitoring a previously recorded track; the stability for new recording is measured by repeatedly "reading" a blank track and then recording on it. At a rotation rate of 30 rps, the test track undergoes $3 \cdot 10^6$ cycles per day; one day of continuous readout is usually an extensive enough test, though the media might be required to handle more reads than this if the drive has a "home" area where it tends to dwell. In our discussion of thermal effects (Chapter 13, Section 3), we found that the actual exposure interval during each pass of the laser stylus is ~ 0.1 μs; so a million readout cycles correspond to less than 1 second of heating or laser exposure. If any cumulative effects are present (such as dye-fade), they might not show up until more cycles are performed.

Stinson and Petronio (1987) studied the readout stability of magneto-optic media and found a very sharp threshold. If the power was low enough to provoke no damage after 10^5 readout cycles, then 10^8 additional cycles could also be performed without any change. Another interesting result of their study was the empirical observation that the threshold write power (the power required to form a noticeable domain with one pulse) is always about twice the maximum allowable readout power. Since the optimal writing power is usually about twice the recording threshold (Chapter 5, Section 3), the readout power must be less than about 25% of the recording power. Other optical recording systems have similar limits for the readout power. In a few cases, the readout limit is even lower if multiple marking mechanisms contribute to recording.

For most applications, erasable media are expected to support 10^6 to 10^7 write/erase cycles. Most erasable media (M-O and phase-change) are not heated as strongly by the optical stylus as write-once media; but still, the recording temperature typically exceeds 200°C, much hotter than any specified environmental limit. Changes sometimes observed during record/erase cycling of erasable media include structural relaxation (M-O materials), compositional segregation (phase-change materials), and irreversible flow (erasable organic media). Even if the recording material itself is perfectly reversible, eventual degradation will occur if the substrate or other media layers are damaged by heat. Recall that polycarbonate softens at temperatures near the glass transition point, $T_g \sim 150°C$. Therefore, some deformation of the tracks on a plastic disk can eventually occur. When it is observed, this kind of deformation can be minimized by encapsulating the recording structure in a solid-sandwich or similarly rigid disk structure.

—— MAJOR CONCEPTS

- The defect level or hard error rate is the most important indicator of media aging. Defects can be created or enlarged by corrosion, stress, or environmental cycling.

- For most applications, optical disks must operate under a wide range of temperature and humidity. They must survive an even wider range of storage and shipping environments without permanent damage or data loss (Table 14.1).

- Arrhenius extrapolations can be used to estimate the room-temperature kinetics of particular failure mechanisms (Eqs. 14.1 and 14.2).

- Temperature cycling is used to quantify media ruggedness or to uncover failure mechanisms. Neither cycling tests nor Arrhenius testing should be used naively as accelerated aging tests.

- Many optical recording materials are prone to corrosion. In some cases, minor additives can form much more stable alloys. M-O media are additionally designed with barrier layers, which keep moisture and oxygen away from both sides of the recording layer.

━━━━ REFERENCES

Collins, G., "Ruggedizing optical disks," *Defense Science and Electronics,* **6**, no. 10, 74 (1987). A discussion of the rigorous conditions a drive must survive in standard military applications.

Frankenthal, R., R. vanDover, and D. Siconolfi, "Duplex coatings for the protection of magneto-optic alloys against oxidation," *Appl. Phys. Lett.,* **51**, 542 (1987). The combination of a barrier layer and a passivation layer to protect M-O recording films against corrosion.

International Electrotechnical Commission. "Test Z/AD: composite temperature/humidity cyclic test," IEC publication 68-2-38 (1974). The formal definition of the Z/AD cyclic environmental stress test.

Kalstrom, D., private communication (1987).

Nakane, Y., N. Sato, H. Makino, and S. Miyaoka, "Principle of laser recording mechanism by forming an alloy in the multilayer of thin metallic films," *SPIE Proceedings,* **529**, 76 (1985). The data include activation energies for failure mechanisms in a SONY write-once medium.

Okino, Y., "Reliability test of write-once optical disk," *Japanese Journal of Applied Physics,* **26**, Supplement 26-4 (1987). Detailed procedures adopted by a Japanese standards organization for Arrhenius lifetime projections.

Robinson, C., R. Payne, and A. Bell, "Amorphous carbon dielectric coatings for magneto-optic recording media," *Topical Meeting on Optical Data Storage, Technical Digest Series 1987,* **10**, 131 (1987). Amorphous carbon used as an anti-reflection and corrosion-prevention coating for magneto-optic media.

Stinson, D., and J. Petronio, "The dependence of maximum readout power on various properties of thin-film magneto-optic media," *Topical Meeting on Optical Data Storage, Technical Digest Series,* **10,** 10 (1987). Magneto-optic media are stable for at least 10^8 readout cycles if the readout power is less than half the recording threshold.

Terao, M., S. Horigome, K. Shigematsu, Y. Miyauchi, and M. Nakazawa, "Oxidation resistance of Pb-Te-Se optical recording film," *Journal of Applied Physics,* **62,** 1029 (1987). A study of the physical effects of various additives on the stability of Te recording films.

X3B11, "Proposed American National Standard 130 mm write-once optical disk cartridge part 1; definitions, test, operating and storage conditions," ANSI document #X3B11/87-010 R2 (1988). A summary of the test conditions and the operating, storage, and shipping environments that standard 130-mm optical disks must satisfy.

Zech, R., "Strategic technology considerations relative to the preservation and storage of human and machine readable records," White Paper submitted by sub-committee C of NARA to the Archivist of the United States (1984). A description of the drawbacks to using digital storage systems for archival applications.

Terms and Acronyms

This glossary is a primer for optical recording jargon. Terms and acronyms that have special importance, or peculiar meanings for optical recording, are defined and explained here. No attempt has been made to define the terms used in this book which have common technical meanings, although every acronym is explained at least at its first usage. The first attempt to standardize optical recording terminology was issued by ANSI subcommittee X3B11 (see J. Freedman, "ODD Terminology," document # ANSI X3B11/86-022). Eventually that terminology proposal was also adopted by ISO, the International Standards Organization. Although not identical, the definitions here agree with the overall intent of the ANSI proposals.

Aberration: phase distortions which degrade the performance of an optical system. Aberrations can be caused by defective optical elements, defocus, misalignment, etc.

Access time: the average delay within a drive between receipt of a write or read command and the instant when the optical stylus begins to read or write data. The access time includes the average seek time, settling time, and latency.

Air-sandwich disk: an optical disk composed of a substrate bonded at its inner and outer edges to another rigid part (usually an identical substrate), with a thin air space covering the recording zone. Air-sandwich disks usually operate in a substrate-incident mode and are usually designed to be double sided.

Antireflection bilayer, trilayer, and quadrilayer: media designs that include reflective layers and/or transparent layers that enhance the absorption of light in the recording layer. Antireflection designs increase media sensitivity and signal contrast.

Apodization: a nonuniform intensity distribution across a lens aperture. Apodization can result from *under-filling* where an incident beam only illuminates the center of the lens. *Over-filling,* in which the beam is much larger than the lens, reduces apodization. The *fill factor* is the ratio of the f.w.h.m. of the beam to the aperture diameter.

Astigmatism: a condition in which a focused beam forms two perpendicular line foci rather than a single point focus.

Average seek time: *see* Seek time.

Axial runout: the peak-to-peak motion of the recording layer of a spinning optical disk in the direction parallel to the rotation axis.

Baseline reflectance: the specular reflectance of optical media in the absence of grooves or written marks. This reflectance value does not include contributions from surfaces other than the media layers, such as the first surface of a transparent substrate.

BER, bit error rate: The raw BER is defined as the ratio of bits recovered in error divided by the total number recovered. The *hard BER* counts only those bits recovered in error on most re-reads. The *soft BER* counts bits recovered in error only occasionally. The *net error rate* is defined as the average rate of ECC decoder failures per bit.

Bias field: an external magnetic field applied normal to the surface of an M-O medium during recording and erasure.

Birefringence: a condition in which the index of refraction in an optical element is polarization-dependent. *Normal birefringence* refers to light rays perpendicular to the surface of the optical element. *Lateral birefringence* refers to light rays parallel to the surface.

Cartridge: the finished assembly of case and disk.

Case: a protective container in which the optical disk is permanently resident.

CAV, constant angular velocity: a technique in which the rotation rate of the disk is held constant, independent of the track radius.

CD, Compact Disc: the read-only optical disk system for digital audio reproduction which was introduced jointly by SONY and Philips. A CD is single-sided, with a diameter of 120 mm.

CDROM: A variant of the CD system which reproduces digitized images, text files, data bases, software, and so on, instead of music. Each-120 mm disk can hold about 600 MBytes of data.

CIRC, cross interleaved Reed-Solomon code: an ECC code designed for CD systems. It is particularly optimized for error detection, long-burst correction, and rapid decoding.

CLV, constant linear velocity: a technique in which the rotation rate of the disk is inversely proportional to the track radius. With CLV, the scanning velocity and data density are constant across the recording zone.

CNR, carrier-to-noise ratio: for a single-frequency signal, the ratio of the carrier power to the noise power at a neighboring frequency, expressed in dB. The measurements are usually made over a 30-kHz bandwidth. CNR should not be confused with SNR, the overall signal-to-noise ratio for the data channel.

Coercivity: the minimum external field required to switch the magnetization of a hard magnetic material. If the coercivity is x Oersted, the minimum switching field is x Gauss.

Concentricity: the radial distance between the best-fit center of a track and the rotation axis or the center of the disk's inner diameter.

Cross-talk: interference in the readout waveform due to neighboring tracks, which may be partially visible to the optical stylus. *Erasure cross-talk* results when a previously written track is not completely erased. *Servo cross-talk* is the tendency for tracking errors to produce spurious focus-error signals and vice versa.

Diffraction limit: the smallest optical spot that can be formed by an optical system in the absence of aberration. A lens or system is said to be diffraction-limited if it achieves a Strehl ratio greater than 0.9.

DRAW, direct-read-after-write: optical media in which the marks are visible immediately after the recording exposure (say, within 1 μs.) DRAW systems exploit this characteristic to identify any hard errors as soon as they are written.

Duty cycle: the fraction of time that a binary signal is high.

ECC, error-correction code: an encoding scheme that appends generalized parity bits to a block of data before recording, and then uses the redundant bits to locate and correct errors after the data are retrieved. An ECC operates reliably only if the actual number of errors is below some (code-specific) correctable limit.

EDAC, error detection and correction: a strategy that combines an ECC with other methods (such as certification, fencing, DRAW, and interleaving) to effectively eliminate errors from the recovered data stream.

Erasable media: recording media on which individual bits of data can be replaced by new data in real time. *Reversible media* is an equivalent term.

Erasure cross-talk: *see* Cross-talk.

Error burst: a string of bit errors. A *guard space* parameter defines the minimum number of consecutive correct bits that separate two bursts.

Fill factor: *see* Apodization.

Form factor: the outer dimensional constraints for a standard-sized drive. The description of a particular form factor (e.g., $5\frac{1}{4}''$) usually bears a loose, historical connection to the actual dimensions.

Front surface: the first surface on which light impinges. In front-surface inspection or readout, the illumination is air-incident, not focused through a transparent substrate.

F.w.h.m., full width at half maximum: the diameter of a laser beam or focused spot measured between two points where the intensity is half the central maximum.

Grooves: concentric circular features (or a tight spiral) formed into the substrate to serve as a guide for tracking. The grooves correspond to the portions of the photo-resist master disk which are exposed and developed away during mastering.

Guard space: *see* Error burst.

Hard BER: *see* BER.

Interleaving: a technique of mixing the data from several ECC code blocks to make the channel more tolerant of isolated, long error bursts. Interleaving makes a long-burst error equivalent to several shorter bursts.

Kerr rotation: a magneto-optic effect in which the polarization of a light beam is rotated slightly upon reflection from a magnetized layer. The direction of polarization rotation depends on whether the magnetization is predominantly parallel or antiparallel to the beam incidence direction. Typical M-O films exhibit Kerr rotation angles less than 1°.

Land area: on pregrooved substrates, any area on the surface which corresponds to unexposed portions of the photoresist master. For write-once and erasable media, the land area further excludes written marks or pits.

Laser diode: variously called a diode laser, semiconductor laser, or injection laser. Laser diodes used for optical recording are driven by direct current injection and emit light at near-infrared wavelengths.

Laser feedback: a condition in which light is reflected back into the cavity of a laser. Feedback can alter a laser's efficiency, spectrum, power output, and noise.

Laser isolation: any optical technique that prevents laser feedback.

Latency: the average time required to begin reading or writing data on a random sector on the current track. The latency for readout is exactly half of one rotation period.

Lateral birefringence: *see* Birefringence.

Mark or pit: a region with altered optical characteristics created by a high-power exposure from the optical stylus. The visible mark is called a *pit* when it corresponds to ablation or flow of material in the recording layer.

Master: a glass disk on which an optical disk format is formed. A stamper created from a master is used to make replicated substrates.

Mirror area: a land area that is not adjacent to grooves and contains no preformat or data marks.

M-O, magneto-optics: refers to methods or materials in which magnetic fields are made visible. In M-O recording, data are stored as magnetic domains and recovered optically, usually using the Kerr rotation.

Modulation codes: any technique that uses the modulated laser power, mark pattern, and corresponding readout signal to represent digital data. A modulation code can store information in the variable placement of pulses and marks (*mark-position modulation*) or in their lengths and spacings (*mark-length modulation*).

MTF, modulation transfer function: the ability of an optical system to image patterns of increasing spatial frequency. The MTF and the image contrast drop to zero when the mark spacing equals the *resolution limit*.

NA, numerical aperture: the sine of the incidence angle of a marginal ray from a positive lens.

Net error rate: *see* BER.

Normal birefringence: *see* Birefringence.

Optical card: a rectangular optical recording medium on which the data are not arranged in circular tracks. The credit-card-sized Drexon® Laser Card is the prototypical optical card.

Optical stylus: the spot formed by focusing a laser beam through a diffraction-limited objective lens which is used to record and read marks on optical recording media.

Outrigger tracking: a technique for generating a tracking-error signal by comparing the signal levels from two low-power focused spots on either side of the optical stylus.

Over-filling: *see* Apodization.

Overhead: the amount of recording space or communication time taken up for functions other than direct storage and transmission of data. Major contributions to the overhead come from error correction, addressing, and formatting.

PBSC, polarizing beam-splitter cube: a beam splitter formed by cementing two 45° prisms together around a multilayer coating that reflects nearly all the s-polarized light and transmits nearly all the p-polarized light.

Phase-change: an optical recording process in which the recording layer is changed from crystalline to amorphous, or vice versa. In some materials, a large change in reflectance accompanies the change of phase.

Photodetector: a solid-state electronic device that converts light intensity into a corresponding electrical current.

Pitch: the spacing between the center-lines of adjacent tracks.

Protective layer: a thick, transparent layer between the recording layer and the objective lens, which protects the recording material and keeps dust out of focus. For substrate-incident media, the substrate itself serves as the protective layer.

Push-pull tracking: a technique in which the phase image of a tracking groove is sensed by a two-element split detector to generate a tracking-error signal.

QWP, quarter wave plate: an optical element that introduces a single-pass retardation of $\lambda/4$.

Radial runout: the peak-to-peak radial motion of a track relative to the rotation axis. The radial runout is approximately twice the concentricity.

Read-only media: optical media with a large amount of information replicated into the substrates. New data cannot be written onto read-only media.

Reed-Solomon codes: a class of extremely powerful ECC codes. The data are handled as c-bit "characters"; usually $c = 8$ and the characters are bytes. The decoding algorithm is capable of identifying and correcting multiple faulty characters, wherever they occur, whether randomly or in long bursts.

Recording threshold: the smallest recording power that produces marks.

Recording zone: the annulus of an optical disk which is intended to support optical recording. The recording performance of an optical disk is guaranteed only within the recording zone.

Resolution limit: for an optical system scanning a periodic array of marks, the spacing at which the image contrast drops to zero. (The image of an isolated mark never disappears completely, no matter how short it is.)

Retardation: the maximum optical path difference through a birefringent protective layer for coincident orthogonally polarized beams, measured in nm. Single-pass retardation is measured in transmission; double-pass retardation is measured in reflection or calculated as twice the single-pass value. Retardation can vary strongly with incidence angle.

Reversible media: *see* Erasable media.

RLL, run-length limited code: a modulation code for digital data in which information is encoded in the intervals between signal transitions. The intervals are constrained to be particular multiples of a (high-frequency) channel clock period.

Second harmonic: the Fourier component of a periodic signal which occurs at twice the fundamental frequency. A 50% duty-cycle signal, such as an ideal square wave or sine wave, has no power at the second harmonic frequency.

Seek time: the time required for a head to move to a new track. The *average seek time* is defined for a motion equal to one-third full stroke, or one-third the width of the recording zone.

Sensitivity: the laser power required for optimal recording at a particular scanning velocity with a particular optical stylus (wavelength, Strehl ratio, *NA*, etc.).

Servo cross-talk: *see* Cross-talk.

Settling time: the time required for the tracking servo to lock onto a newly acquired track and eliminate transient tracking errors.

Shot noise: electronic noise that arises because of the quantum nature of light and/or electrical current. Data channels are usually not dominated by shot noise unless the detector illumination and photocurrent are very small.

SNR, signal-to-noise ratio: the ratio of the average signal power (for pseudo-random data) divided by the total noise power in the data channel, measured in dB. SNR is a much more fundamental measurement than CNR, but it is also much more difficult to measure.

Soft BER: *see* BER.

Solid-sandwich disk: an optical disk formed by laminating two substrates together. The disk operates in a substrate-incident mode and is usually designed to be two-sided.

Strehl ratio: the central intensity of a focused spot divided by the intensity that would theoretically be present in the absence of all aberrations. The Strehl ratio is always less than 1.

Substrate: the relatively thick part on which the media layers are coated. For *substrate-incident* operation, the substrate must be transparent so that the laser beam can be focused through it.

Two-axis actuator: a combination tracking and focus motor, that operates in a closed-loop servo system to position the objective lens precisely relative to the optical disk in both the axial and radial directions.

Under-filling: *see* Apodization.

WORM, write-once-read-many: the broad class of optical recording media on which data can be recorded but not freely altered. Data on write-once media can be altered by writing additional marks, but individual files cannot be rewritten.

Index